Praise for *Investigating Ghosts*

"In the growing literature of sci[...] paranormal practice, this book [...] ghost hunting should be done. If we are lucky, some of this might sink in."

—**Brian Regal**, Kean University, author of *Searching for Sasquatch: Crackpots, Eggheads, and Cryptozoology*

• • •

"A great book. Benjamin Radford is one of those rare individuals who devote time, competence and passion to the scientific investigation of unusual claims. It would be much easier and profitable to follow the tide but the fact that Ben prefers to go against the flow is a testimony to his honesty."

—**Massimo Polidoro**, psychologist and author of *Final Séance* and *Secrets of the Psychics*

• • •

"This book presents a combination of the excitement and emotional tingle typically provided by ghost stories, a critical analysis of the reliability and scientific value of such accounts, an explanation of how ghost experiences can occur even if ghosts do not exist, and a prescription for how any future ghost research should properly be conducted. Ghost hunter and skeptic alike will learn from his clear-headed analysis. This book is highly recommended both for anyone with a serious interest in ghostly phenomena and for readers who simply enjoy reading about ghosts."

—**James Alcock**, Department of Psychology, York University

• • •

"Interested in the reported phenomena of ghosts and serious research into paranormal claims? *Investigating Ghosts* can open the eyes and minds of today's paranormal investigators—if they dare to look. A comprehensive review of ghost hunting techniques, this volume describes the best practices of investigation that lead a useful result. Radford drills down into the modern approach to investigating haunting claims and how to correct it, covering the spectrum of viewpoints in this well-referenced volume."

—**Sharon A. Hill**, Science and society specialist and founder of Doubtfulnews.com

• • •

"This is without doubt the most comprehensive book on ghost investigation that I have read. It is written in a lively style that will engage the reader from start to finish. It should be read by everyone with an interest in paranormal claims."

—**Christopher French**, Head of the Anomalistic Psychology Research Unit, University of London

INVESTIGATING GHOSTS

The Scientific Search for Spirits

Benjamin Radford

Rhombus Publishing Company
Corrales New Mexico

Publisher Cataloguing-in-Publication Data
Radford, Benjamin, 1970-
  Investigating ghosts: the scientific search for spirits/ Benjamin Radford. —First edition
          pages cm
Includes bibliographical references and index.
ISBN 978-0-9364-5516-7 (pbk: alk paper) ISBN 978-0-9364-5513-6 (ebook)
1. Ghosts—investigation. 2. Folklore. 3. Parapsychology. I. Title.
BF 1472.R34 2017
133.109—dc 232017029026

Designed by Christopher Fix
Edited by Celestia Ward
Front cover by Marty Blake Graphic Design

"It is error only, and not truth,
that shrinks from inquiry."
– Thomas Paine

Dedicated to Bob Carroll–and Daniel & Sharon,
who share the vision.

INVESTIGATING GHOSTS

INTRODUCTION

This book is the result of about twenty years of personal research into ghosts and hauntings. It isn't really about ghosts—since, as will become clear, we don't know for certain that ghosts exist, or, if they do, anything about their nature. Instead, as the title suggests, it is specifically about the *investigation* of ghosts and explores the intriguing question of how to apply scientific analysis, logic, and critical thinking to such an elusive (yet paradoxically common) phenomena.

I attempt to cover all aspects of a scientific ghost investigation, from the psychology of the ghost experience to EVP, on-site investigation, and so on. Unlike the legions of self-published and self-described ghost hunters who populate bookshelves with anecdote masquerading as evidence and speculation presented as fact, I've consulted many of the world's top experts on various aspects of the ghost phenomenon—as well as professional psychologists, folklorists, and other academics. This multidisciplinary approach provides much deeper insight into the topic, going far beyond the typical "here's my spooky experience" books.

The reader might charitably ask what my qualifications are for writing this book; the answer is that—unlike most other authors of ghost hunting books—I don't claim to be an expert on ghosts *per se*, since of course one cannot be an expert on a phenomenon not proven to exist. I am, however, a demonstrated expert on ghost folklore, investigation techniques, and other areas related to ghosts. This is a distinction I trust readers will recognize and appreciate.

I am a "serious" author, co-author, or editor of more than twenty books and a researcher and journalist for international science news organizations. I have an undergraduate university degree in psychology and a Masters degree in education, and my research has been published and cited in several peer-reviewed publications including medical and law journals. At the same time I am also a ghost investigator and have spent considerable time and effort trying to determine the best way to scientifically find out whether ghosts exist. My position straddling two worlds provides me with a unique perspective.

I am agnostic about whether ghosts exist or not; I have my doubts (based on the lack of scientific evidence to date) but remain open to the possibility. I firmly believe that you won't know if you don't look, and I have never mocked sincere ghost hunters for their efforts. I don't think the topic is too silly to spend time on. Indeed, I have personally conducted in-depth, on-site investigations at dozens of haunted houses over the years, spending many long nights and cold hours researching, documenting, interviewing, and searching for evidence of ghosts. I'm not some pointy-headed academic sniffily dismissing ghost reports from a window in my lofty ivory tower; I've been there and done that. You may or may not agree with my conclusions, but you can't say I didn't try to understand and explain the phenomenon.

My goal with much of my research—and this book specifically—is to help bridge the gap between skeptics and believers, scientists and ghosthunters. You will find a variety of voices and perspectives in this book, from psychics to physicists, fervent believers to strident skeptics. My purpose is to help each side understand the other and hopefully increase the quality of ghost research.

Ghost Popularity

Ghosts and hauntings are by far the most common type of paranormal investigations. There are several reasons for this. The first is a direct result of the hugely popular "reality" cable TV show *Ghost Hunters* and its spin-offs and imitators. Such shows depict teams of amateur, ordinary folks with no particular investigative or scientific backgrounds as successful ghost investigators. Another reason is that, compared to other supposedly "unexplained" phenomenon, ghost reports are very common. Daniel Loxton, writing in *Junior Skeptic* magazine, notes that "Haunting is one of the most common kinds of paranormal belief in the U.S. and

The Witch of Endor, depicting a Biblical spirit summoning. Engraving by Kunz Meyer-Waldeck.

around the world. The number of Americans who believe in ghosts may even be growing rather than shrinking. According to one 2009 survey, roughly one out of every five Americans believes they have personally been in the presence of a ghost—double the number who made the same claim during the 1990s" (Loxton 2016, 64). Ghost communication is found in a wide variety of old texts ranging from Homer's *Odyssey* to the Bible (for example Samuel I 28:3-25). Loxton wryly notes that "People across the ancient world believed it was possible to encounter spirits, and even to communicate with them. In Egypt around 3,000 years ago one man wrote a letter to his dead wife, accusing her spirit of misfortune he didn't deserve" (66).

Not everyone lives next to a lake reputed to hold a monster or a wheat field where crop circles mysteriously appeared, but nearly every town or city has at least one (and often several) reputedly haunted places. Any old building, school, abandoned mine, decrepit house, or cemetery will do. Because the evidence for ghosts is so general and ambiguous (ranging from "spooky feelings" to ghostly photos and EVPs), just about any building or location may generate "evidence" if enough people look hard enough and the standard of evidence is low enough.

Sadly, the standard procedure for most ghost investigations the public sees on television or reads online is badly flawed. Ghost hunting can be a deceptively tricky endeavor. Very ordinary events can be—and have been—mistaken for extraordinary ones, and the main challenge for any ghost investigator is separating out the truth from the jumble of myths, mistakes, and misunderstandings. Often, it is very easy to accidentally create or misinterpret evidence: Is that flash of light on a wall from a flashlight reflection—or a ghost? Are the faint sounds recorded in an empty house spirit voices—or a neighbor's radio? It's not always clear, and ghost hunters must be careful to weed out the red herrings and false clues in order to focus on the real ones. (When I refer to "ghost hunters," throughout this book I'm referring to ghost investigators in general, not specifically to the *Ghost Hunters* TV show team unless otherwise noted.)

Using This Book

This book is a guide to science-based ghost investigation written for both ghost hunters and laypeople who wish to understand the field and topic. I should begin by clarifying some misconceptions.

Many people who are interested in the paranormal believe that one method of investigation is as good as another, that there is no "correct" way to investigate the unexplained. Christopher Moon, editor-in-chief of *Haunted Times* magazine, wrote in 2010 asking "if ghosts...haven't been proven to exist, then how can we say who is going about investigating it the right or wrong way? Simply put, we can't."

Actually we can. If the goal of investigation is to understand an unexplained phenomenon, then the methods that produce information solving the mystery are the right ones; the methods that do not help solve the mystery are the wrong ones. It's as simple as that. Paranormal subjects must be investigated just like any other subject: through critical thinking, evidence analysis, logic, and scientific methodologies. Of course, some methods of investigation are better than others. The best way to approach investigation is to use the same guiding principles that professional investigators and detectives use everyday: the scientific method. Assuming that all methods of ghost investigation are equally good is simply wrong, and it causes many ghost hunters to waste untold time, effort, and money following worthless techniques that don't get results.

It is true that hard evidence for ghosts has never materialized. Why is conclusive proof so elusive? There are only two possible explanations for this. The first is that these phenomena do not exist, and all the evidence for them are the result of hoaxes, honest mistakes, misidentifications, and psychological misperceptions. This doesn't mean that the search should end, just that the reason for the lack of good evidence must be dealt with.

The second possibility is that ghosts are real and do exist, but that the efforts to confirm their existence have so far failed because the search is being conducted in the wrong way, researchers are not verifying their assumptions and asking the right questions. The methods used to investigate these mysteries over the past decades have, with a few exceptions, been overwhelmingly pseudoscientific. Much "research" in the paranormal is notable for its sloppy scholarship, bad logic, and poor scientific methodologies.

One common (but apocryphal) definition of insanity is doing the same thing over and over again and expecting different results. For well over a century, the search for ghosts has relied mostly on sightings and séances. In the last decade or so ghost hunters have employed new technology (such as EMF detectors and night vision cameras), yet all the high-tech gear has not led to a single piece of hard evidence for ghosts. Why has the evidence for ghosts gotten no better over the years and decades? Again, either because they do not exist, or because investigators who search for them are using flawed methods.

What would qualify as strong scientific evidence for ghosts? Ideally, some phenomenon that is repeatable and can't be explained by any other means. Some ghost investigators suggest that there is no evidence that would satisfy scientists or skeptics. This is simply wrong. It's true that there is not one single *specific* piece of evidence that could conclusively prove that ghosts exist. That's not how science works, whether the subject is normal or paranormal.

Police detectives and crime scene investigators use time-tested, proven methods to solve crimes and serve as a good example of investigative methods that work. Let's say, for example, police are called to investigate a burglary. There are many different methods that detectives could potentially use to solve the crime. Police could consult a local psychic to identify the criminal, or they might simply wait for the criminal to turn himself in. Another way would be to carefully search for and examine evidence at the scene for fingerprints or DNA. Any of these methods *could theoretically solve the case*, but only one way—methodical, scientific investigation—has proven useful in solving crimes and mysteries. The same applies to ghost and other paranormal investigations.

There are several good books on paranormal investigation in general, on the history of ghosts, on ghost folklore, on scientific research, and so on which can be found in the references. All these offer useful, valid approaches but no single book has yet combined these areas into a multidisciplinary approach. I bring nearly twenty years of field experience in ghost investigation and research—not just accepting or dismissing extraordinary claims from an armchair, not just doing research from behind a computer screen using Google, but actually investigating dozens of reputedly haunted locations around the world.

In 2010 I wrote a book titled *Scientific Paranormal Investigation: How to Solve Unexplained Mysteries* offering practical, real-world advice on investigating a variety of paranormal claims. Its scope was necessarily wide, covering everything from lake monsters to psychics to Bigfoot to ghosts (I dealt with vampiric monsters separately the following year in my book *Tracking the Chupacabra: The Vampire Beast in Fact, Fiction, and Folklore*). I soon realized, however, that ghost investigation merited its own book and I couldn't do such a broad topic justice in a mere chapter or two.

Thus this book was born. Readers will find some unavoidable overlap in a few sections with *Scientific Paranormal Investigation* because many of the fundamental principles are the same, and those who read that book in conjunction with this one will get the most out of both. However most of the material presented here is new and greatly expanded, drawing from my earlier research, and my field investigations using these techniques.

This book is organized into twelve chapters grouped into three main sections.

Part I, "Approaching Investigation," offers practical information and advice on how to apply scientific methods and ideas to ghost investigations. Chapter 1 offers a brief overview of ghost investigation from a historical perspective; though the topic has exploded in popularity in recent decades, it has a long and colorful history. Chapter 2 reviews how to investigate general paranormal phenomena, adapted from chapter 3 of *Scientific Paranormal Investigation*. Chapter 3 covers the phenomenology of ghosts—that is, understanding the idea of ghosts and their nature. If you're looking for something—and certainly something as elusive as ghosts—you must understand some of the ideas about that thing if you want to have any hope of finding it. Chapter 4 examines evidence-based techniques for applying scientific methodologies to ghost investigations and reveals why many widely used methods are unscientific. Chapter 5 covers some of the devices and equipment that can be used to help prove or disprove the existence of an unknown presence, as well as those that are a waste of time and money.

Part II, "Analyzing Evidence," looks at four different types of evidence commonly offered for ghosts. Chapter 6 provides an overview of ghosts caught on camera, a history of ghost photography, and expert discussions on examining anomalies in photographs and on video. Chapter 7 examines one of the best known and widely collected types of ghost evidence: ghostly voices or Electronic Voice Phenomena (EVP). Chapter 8 looks at claims of ghostly writings, ranging from spirit-dictated automatic writing to channeling. Chapter 9 reviews another common type of claimed evidence: experience. Despite not having tangible, hard evidence that can be examined under a microscope, many ghost hunters claim they have powerful personal experiences with undead spirits; this chapter examines some possible explanations for those encounters.

Part III, "Investigation Case Studies," offers in-depth examinations of real-world claims of ghost photos and hauntings. Chapter 10 includes analyses of a half-dozen ghost photos and videos, complete with detailed instructions for what to look for in establishing a supernatural claim. Chapter 11 is a detailed examination of one of North America's most haunted locations, Ontario's Ft. George, and my investigations there. Chapter 12 tracks down the true story of one of Ft. George's best known ghosts. The conclusion briefly describes a dozen or so other ghost and haunted house investigations I've conducted and offers suggestions for further reading.

My purpose is to help sincere ghost investigators adopt better and more scientifically valid methods of collecting and analyzing evidence. If you are content to see the same old stories and ambiguous photos recycled as evidence for ghosts, then this book probably is not for you. My goal is to help intellectually honest ghost investigators recognize the lapses in their methodologies and procedures, the errors that are preventing good quality evidence for ghosts from being collected—assuming, of course, that ghosts exist. If they do not exist, then the investigation techniques I describe here will help clarify that.

There are many reasons to investigate a ghost or haunting scientifically, using critical thinking, logic, and scientific methodologies. The most important one is of course that it *works*; the methods and procedures I outline in this book have proven themselves over and over in solving mysteries and explaining "unexplained" phenomena. If you prefer that mysteries remain unsolved and would rather not look too closely at a phenomenon lest its secrets be revealed through logical deduction and perseverance, this book is not for you.

Practical skepticism and intellectual curiosity aside, there's another important reason to solve these mysteries, and it's a very personal and humanitarian one: People's lives are often disrupted by belief in ghosts and spirits. I have personally encountered many cases where this is true, and most ghost hunting groups can tell you tragic tales of people who have contacted them fearing for their safety and sanity. Whether or not their houses were truly haunted—and I found no evidence they were in the cases I investigated—the *belief or assumption* that they were haunted was in some cases doing very real psychological damage in the form of stress-related health issues, sleep disturbances, relationship strife, divorce, drug use, and so on.

As Marley Gibson, Patrick Burns, and Dave Schrader note in their ghost-hunting book *The Other Side*, "Ghost hunting can be an exciting field to get into, although we must stress that more often than not it's tedious, routine, and boring to the average person. Moreover, with the exception of a very small number of people who write books, work in television, or operate haunted-tour companies, ghost hunting is pretty much just a hobby for most people" (Gibson, Burns, and Shrader 2009).

At the same time, ghost investigation is not a joke, and it's not a game. Despite melodramatic warnings from TV ghost hunters and others, it's not dangerous insofar as physical threats from real or imaginary ghosts, demonic entities, and the like (ghosts have never seriously injured or killed anyone, sensational reports notwithstanding) but the idea of ghosts can be dangerous to those who fear them and have been influenced by dramatic TV shows and books.

Many books written by ghost hunters and others involved in hauntings report experiences that frightened or disturbed them, ranging from pets with puzzling behavior (imagine assuming that every time a dog or cat acts strangely a ghost must be present); to closing off certain rooms in concession to a ghost believed to desire that; to selling a house and moving to a new location, with all the emotional, financial, and other associated stresses.

Though they attribute disturbing and strange phenomena to ghosts, it's clear *that their belief* in ghosts and their resulting reaction to the experiences are causing the most distress. Their stark lack of skepticism and inability (or unwillingness) to thoroughly and scientifically investigate the evidence leaves them unable to explain the experience. I hope that my work will help those who are seeking explanations and reassurances that many, if not most or all, seemingly unexplainable events are in fact plausibly explainable with diligent investigation and an open mind.

Whether or not ghosts exist, it is clear that many cases initially assumed or believed to be caused by spirits were in fact caused by mistakes, misunderstandings, flawed investigation, misperceptions, and so on. Everyone—skeptic and believer alike—benefits from clarifying the situation, improving the quality of evidence for ghost experiences, and distinguishing fact from fiction. When we better understand the phenomena and experiences that can be sincerely mistaken for ghosts, we can more effectively rule those out as explanations going forward, narrowing the focus on the best evidence for ghosts. For that reason, this book is for anyone seriously interested in understanding and solving the riddle of ghosts.

An investigator's job is neither to prove nor disprove ghosts in general or at a specific haunting: the goal is to sort out good evidence from bad, fact from myth, and follow whatever valid evidence remains (after applying filters to screen out logical fallacies and bad evidence) to a logical conclusion. Whatever the result is—whether in support of a mundane explanation or a possibly supernatural one—it should be accepted.

I have read dozens of books on ghost hunting and seen hundreds more on library and bookstores shelves. If these books written by self-professed ghost experts have a common theme, it's the tendency to present speculation as established (or at least strongly supported) fact. Ghost hunting books are littered with blanket statements that, for example, ghosts act a certain way or have certain qualities.

Many feel that writing a book (even a self-published one) about ghosts gives them immediate credibility—after all, this is a field populated by self-proclaimed experts, and where appearing on local TV (or better yet a cable TV series) is seen as the Holy Grail, the ultimate legitimization (instead of, for example, gathering better quality evidence).

Why do so many "experts" on ghost hunting write as if they know more than they do? A series of experiments published in the July 2016 issue of *Psychological Science* offers an answer. People often "overclaim" their knowledge to appear smarter or authoritative than they really are, but sometimes people genuinely overestimate their knowledge about a topic. As *Scientific American Mind* noted, "Researchers at Cornell University tested people's likelihood to overclaim in a variety of scenarios. In the first two experiments, participants rated how knowledgeable they believed themselves to be about a variety of topics, then rated how well they knew each of 15 terms, three of which were fake. The more knowledgeable people rated themselves on a particular topic, the more likely they were to claim knowledge of the fake terms in that field.... Researchers point out that people who believe they know more than they do may be less inclined to pursue further education, or they may give advice about topics they do not fully understand. So the next time you are offered advice from a self-professed expert, you may want to take it with a grain of salt" (Schmerler 2016).

This may help explain why many self-professed "experts" in the paranormal field don't read or consult skeptical resources or information: they don't think they have to. To them, personal experience is their primary educator—supplemented by books, TV shows, and other experts who share their views—and thus skeptical literature is either not on their radar or assumed to be irrelevant. This intellectual insularity sabotages their work because their views, ideas, and positions are rarely subjected to challenge or criticism. There's an old saying that a person who does not understand their opponent's arguments does not fully understand their own—this is why in scientific ideas, theories, and results are published and subjected to peer review and criticized. Scientists understand that the best way to test the quality and validity of competing ideas is to challenge them. It's not a matter of attacking or insulting anyone; instead it's a method for revealing error and improving the quality of the work. This scientific process is virtually nonexistent in ghost hunting.

PART I
APPROACHING
INVESTIGATION

CHAPTER 1
A Brief History of
Ghost investigation

Though many people's exposure to what might be called ghost hunting or ghost investigation is fairly recent—minted, somewhat unfortunately, by the prevalence of cable TV shows—the search for ghosts has in fact been going on in some form for hundreds of years. The full history of ghost research is fascinating and far too detailed to include here but can be found in books such as Peter Aykroyd's *A History of Ghosts,* David Jaher's *The Witch of Lime Street,* and Owen Davies's *The Haunted,* among others. Much of it involves Spiritualism, ghost photography, and twentieth-century mediumship.

As Owen Davies notes in his history of ghosts, "Spiritualism made ghost investigations a mainstream intellectual pursuit" (Davies 2007, 89). Inspired by Spiritualism—and turning a blind eye to the rampant fakery and fraud that plagued the movement since its inception with the ghost-faking Fox Sisters of Hydesville, New York (see chapter 8)—"Societies sprang up to provide a sober, impartial vehicle for assessing the evidence for the return of the dead. In 1851, members of Cambridge University founded the Ghost Club. Another Ghost Club was founded in 1862 by a group of respected London gentlemen... [and] in 1879 some Oxford University students formed the Oxford Phasmatological Society, which existed until 1885...although the Ghost Club would go on to have a long though interrupted life, it was the Society for Psychical Research (SPR), also founded in 1882, that was to be at the forefront of rigorous investigation regarding the spirit world" (Davies 89). As for SPR, Davies notes that "the majority of its founding members soon came to the conclusion that the spirits of the dead did not appear to the living" (Davies 89).

This skepticism arose from various analyses of ghost reports, and "Many of the cases were stated to concern 'spirits,' but what sort of spirits was often left unresolved, presumably because of the difficulty of determining whether manifestations were the work of witches, devils, fairies, or ghosts" (Davies 109). That this thorny—and in all likelihood insurmountable—

problem remains can be seen in the pages of books written by ghost experts who authoritatively decree that there are many specific categories of ghosts (demonic, residual hauntings, etc.). Ghosts, after all, could presumably be merely diabolical hallucinations cast on us fallible, fragile humans by Satan, God, or some other unknowable entities for whatever purpose.

Unlike today's ghost-hunting "sensitives" who typically offer messages and impressions from spirits, early psychic mediums claimed to actually produce hard physical evidence of ghosts. As Davies notes, "By 1850 the spiritualist movement had already caused a sensation across Europe and America. Initially communications were conducted via knocks, raps, and the movement of tables, but as spiritualism developed so the supposed spirit manifestations became more elaborate and more physical... Spiritualists could explain the appearance of the spirits of the dead in rooms in terms of an ethereal materialization of the promordial fluids attracted by the magnetic aura of the medium. If this was so, and such matter could be seen, touched, and smelt, then logically it could also be scientifically analyzed. The skeptics were constantly demanding proof, and with the first manifestations of ectoplasm it seemed that the very essence of ghosts was literally within grasp" (Davies 130).

This ectoplasm appeared as a sort of gauzy, streaming white substance that seemed to come from the mouths, chests, and other orifices of the mediums. Photographs from this era show spirit mediums exuding gauze, sometimes including bizarrely photographic images of faces. Unfortunately it all turned out to be faked: "Despite several decades of ectoplasmic emanations, close examination revealed them to be nothing more than mundane household items such as muslin, cheesecloth, gelatine, and frothy egg whites" (Davies 131).

Foreshadowing today's "ghost industry" (ghost-themed "reality" TV shows, ghost tours, etc.), early purveyors of ghost claims and evidence exploited a paying audience. This seeming improvement in the quality of ghost evidence (spirits communicating though musical instruments, the appearance of ectoplasm, etc.) was a direct result of spirit mediums needing to improve the sensationalism of their (fraudulent) performances: "From the 1860s onward, spiritualist séances became more elaborate and more theatrical in their presentation. Mimicking the simple rappings or tableturning of early spiritualism was simple and dull fare for a paying audience" (Davies 158). Ghost experience purveyors therefore turned to more elaborate magicians' illusions to keep their audiences interested and returning to see ever more dramatic evidence of ghosts—all of it faked.

Most of the Spiritualists of the day—Ira and William Davenport, Eusapia Palladino, Margery Crandon, and others—were repeatedly exposed as hoaxers but still managed to draw audiences (often by taking their shows to new towns where their reputations had not yet preceded them). On the rare occasion that Spiritualists publicly admitted to fraud (for example by being caught red-handed), many even managed to persuade their fans and audiences that their abilities really were genuine and they only resorted to fakery when their powers were dim or the spirits uncooperative.

Indeed "Even the most devout believers in ghosts over the centuries recognized that many hauntings were frauds" (Davies 165). While sometimes the ghost hoaxes were elaborate (involving, for example, dark-garbed accomplices in seance rooms, optical illusions, or ventriloquism), most "merely consisted of individuals prowling around in a white sheet emitting groans... [though] to create a ghost scare one did not even need a sheet. Appearing in white clothing at night was sometimes sufficient to terrify people" (Davies 169). In fact the human imagination (fueled by spooky stories, ghost lore, and the twin powers of expectation and suggestion) can easily make monsters out of mild shadows. Indeed, "The act of dressing up as a ghost and wandering the night-time streets for the purposes of scaring lone pedestrians is a practice with a longstanding history. It's likely that for as long as people have believed in spirits, unscrupulous individuals have taken on their guise for a variety of purposes," notes Jacob Middleton (2013). This was an especially popular pastime in Victorian England, with hundreds of such spectral hoaxes recorded. "The behaviour of these pretend spirits was based not on the spectres which appeared in literature but upon well-established rural traditions"—in other words the hoaxers drew from folklore, legends, and popular beliefs about what ghosts are, how they look, and how they act—just as modern ghost hunters do.

Typically "the best strategy to create hauntings in confined spaces was to simulate auditory or noisy ghosts, which people did not necessarily expect to be accompanied by any visual apparitions.... Basic poltergeist phenomena such as knocking and rapping on walls were fairly easy to orchestrate by a variety of subterfuges and with the help of accomplices" (Davies 172-173). Objects apparently moving on their own, as attested to by eyewitnesses, has a long history of fakery. Davies offers many examples, including The confession of "a twelve-year-old girl... [who] revealed a simple technique for simulating the ghostly movement of objects. She tied a strand of her long hair round the article she wished to disturb and tugged on it, thereby making it appear as if it had been moved by an invisible hand" (Davies 173).

In the famous Columbia Poltergeist case, teenaged Tina Resch—who claimed to be the nexus of ghostly and paranormal activity in her home—was caught (and photographed) throwing a telephone into the air while acting surprised by the sudden "poltergeist" activity. As Terence Hines noted in his 2003 book *Pseudoscience and the Paranormal*, "The Resch poltergeist turned out to be so elusive that no one ever actually saw a single object even start to move of its own accord. This included the newspaper photographer, who found that if he watched an object, it stubbornly refused to budge. So he would hold up his camera and look away... Examined closely, the photographic evidence in this case strongly suggested that Tina was faking the occurrences by simply throwing the phone and other 'flying' objects when no one was looking" (Hines 2003, 98-100).

As far as today's incarnations of ghost hunting, many apparently modern ghost hunting techniques can be traced back to British psychic researchers, among them Eleanor Sidgwick (1845-1936) and Harry Price (1881-1948). There were many other investigators of that era—including Harry Houdini, William Crookes, and Sir Arthur Conan Doyle—whose (mis)adventures are equally enlightening but beyond this book's scope.

Eleanor Sidgwick

Researcher Michaeleen Maher traces back modern ghost investigation techniques to Eleanor Sidgwick, who was an investigator for the Society for Psychical Research in the mid-1880s. Born in 1845 into a prominent British political family (her brother Arthur went on to become Prime Minister), Eleanor Mildred Balfour married philosopher Henry Sidgwick in 1876 and on 1880, at thirty-five, she became Vice-Principal of Newnham College in Cambridge.

According to Eleanor Sidgwick's friend Alice Johnson's account in *Proceedings of the Society for Psychical Research*, "From an early age she showed a special aptitude for mathematics," and indeed Sidgwick "took a keen interest in science generally [and] she once remarked to me that mathematics especially appealed to her in her early youth because she thought a future life would be much more worth living if it included intellectual pursuits," Johnson wrote. Eleanor Sidgwick devoted much of her life to science and education but also had a fascination with what would today be considered the paranormal. She and her husband, both together and separately, spent many years seeking evidence for spirits.

In his book *The History of Ghosts*, Peter Aykroyd (father of original *Ghostbusters* actor and cowriter Dan Aykroyd) describes a séance attended by both Sidgwicks in which a medium claimed to be in contact with ghosts. The medium, Eusapia Palladino, "managed to produce from nowhere a fresh melon, which was deposited on the table in front of the sitters [audience]. She also moved, by psychokinesis or telekinesis, a small wicker table" (Akroyd 2009).

Palladino, however, was often caught faking ghostly phenomena in her darkened, fraud-friendly séance rooms; as Aykroyd notes, "Everyone at the séance saw her cheat...and the mighty Sidgwicks were not at all impressed." Palladino continued to perform for paying audiences, trying to stay one step ahead of the skeptics and ghostbusters who continually exposed her tricks; she eventually gave up and died in 1918. According to Alice Johnson, Eleanor and Henry Sidgwick "condemned the tacit encouragement given by the majority of spiritualists at that time to fraudulent mediums, who knew that no exposure would prevent their continuing to drive a profitable trade."

Eleanor Sidgwick (1845-1936) was one of the founders of modern ghost investigation and served as an investigator for, and president of, the Society for Psychical Research.

Mrs. Sidgwick also helped expose fraudulent activity of many other self-proclaimed psychics, ghost summoners, and mystics including the famous occultist and medium Helena "Madame" Blavatsky.

Sidgwick's article "Phantasms of the Dead" in the SPR's third *Proceedings* (1885) journal examined ghost reports and identified numerous potential sources of error including hoaxing; mistaking a living person for a dead one; unintentional exaggeration by the eyewitness; visual or auditory hallucinations or misperceptions, and so on. She was quite open to the possibility of a ghostly encounter but held that if they occurred they were a form of "veridical hallucination." As Maher notes, "Sidgwick brought an exacting and perspicacious intelligence to her analysis" (Maher 327).

"When she summarized the ghostly characteristics that were representative of her sample—and these same characteristics prevail in the credible accounts of ghosts reported today—Sidgwick concluded that (a) there is no foundation for the supposition that ghosts primarily haunt old houses; (b) there is no indication that ghosts are connected with crimes or tragedies; (c) ghosts do not ordinarily appear on anniversaries or special occasions; (d) ghosts rarely appear in the clothes of a bygone age; (e) ghosts may be seen in daylight or in artificial light, at dawn or at dusk, and in various parts of a house or outside in the yard," and so on—over a dozen principles gleaned from a deep analysis of hundreds of the most credible eyewitnesses and reports (see Maher 2015, 328).

This analysis is interesting for several reasons, not least of which because it largely discredits many long-held and widely believed tenets of modern ghostlore (for example that ghosts appear dressed in clothes of the period they're assumed to belong to, or that ghosts are primarily seen in the dark). Nonetheless many modern ghost hunters continue to seek their quarry in scenarios based on these assumptions, their mission thwarted by misperceptions and unrecognized ghost folklore. In science there's a common phrase that "anecdotes are not evidence," meaning that because personal experience can be misleading (or may not be representative of others' experiences), the general trends that emerge through collecting and analyzing a large number of reports are likely to be more accurate. It's the same reason that pollsters and surveyors ask 10,000 people instead of one person. (For a discussion of Sidgwick and her work by her contemporaries see Alice Johnson's article "Mrs. Henry Sidgwick's Work in Psychical Research" in the *Proceedings of the Society for Psychical Research* part 146.)

Harry Price

As psychologist Richard Wiseman drolly notes, Harry Price "infuriated believers and skeptics alike. He exposed famous spirit photographers as frauds (mainly double exposures), tested the alleged 'ectoplasm' materialized by mediums (largely egg white) [and] re-staged an ancient ceremony to transform a goat into a young man (the goat remained a goat)" (Wiseman 2011, 183). Price worked both independently and with several organizations (most prominently the SPR) interested in paranormal phenomena and conducted numerous ghost investigations in the early 1900s. Among Price's advice for ghost investigations: "When going on duty, see that objects are on chalked outlines, and check frequently. When an object is heard to fall, immediately ascertain in which room object has fallen, and draw a rough plan of room, showing direction of flight... If footsteps are heard, try to judge direction, note duration, and record type (heavy, soft, pattering, shuffling, etc.), and at what time they were heard." Regarding apparitions or ghostly figures, Price counsels "If seen DO NOT MOVE AND ON NO ACCOUNT APPROACH THE FIGURE [emphasis in original]. Note exact method of appearance. Observe figure carefully, watch all movements, rate and manner of progression, etc. Note duration of appearance, colour, form, size, how dressed, and whether solid or transparent" (Quoted in Finucane 1996, 129).

Harry Price (1881-1948) was a pioneering ghost investigator who researched many haunted houses, including the Borley Rectory in Essex, England. Mary Evans Picture Library.

Much of this is of course rather obvious advice, and though Price is surely correct that careful observation is necessary, I would strongly disagree with his counsel to not move toward the ghostly figure, since the closer you are the more detail and thus better information is available to an investigator. Staying immobile and far away from the subject of your study, whether out of fear or for any other reason, is unhelpful. Investigation into monsters and magic, whether real or reputed, is not for the timid.

Like self-promoting ghost hunters a century later who succumbed to the desire for fame and publicity by faking or staging ghost evidence, Price was not only a debunker of frauds, but was also suspected of such conduct. Nonetheless, as ghost researcher R.C. Finucane concluded, "Despite his sometimes questionable tactics and motives, in his own flamboyant way Harry Price drew attention to the need for a more disciplined approach to psychic investigations" (Finucane 1996, 218). Others followed in Price's footsteps—sometimes honorably but often not—including prolific Hans Holzer (whose scholarship and methods were criticized by skeptic and believer alike); Ed and Lorraine Warren, and others.

These days ghost hunting has become greatly democratized, and anyone with time and interest can become a ghost hunter. Hundreds of hotels, restaurants, and myriad other buildings across the country and around the world cater to amateur ghost hunters.

I have neither the flair for sensationalism nor the bent towards charlatanism that Price did, but I hope that my own efforts (and yours, should you pursue it) in ghost investigations—skeptical as they may be—may also help nudge this field into better discipline, better science, and better standards of evidence. For the serious researcher, the person who wants to

Hundreds of locations around the world offer amateur ghost hunters the chance to seek out spirits, including San Diego's famous Whaley House. Photo by the author.

know the truth about ghosts but recognizes that the effort so far has been largely fruitless, the situation is untenable. Those for whom stories and anecdotes are sufficient will blithely carry on—as they have for well over a century—spending (or wasting, depending on your point of view) years of their lives in a fruitless pursuit of good evidence for the afterlife yet content to consider ambiguous reports, sightings, and sounds as somehow proof of spirit communication.

It's not hard to image these early, eager ghost hunters convinced their investigations were on the cutting edge of paranormal research, and that they were on the cusp of discovering important, verifiable information about the afterlife. Today's ghost hunters approach the subject with the same optimistic conviction despite not a mote of progress over the past one hundred and thirty years—not a single verifiable fact about ghosts having been established. I mention this not to be cynical or snarky, but merely to put the pursuit of ghost hunting in its proper historical context. If today's ghost hunters and paranormal investigators wish to have more success than their spirit-seeking forefathers, they should carefully evaluate their methods to be sure they are grounded in science.

CHAPTER 2

Investigation
Guidelines Summary

There is no one "right" way to investigate paranormal and ghost claims, except through the use of critical thinking and scientific methods. The techniques I present here have proven useful and effective in solving mysteries. They are drawn from many sources including professional investigations (such as procedures used by police detectives, FBI agents, and investigative journalists), scientific methodologies, formal and informal logic, psychology, personal experience, and other investigators—along with a dose of common sense. This chapter is adapted and summarized from chapter 3 of my book *Scientific Paranormal Investigation*.

Skeptical Principles

In his wonderful book *The Demon-Haunted World*, Carl Sagan (1996) suggests some guidelines for baloney detection, including the following:

1) There should be independent confirmation of the facts of the case, not just from the proponent.

2) Suggest more than one hypothesis to explain a given phenomenon, and try to come up with ways to discriminate between them to see which best fits the facts.

3) Be willing to abandon a hypothesis if it is not useful; don't force a pet explanation to fit the facts.

4) In a chain of argument, each step must come logically from the previous one, and all links in the chain must be valid.

5) Hypotheses and propositions must be falsifiable (able to be proved wrong) and testable. Claims that cannot be proven one way or the other are of limited use.

One investigative principle that comes up often is Occam's razor. The basic premise is that if you have a phenomenon to be explained and two or more different theories are proposed as solutions, the simplest one (or the one with the fewest assumptions) is much more likely to be the correct answer. For example, if the topic was a ghost that is seen late at night at the foot of a friend's bed as he drifted off to sleep, is it more likely that he was dreaming (or had a hypnagogic hallucination while falling asleep), or that the ghost of a dead person just happened to appear at exactly a time when he was nearing (or in) a dreamlike state? Either is *possible*, but which is more likely?

In determining the best way to solve a mystery, it is first important to understand the nature of mysteries. *Webster's Collegiate* dictionary defines *mystery* as "something not understood, or beyond understanding." Yet this definition actually confuses the issue, because the two definitions are not interchangeable; "something not understood" is rather ordinary, while something "beyond understanding" is quite extraordinary. The former implies a temporary ignorance of the true situation due to a lack of information, while the latter states rather dismissively (and omnisciently) that the event is beyond understanding and in fact *has* no explanation, no knowable solution. There is no shortage of things that at one point were not understood but later became clearly comprehensible. For example, for millennia no one knew how diseases were spread until germ theory was developed. Why some people caught the plague and died was a mystery to people in the 1500s, but it is no longer a mystery today. It was solved through scientific investigation—and it was a mystery created by a temporary lack of knowledge, not some supernatural event beyond human understanding.

To an investigator, a mystery is simply an event out of context. The investigator's job is to find a context in which the mysterious phenomenon makes sense. Think of a completed jigsaw puzzle as a solved mystery. As an investigator you will be given a few pieces of the puzzle (for example in the form of photographs or eyewitness reports). Some information may be bogus puzzle pieces (such as hoaxes, lies, or incorrect information), and you must verify the truth of each fact before you use it in the puzzle. From a few pieces of the puzzle, you must assemble the rest of the solution.

Often, the mystery is created when the facts are not merely lacking a context but put into the wrong context. A person claiming that an event is mysterious or paranormal is presenting you with a jigsaw puzzle with a few obviously wrong pieces jammed in there saying, "Look! This doesn't fit! This must be a mystery!" They have (usually unintentionally) added their own pieces—fashioned from misinformation, bad logic, or faulty assumptions—to fill in the gaps and constructed the wrong frame around the pieces of evidence. They can't think of any other way to make the pieces fit, and their "solution" is that the event is an unexplainable mystery. It may in fact be a paranormal event or unexplained mystery—but that can only be determined once all the other pieces are put in place.

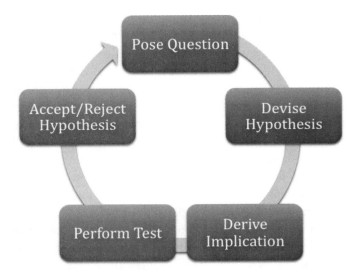

Five steps to a scientific approach.

In many ways solving a seemingly paranormal mystery is like solving a crime. Police work is based on scientific methods: collecting and examining evidence, constructing alternative theories about how the crime was committed and by whom, using science to test those theories, and so on.

Lewis Vaughn (2005) lists five steps involved in a scientific process: 1) Identify the problem or pose a question; 2) Devise a hypothesis to explain the event or phenomenon; 3) Derive a test implication or prediction; 4) Perform the test; and 5) Accept or reject the hypothesis.

When using these steps to investigate mysteries, identifying a problem will help frame the key questions. Sometimes the question comes down to whether a given phenomenon exists (for example, is there actually a Bermuda Triangle where unknown, deadly forces are at work, or is it merely a fictional construct?). Often the problem is identifying the nature or origin of a phenomenon (for example, there is no question that crop circles exist; the issue is who or what made them).

Devising a hypothesis involves seeking alternative explanations. Usually the first theory (or paranormal explanation) provided to an investigator will be the *last* one examined. Often it is not examined at all, because investigations begin with the most likely explanation, and normal explanations are found before the investigator gets to the paranormal ones.

This is basic detective methodology and applies to any mystery, "paranormal" or otherwise. For example, police know that homicide victims are usually killed by someone the person knows (such as a friend or family member). Stranger slayings are very rare, so detectives naturally begin by looking at the most likely suspects (hypotheses) first. If, in the course of the investigation, it becomes clear that the victim was *not* killed by someone he or she knew, only then do the police begin investigating the less likely suspects (hypotheses). When doctors are presented with a pain or symptom, the most common possible causes are assumed (and ruled out) before testing for rarer disorders. This is a variation of the principle of Occam's razor.

When examining a photograph claimed to be of a ghost, for example, an investigator would devise a series of hypotheses that might include: a hoax; a camera artifact (such as a flash reflection); an optical illusion; a real person mistakenly photographed; and finally a ghost. This initial focus on naturalistic, normal explanations has the added benefit of giving the investigator a place to start. Since the nature of paranormal phenomenon is by definition unknown, devising valid hypotheses and tests to examine that phenomenon is very difficult. A ghost might be any size or form; it may or may not appear in photographs, it may or may not leave "cold spots," emit electromagnetic fields, and so on. With so many variables (and without even an established, evidence-based definition of *ghost*), collecting evidence of ghosts can be like grabbing a fistful of rain.

On the other hand, by starting with alternative, scientific explanations whose characteristics are known, an investigator can accept or reject those hypotheses. Once alternative explanations are selected, they are individually tested. Each explanation or hypothesis will have its own logical implications. In the study of logic this is called a conditional syllogism and takes the form of, "If A, then B," or "If A is true, then B should be true."

Guidelines for Skeptical Paranormal Investigation

Here are some guidelines for investigating paranormal claims.

1) As an investigator, you will be dealing with *specific* cases and claims. For example, general claims might be that house X is haunted. Specific claims would be that a ghost was seen or photographed on one occasion, or under certain conditions, at house X. General claims are not testable or falsifiable (you cannot prove or disprove the existence of all ghosts, but you can prove or disprove specific claimed examples or reports of ghosts). Ask the right questions: you must be able to focus on the relevant issues and know what to look for. In many cases what seems like one simple question must actually be broken down into several different ones for independent analysis.

2) Establish the claims clearly and thoroughly. It is essential to find out what exactly is being claimed, by whom, and under what circumstances. As psychologist Ray Hyman points out in the dictum named after him ("Hyman's Categorical Imperative"), before trying to explain a claim, make sure that there is something to explain.

3) Remember that the devil is in the details. Mysteries are easy to create; all you need is to change or omit some important details, or leave false assumptions unchecked. Countless cases of strange or mysterious phenomena have been solved through little more than correctly establishing the particulars and connecting the dots.

4) Realize that questions will sometimes remain after proposing a solution, and it is rarely possible to absolutely prove a case to everyone's satisfaction. Mystery mongers, instead of offering better and more plausible explanations, will sometimes try to nitpick at details. In real-world cases, information is often incomplete or fragmentary, for many reasons: eyewitnesses can be mistaken, records can be lost, etc. There is often no way to know with absolute certainty what happened. Science does not operate on certainties but instead on what fits the facts, what is most likely and probable. An investigator is under no obligation to explain phenomena for which insufficient evidence is offered.

5) Remember where the burden of proof lies and be selective about what cases you tackle, so choose those with good evidence. The burden of proof

is on the person making the claim, not on the investigator to disprove it.

6) Follow the evidence objectively to its conclusion. Don't begin by assuming that a given investigation will turn out a particular way, and don't go into an investigation trying to prove or disprove it. Seek and consider all evidence, not just that which supports a favored theory or explanation.

7) Do sufficient background research on the topic; have a good grasp of the issues before you begin so you know what to look for and what types of questions to ask. You must ask the right questions to get the right answers.

8) Stay focused on the important issues and questions at hand. When investigating a case, especially a complex one, it is easy to become sidetracked and go in several directions at once. Many paranormal proponents and untrained investigators have a difficult time focusing on one aspect of a case at a time and separating out individual claims to determine if they are true or false. Each individual claim should be thoroughly evaluated and determined as true or false before moving onto the next claim. Quality, not quantity, of evidence is what's important. One uncorroborated personal experience is no more useful than a hundred uncorroborated experiences. Another way to put it is "the plural of *anecdote* is not *evidence*."

9) Recognize that investigations often draw upon a wide variety of disciplines, including psychology, forensics, folklore, sociology, scientific methodologies, research and library work, detective work, evidence evaluation, etc.

10) Demand specificity and clarity from people about their claims; do not accept fuzzy logic, made-up words, or vague answers to simple questions. Vagueness is a weasel area that can be used to try to explain away failed results. Scientific experiments and tests do not advance on generalizations.

11) Do good scholarship. Get your facts and quotes right. Double-check original sources; when possible interview original eyewitnesses. Seek primary sources and documents instead of second- or third-hand information.

12) Get a wide variety of claims about the topic; consult five or more sources to see the variety of claims. Different sources may contain dramatically different information and provide clues about what happened.

13) Look for implications and hidden assumptions underlying claims: If a given claim is true, then what else would (or should) be true? Look for keys and linchpins in cases; what assumptions are at the crux of the claim? What assumptions, if false, make the mystery disappear? What is the underlying premise for the mystery?

14) Keep calm, especially when conducting field investigations. There may be times when an investigator is in an unfamiliar area (such as woods or a reputedly haunted location) searching for something or waiting for something to happen. This guideline seems obvious, but TV shows like *Ghost Hunters* and *Ghost Adventures* are filled with very emotional and suggestible "investigators." Whether they are actually terrified or just playing to the camera, the fact is that panic and jumping at shadows does not solve mysteries. If something odd or startling happens, a competent researcher must put aside any natural fear and immediately investigate. Often ghost hunters are too busy running out the door, crying, or curling up in the fetal position to do any investigation.

15) Look for the social context of a claim; reports of mysterious phenomena do not occur in a vacuum. For example, the story of the *Amityville Horror* hoax was created just as *The Exorcist* was hugely popular in the public's consciousness; that fact by itself doesn't "explain" the case, but it does provide a context in which to view the story.

16) Re-creations and re-enactments can be very helpful in trying to determine what happened, and how. But be careful to not infer too much from the results; just because you can duplicate a phenomena doesn't mean the original event necessarily occurred that way, and if you can't, that doesn't mean it didn't happen that way (as the circumstances of your re-creation may not be exact).

17) If you can't find an answer, keep trying. Re-examine all the assumptions, and double-check important facts. Don't be afraid to say, "I don't know." Give it your best guess, based on the evidence, and if you publish an article on it or reach a conclusion, be honest about the limitations of your research.

18) Look not only for positive evidence but also for negative evidence. Often what did not happen is just as important as what did happen. One

famous fictional example of this type of reasoning can be found in the Sherlock Holmes story "The Silver Blaze." The mystery contains the following exchange between a Scotland Yard detective and Holmes:

> Detective: "Is there any other point to which you would wish to draw my attention?"
>
> Holmes: "To the curious incident of the dog in the night-time."
>
> Detective: "The dog did nothing in the night-time."
>
> Holmes: "That was the curious incident."

The dog in question did not bark at the approach of a specific unknown person, and Holmes "grasped the significance of the silence of the dog: Obviously the midnight visitor was someone whom the dog knew well." That is, the fact that something did *not* happen (in this example, a dog did not bark) when we would have expected it to gives us information about what *did* happen.

19) Whenever possible, construct timelines for events. If a glass of milk spills before someone touches it, that is a mystery; if it spills after a hand knocks it over, there is no mystery. Establishing the exact chronology of events can make the difference between a baffling mystery and a solved case.

20) Always treat all eyewitnesses and claimants with courtesy and respect. During investigations, you will, by definition, be talking with people who are approaching the topic from a different point of view (or who are already convinced of the validity of only one interpretation of the event they experienced). Remember that good investigation is about finding the facts and revealing the truth; it is not about attacking a person's credibility or motives. The question of whether an eyewitness truly saw a ghost is a factual issue, not a personal one. You must make a clear distinction between questioning a person's logic or reasoning and attacking him or her as a person. Ridicule or mockery of sincere people has no place in investigation. Not only will it tarnish the reputation of yourself and other investigators, but it is counterproductive and will sabotage your efforts. With the occasional exceptions of frauds and hoaxers, most people who experience and report paranormal phenomena are sincere, honest people who simply didn't understand something they experienced. They need compassion and a sincere effort to help, not ridicule.

Case Study in Flawed Investigation: *Paranormal Lockdown*

A 2016 episode of the show *Paranormal Lockdown* provides an example of how wild speculation and going beyond the evidence can derail an investigation. In the episode (titled "Monroe Demon House," airdate December 16, 2016), ghost hunters Nick Groff and Katrina Weidman meet with Eddie Norris, the owner of what is claimed to be the best-known haunted house in Indiana. According to the promotional copy, "The season premiere takes them inside the forbidding Monroe House in Hartford City, Ind., where ghostly happenings and evidence of ritualistic occult activity that have spooked the homeowner. Former residents and construction workers have fled the property after coming face to face with a dark entity, leaving the home uninhabitable."

The show follows a familiar template, with Norris giving Groff and Weidman a tour of the home as he relates various unexplained events he's experienced or heard about secondhand. No evidence or proof is offered for the "dark entity" or any other past paranormal events, though Norris produces an object that becomes central to the episode: a necklace and pendant with hair caught in it, found under the house by hired workers.

It's not clear what connection or significance the necklace might have to the house or any ghostly goings-on therein. It could have been tossed there by

An advertisement for the show *Paranormal Lockdown* on the Destination America network promises that the investigators won't leave until the audience believes.

a child who didn't want to bother untangling her hair from the cheap bauble. It could have been left by someone crawling around in the small space whose hair or necklace got caught on a nail or something sharp, or any number of other mundane explanations. Or, as Groff ominously notes, "He found some weird objects that were discovered in the basement and we don't know what they are, or why they are used for, but they could possibly be [*sic*] to the occult... the objects Eddie found could have been used as part of a dark ritual that served to bridge the spirit world and ours."

On camera, Norris presents the necklace and hair in a piece of cloth and plastic. Upon seeing it Weidman immediately exclaims, "That's totally ritual. It has to be ritual... It's jewelry wrapped in hair, wrapped in cloth, wrapped in a plastic bag buried in someone's basement.... There's a definite intent in doing that."

What Weidman doesn't understand is that the item—as Norris presents it to her, Groff, the camera (and by extension the audience)—is not necessarily the same as it was when Norris's unidentified workers found and presented to him. Weidman does not know—and cannot know—that the necklace *was* in fact wrapped in cloth or wrapped in plastic when it was found, nor that it was even "buried" in a basement. There is no evidence whatsoever that the necklace was found wrapped in cloth, sealed in a plastic bag, and buried under the house. All she knows (based on secondhand information provided by Norris) is that a necklace with hair caught in it was (allegedly) found in the crawlspace under the house.

The workers could have found it lying on the ground in the crawlspace—perhaps tossed there or lost there—and *they* are the ones who used a nearby scrap of cloth and/or piece of plastic (both common in crawlspaces) to wrap it up and take it out from under the floors to show Norris. Groff and Weidman make no effort to confirm the information told to them by Norris in terms of where the items were found; they could have verified this by interviewing the workers who found the necklace ("How exactly was this wrapped, if at all, when you found it, and where exactly was it?"), but they are nowhere to be seen. Normally the details of such an item's history (what researchers call *provenance*) wouldn't likely be so important, but in this case the wrappings were being used as the sole basis for wild speculation about its allegedly occult past. Keep in mind that it's likely that Norris offered the show producers several objects related to the house, and they chose to focus on the necklace as the weirdest and potentially creepiest of the lot for dramatic purposes.

If Groff and Weidman are certain that understanding the necklace's significance is key to their investigation, there are several experts they could have consulted. Is the piece a valuable gold-and-diamond chain and pendant, or a cheap bauble available at Wal-Mart for under ten dollars? Was it made and marketed five years earlier, or a century ago? Can analysis reveal any clues about the person whose hair is caught in the chain? Was it a young girl, an old woman, or even a man? If the hair follicle contains any roots, it may even be possible to extract DNA and determine the person's race and other identifying characteristics. There are many experts that could have shed light on the necklace, including a jeweler, a forensic hair analyst, a geneticist, or an anthropologist.

Instead Groff and Weidman invite a colleague, Michelle Belanger (credited as "an expert in all things occult"). Belanger notes, correctly, that many magic rituals (including folk magic, Wicca, and voodoo) involve parts of people's bodies such as hair and fingernails, or personal items (rings, necklaces, etc.). She notes that since "there's no obvious symbols carved onto it or drawn onto the cloth I can't identify a specific group or tradition beyond it looks like something intended to hex or curse somebody" and later speculates that "I think this was done not only to bind somebody, but to shut them up."

Belanger, of course, can only go by the limited, speculation-tainted information she is given by Groff and Weidman about the necklace. I'm not suggesting that Norris, the *Paranormal Lockdown* cast and crew, or anyone else is necessarily hiding or fabricating anything; instead, merely that they fail to properly investigate and verify their assumptions at virtually every step, making leaps of logic and guessing far beyond the evidence. Given the well-established threat to scientific, objective investigation that psychological priming and confirmation biases pose (not to mention ratings-driven television), it is all the more important that viewers recognize that "reality" television shows are entertainment, not investigation.

Just about anything found under the crawlspace could easily be spun into fodder for mystery mongers, and ghost hunting shows routinely exploit this ambiguity. This looks like an ordinary nail—but is it possible it was used in some ghastly occult ritual torture? Look over there! A rusty razorblade in the dirt! Could that have been used in a suicide attempt? And here's something faintly marked on the wall, it looks like "M.J. + L.S. = love 4 ever!" Is this evidence of a love triangle gone horribly wrong? Let's find out by researching everyone who lived on this block for the past 50 years to see if we can identify who it was! Examples like this demonstrate to investigators how important it is to avoid these flaws in their own work, and the resulting wasted time and effort.

Case Study in Flawed Investigation: *Kindred Spirits*

In an episode of the ghost hunting show *Kindred Spirits* titled "Breaking and Entering" (airdate November 18, 2016), former *Ghost Hunters* cast members Amy Bruni and Adam Berry investigate a supposedly haunted home owned by a woman named Meghan.

Berry announces, to a room in which he assumes a ghost is present, "We don't mean any harm to you and our main goal is to find out if someone is trying to communicate with Meghan." Berry either misspoke or is lying, because it's clear that he and Bruni are already convinced that someone is trying to communicate with the homeowner; in fact that is the (unproven) assumption the ghost hunters are operating on. As Bruni states when also addressing the ghost, "We're looking for someone specifically who may have lived here at one point, maybe you lived here with your family. Maybe you don't realize that this house belongs to Meghan now" (Bruni 2016).

Berry's slip of the tongue accidentally reveals which vital step both he and Bruni failed to do in this case (and throughout the whole series): First determine or prove that a ghost is in fact present in the home. Only after that fact is established can or should they proceed to trying to identify who that ghost may have been. This is one of the most common mistakes in ghost hunting: Trying to establish the identity of a ghost (through a psychic medium, historical research, etc.) before establishing that the ghost exists at all.

Berry and Bruni ask a series of questions, hoping to elicit either some sort of immediate reaction (a chair falling over, a noise, etc.) or an EVP (upon replaying the recorded conversation). They ask, "How many of you are here? How many years have you been in this house? Are you male or female? Do you have children?" and so on. They then ask the speculated specter to throw an object to get their attention. Still nothing happens, so they then ask the ghost to "get our attention some other way. Come on, where are you?" which once again results in absolutely nothing happening. Berry then comments to Bruni that "It's not ready for those games," and Bruni concurs: "No, it's not."

Berry and Bruni repeatedly sought some sort of indication that a spirit was present, asking it various questions and to make its presence known, and both agreed that nothing happened. The illogical conclusion they drew was that the ghost wasn't feeling cooperative—not that there was no ghost.

Note that if something happens seemingly in response to their efforts (i.e., some sound is heard, or a picture falls off a wall), then that's taken as evidence of the ghost. Similarly, if absolutely nothing happens, that is *not* taken as evidence that they were wrong about a ghost being present, but merely that the ghost chose not to make its presence known. This is of course not how science works: if you conduct an experiment (which is what Bruni and Berry's test was, albeit a poorly controlled one), then you can't just interpret any or all contradictory results as proving your point. In science that's what's called an unfalsifiable theory or claim (it can't be proven or disproven), so it's useless. An experiment in which any result—or no result at all—confirms (and thus offers "evidence" for) your assumptions is no experiment at all.

This sort of pseudoscience and fundamentally flawed methodology might be expected from an amateur group of weekend ghost hunters, but this show aired in 2016, when the two stars have, they claimed, a combined thirty years of ghost hunting experience. A third of a century working in any other career would result in demonstrably better results, but not in ghost hunting, where thirty minutes of ghost hunting experience can yield exactly the same results as thirty years.

CHAPTER 3

A Phenomenology of Ghosts

This chapter examines some of the common assumptions about ghosts—what they are, what they want, how the communicate, what methods are effective in contacting them, and so on. As Owen Davies notes, historically "Ghosts shared certain characteristics with fairies, angels, and devils, and the tricky task of distinguishing between them often depended on the context in which they appeared: and this in turn changed over the centuries according to religious, philosophical, and scientific developments" (Davies 2007, 13).

Unexplained or Unexplainable?

Ghosts are unexplained—but there is no reason to think they are *unexplainable.* Confusing the two is a very common error in ghost investigations. There are countless phenomena that at one point were mysterious and unexplained, ranging from how diseases spread to why the sun rises and sets. As the ancient scientist Hippocrates observed, "Men think epilepsy divine, merely because they do not understand it. But if they called everything divine which they do not understand, why, there would be no end to divine things." Basically the idea is that, "If *I* can't explain it, then no one can."

Yet just because one person can't find an explanation for something they experienced doesn't mean that someone else may not know exactly what it was. No one knows everything; that's why we have experts. But when it comes to unusual phenomena and personal experiences, people rarely seek out experienced scientific investigators. Instead, they simply proclaim it a paranormal mystery.

Joshua Warren, author of *How to Hunt Ghosts: A Practical Guide,* makes this basic mistake early in his book, asking, "When you are not absolutely sure what you seek, how do you know when you find it? The best method is to weed out all ordinary possibilities. What remains is most likely the product of a phenomenon still misunderstood by science" (2003, p. xii). Warren begins well enough—investigation is a process of deduction and eliminating possibilities—but he errs gravely in the last step, committing a logical fallacy called arguing from ignorance. He's saying that if you can't explain something it's likely paranormal, which is simply false; if you can't explain something, all that means is that whatever tools, methods, equipment, and procedures you have tried so far haven't worked, or that you just haven't discovered the answer.

Imagine another real-world mystery that a person may not be able to understand, say a strange rattling under a car's hood, or an unexpected computer crash. If a person tries everything they can think of to diagnose the problem and fails, that in no way implies that the cause "is most likely the product of a phenomenon still misunderstood by science"; it just means that the person needs to get an expert opinion or try something different. Ghosts and other supposedly paranormal topics are not in some special category where a failure to understand or explain the phenomena (after a given effort of anywhere from minutes to hours) means that "a phenomenon still misunderstood by science" is the most likely explanation.

Warren writes that "As we learn more about the spirit realm, our ways of studying it will surely develop and mature" (xiii). He seems unaware that the body of knowledge about ghosts and the spirit realm has been stagnant for centuries and shows no signs of increasing. There is not a single fact that humans have ever learned "about the spirit realm"; there is nothing that we "know" for sure about ghosts today that we didn't know about them a decade ago or a century ago. Outside of ghost folklore—which as an ever-changing sociocultural phenomena can be documented and studied—it's all guesswork, fantasy, speculation, and conjecture. Warren has faith that "ways of studying" ghosts will mature, but the irony is that new technologies (all the EMF detectors, tricorders, infrared cameras, and so on) used by Warren, the *Ghost Hunters*, and other groups have produced exactly zero hard scientific evidence of ghosts. It's a spectacular failure; they have done naught but create new ways to fool themselves and others. Until and unless the specific unique characteristics of a genuine ghost (or ghost experience) are identified, there can be no device that can be calibrated to detect it.

In their book *Ghostly Encounters: The Hauntings of Everyday Life*, Dennis and Michele Waskul note that "given all their otherworldly powers to defy the known laws of nature, the majority of everyday ghosts are dramaturgically impaired. Ghosts are most often indifferent to the living" (2016, 10). It's important to realize that apparently odd, peculiar, or strange things happen in our everyday lives—and usually pass unnoticed. The cat or dog acts strangely for no apparent reason; we discover we had more (or less) money in our pocket or purse than we remembered; we happen to look at a digital clock at 12:34, or 11:11; on a crosstown drive we seem to catch all green lights—or all red ones; keys get misplaced at an especially bad time; an old friend calls out of the blue not long after you thought about him or her; and so on. "When something odd occurs, we either ignore or investigate. If we choose to investigate, most times we find an answer, and sometimes we do not, but either way we minded it. Oftentimes, if an answer is not found and the oddity is mundane enough, it is easy to just scratch your head and move on with your business" (12).

When afraid, alarmed, or psychologically primed to the idea that something unusual and unknown is going on, our sensitivity to anything odd or out of the ordinary goes up, and things that we would otherwise ignore (or perhaps not even notice) can take on added significance. Common occurrences such as flickering lights, dead batteries, unexplained but fleeting unease, computer crashes, blurry sections in photographs, video glitches, and so on can be, and have been, claimed as possible evidence for ghosts. Not only does this unconscious psychological bias lead us to pay attention to such mundane mysteries, but it also imbues them with added significance, making them much easier to remember. A flashlight that happens to go out during a power failure will be soon forgotten, but a flashlight that happens to go out in a dramatic moment when a ghost hunter is asking for a sign from an invisible spirit will be remembered for a lifetime.

Communicating with Ghosts

Warren advises that one of the most important aspects of ghost investigations is "trying to decide exactly what kind of activity you're dealing with" (Warren 2003 111)—in other words, which of the five more or less arbitrary categories of ghosts that Warren thinks exist. These "categories" put the cart so far before the horse that the poor equine would barely be able make out that distant speck on the horizon and wonder if it's supposed to have something to do with him.

Perhaps most obviously, any speculation about a potential ghost's motivations is a frivolous and pointless task because there's no way to independently confirm it. No matter what answer a ghost hunter comes up with as to why whatever phenomenon he or she perceives as a ghost "does" something (appear at a certain location, make a specific sound, etc.), another ghost hunter might come to a completely different—yet equally valid—conclusion based on the same logic and "evidence." There's no verifiable, provable right or wrong answer as to why a ghost does anything, and therefore as an investigative technique it's a dead end.

Even if a ghost exists, and even if it can (and chooses to) communicate its motivations to a ghost hunter, and even if the ghost hunter correctly guesses the ghost's intent based upon taps or knocks or some other inherently ambiguous method, that doesn't solve any mystery. A ghost hunter concluding, "I believe this ghost wanders the hallway mourning his dead wife," even if completely true, doesn't explain anything or give any information upon which to further our knowledge of ghosts. It's a waste of time and effort. Determining why a ghost seems to do something is no more useful than asking it what its favorite color is; there is no independently verifiable right or wrong answer.

Asking why a presumed ghost acts a certain way is akin to asking why a Bigfoot, fairy, or genie acts a certain way, or performing tortuous mathematical and theological calculations to determine how many angels can dance on the head of a pin. It's all guesswork and speculation: until and unless ghosts are proven to exist there's no point in wondering what human motivations to ascribe to them.

Just as spending time deciding why an apparition has chosen to manifest itself is pointless, there's no point in spending time trying to figure out what type of spirit is in a place. Is it Type A, B, C, or D? The answer, of course, is that it doesn't matter; it's not like a mechanical problem in which a person must first assess the situation to determine what tool to use for the specific job (wrench, screwdriver, pliers, hammer, etc.). No credible ghost investigator ever said, "Well, I was baffled by this paranormal haunting for weeks until I realized I'd made a silly mistake: I re-read a ghost hunting book and found out I wasn't dealing with a residual haunting entity, it was really a poltergeist! I felt pretty silly, but once I figured that out I solved the mystery and proved the ghost existed."

The important thing is determining whether a given apparently mysterious phenomena (of whatever sort or category) has a mundane explanation. Guessing at—or claiming to know—why a ghost did something, or what kind of spirit it might be, is like trying to determine what musical note a sound is before proving or verifying that any sound exists, or trying to figure out what color a light is when it's not clear a light is even present. These ghost hunters are essentially asking, "If you could hear something right now, what would it sound like?", though it seems more credible when dressed up in the pseudological trappings of veteran ghost hunters.

Once again, when and if ghosts are proven to exist—and their differing properties can be scientifically quantified and categorized—it will be useful and important to distinguish between types of spirits and apparitions. Until then it's merely a parlor game distracting amateur ghost hunters from the task at hand.

Ghost Typology and Communicating with Ghosts

Many ghost hunting books begin by boldly asserting that there are a specific number of types of ghosts (curiously, the exact number varies somewhat, from two to a half dozen or so). For example Rich Newman, in his book *Ghost Hunting for Beginners*, claims that there are three types of hauntings (Intelligent, Residual, and PK). He offers no source or reference for this, essentially offering a version of "they say..."

But the simple fact is that no one knows if ghosts exist, and therefore no one can be sure how many types of ghosts there are. Ghost reports and sightings can of course be catalogued, analyzed, and categorized, but ghosts themselves cannot. This is a basic mistake, confusing a type of ghost for a type of ghost report; they are not the same thing at all, and ghost hunters confuse the two at their peril. A ghost report is merely a record of something that someone—for whatever reason and under whatever circumstances— could not explain and chose to attribute to an unseen spirit and may or may not reflect an actual ghost appearance. Warren writes that "Determining why a conscious specter stays around is one of the most challenging questions facing the ghost hunter.... Understanding the psychology of a ghost is an even more daunting task" (49).

EVP, which is covered in detail in a later chapter, provides a good example of the premises and hidden assumptions involved in attempting to communicate with ghosts. Newman enthusiastically (and uncritically) endorses the reality of EVPs. He offers advice gleaned from his decade-long career investigating ghosts: "While you are asking your EVP questions, you should follow a few guidelines," including using the present tense when speaking to ghosts; avoiding references to death; asking yes or no questions; and "ask questions that are specific to the location. Examples: do you like the new paintings in the parlor? Is that you opening the bedroom closet?" (Newman 2011, 88).

These are exactly the wrong questions to ask, for the simple reason that the answers are unverifiable. To determine whether or not you are communicating with a ghost you need to elicit factual, verifiable information. Asking a ghost's opinion of a painting is completely pointless; whether the answer is yes, no, or no response, there is no right or wrong answer to such questions, and therefore the questions cannot inform the investigation. A meaningful response to a question such as "Did you die here in a fire?" can be researched and possibly independently verified; any response to a question such as "Are you happy?" or "Do you like the drapes?" is meaningless.

Communicating via Singapore Theory

Newman also endorses "Singapore Theory," which assumes that "playing music from a particular era (that, presumably, of when a spirit was actually alive) will instigate a response on the part of the ghost... Since you do not know what particular era a spirit may be from, you will probably want to keep a folder of MP3s that range across time... [including] classical music, some Civil War-era songs, jazz from the turn of the century, blues, and more... By re-creating the environment the spirit was once comfortable in while alive, you may get the responses you want and capture some evidence of the haunting" (90-91).

Ghost hunters have used some version of this for decades: for example, hiring re-enactors to perform scenes a ghost might have experienced, or using antique items that were common during the era in which a ghost they're trying to contact was alive (such as using Civil War-era items to try to contact Gettysburg spirits). In her book *Dead Whispers: Ghostly EVPs*, A.E. Angel describes how the lead investigator for her paranormal group, Whaling City Ghosts, "might play an authentic Native American drum for the spirits, or purchase an antique toy for a child ghost." When the technique is formally described—instead of simply put into practice—it may be known by various names including "familiarization theory," but when applied specifically to music intended to provoke ghostly response, "Singapore Theory" is the term given.

At first glance Singapore Theory seems vaguely plausible: if there's a spirit present, and if it can hear, and if you know what music he or she liked when alive, then perhaps one of these famously fickle ghosts might respond favorably to that music by making contact. However a closer examination of the circumstances of ghost hunting reveals that none of those conditions are present: Ghost hunters do not know—and *cannot* know—for certain that a ghost is present (if a scientifically valid way to detect the presence or absence of ghosts existed, then we'd have proof of spirits). More to the point, even if a ghost was suspected of being present, it would be virtually impossible for a ghost hunter to correctly identify a particular piece of music that a particular long-dead unknown person might have listened to, much less enjoyed or had some connection to, at some point anywhere from months to centuries earlier.

A bit of historical perspective helps inform the discussion. To take the United States as an example, hundreds of thousands of immigrants from Germany, Italy, France, Ireland, Spain, and elsewhere helped settle this country. Chinese laborers, for example, worked on railways and in laundry houses in the Old West; many of them spoke little or no English. Unless a ghost hunter happened to find a song that was popular around 1850 in Shanghai, for example, which a young man destined to die in the Old West might have learned to play on a *Pipa* (fretted lute) or *Yehu* (fiddle), the chance of musically connecting to this hypothetical ghost are slim.

What if the ghost you're trying to communicate with is Navajo or Hopi, and the only music meaningful to her are traditional tribal dances she grew up with? What if the ghost you're trying to communicate with was born in Russia in 1790 and never spoke a word of English and certainly never listened to any Civil War-era songs or jazz?

Just because a person lived during a certain era doesn't necessarily mean they listened to and enjoyed whatever music was popular in a specific area at that time. For example, though the jitterbug was especially popular in the 1930s and 1940s, and Elvis Presley was popular from the 1950s onward, many people of the era didn't like—nor listen to—that music at the time, and many people still listen to particular types of music decades after its heyday. Mozart and Beethoven are world-famous, but that doesn't mean their music was familiar at the time all over the world, from Indonesian fishing villages to Brazilian farms during their time of celebrity.

If you could somehow know (or determine with a high likelihood of accuracy) that a given location had only been visited by a few people who could possibly have died there—and you have thoroughly documented those people's backgrounds—then you might conceivably be able to select music that they might have listened to. For example if a ghost hunter visited a remote cabin far out in the Nevada desert that was only known to have housed a single Gold Rush miner hermit, or a compound in Antarctica where only a few dozen people had lived, then you could have a chance at selecting music that people who once lived (and possibly died) there might have enjoyed. There is simply no way to accurately identify every single person who may have died in a particular place otherwise.

But in fact most locations where ghosts are reported (historic hotels being a perfect example) are exactly the places where thousands, or tens of thousands, of travelers from all over the world have stayed at one time or another. Hubs of travel—such as airports, bus stations, train stations, and hotels—are exactly the locations where people of wildly varied cultures, languages, customs, and musical preferences are likely to have visited (and perhaps died) over decades and centuries. Assuming ghosts exist, realistically and statistically the chance of any given particular jazz or Big Band tune that a ghost hunter happens to have and chooses to play in a particular location being familiar to a particular ghost is vanishingly small.

Nor is there any established range for ghosts: Does a ghost haunt only the room where he or she died, or a whole house, or a whole neighborhood, or state? Sometimes ghosts have been reported not where they died but where they lived and worked—their businesses and saloons, for example. Depending on which arbitrary "ghost rules" a person assumes ghosts obey, any ghost might haunt any location—making the task of guessing their taste in music that much harder.

Illustration by Celestia Ward
of Two Heads Studios

Unless ghost hunters can somehow correctly identify the age, race, religion, gender, social class, nationality, and other personal information of a particular ghost, there is virtually no chance that whatever music they select to prompt the ghost would be relevant. The ghost you are trying to woo into conversation with what you imagine might possibly be familiar tunes to them might have died five months ago, or five hundred years ago. He or she might have been raised on blues or jazz or classical or hard rock or rap or music from other countries or prehistoric tribal songs. It's even possible that the person never heard any music at all while alive, if for example he or she was born deaf or died shortly after birth.

Without knowing any of the correct biographical details of a ghost it is virtually impossible to accurately predict what music they might have heard, much less enjoyed. Keep in mind that recorded popular music has only existed since about the 1930s. Thus as a practical matter it would be difficult for a ghost hunter to even obtain and play recorded music that anyone before that era would recognize.

Even if a ghost hunter could somehow correctly determine a ghost's favorite *type* of music, that would be of little help since in reality most people's musical tastes are far more specific. They might like rock and roll, for example, but that doesn't mean they like anything that might be included in that category, from Guns N' Roses to Air Supply; a person who likes country music might like Johnny Cash but not the Dixie Chicks, and so on. No music style is homogenous; because not all jazz, bluegrass, or rock is the same, the likelihood that whatever MP3 music files Rich Newman or another ghost hunter might have brought to play would just happen to be music that the dead spirit would recognize and respond to is remote at best.

Ghost hunters using Singapore Theory are instead forced to draw from pop culture stereotypes and tropes. They make (largely baseless) assumptions about what sort of stereotyped ghost they expect might haunt the location (a gunslinger, a slave, a soldier, etc.). As with most ghost-hunting protocols, there's no logic, evidence, or science behind the method; it's based on little more than speculation and guesswork.

To see just how absurd Singapore Theory is, imagine ghost hunters a century from now trying to use it to communicate with an American alive today: Without a clue about the age, race, gender, or culture of that hypothetical person, what music could they possibly choose that would be liked or familiar to him or her? Eazy-E? George Jones? Yanni? Taylor Swift? The Beatles? Aerosmith? Mozart? Youssou N'Dour? Ludakris? Shania Twain? Megadeth?

Lady Gaga? Andy Prieboy? Ricky Martin? Michael Jackson? Shakira? Vivaldi? Bob Marley? The Everly Brothers? Nirvana? Ragheb Alama? Frank Sinatra? Warren Zevon? B.B. King? Woody Guthrie? M.C. Hammer?

All these musicians—and thousands more around the world—created popular music at one time or another, among people of a certain age and sociocultural demographic. But just because a person was alive at a time when a song was popular doesn't mean they ever even heard it; as a rule, Baby Boomers listen to different music than their parents did, and than their children do. But that's not always the case: new generations are being exposed to music from many decades earlier, and thus some teenagers today are just as familiar with Miley Cyrus as the Beatles.

The fact that Singapore Theory and other such methods are taken seriously by many ghost hunters as a proven and credible technique should be concerning; if these experts, who write books and teach classes on investigation, don't recognize the absurdity of this ghost hunting technique, what does that say about their other advice and instruction?

Disorder in the House

It's difficult to overstate the lack of coherent research methods and assumptions about ghosts within the ghost hunting and paranormal communities. A chapter in the book *Ghosts, Spirits, And Hauntings* by ghost hunters Larry Flaxman and Marie D. Jones shows just how disorganized the ghost hunting field is.

Though both are clearly believers in the existence of ghosts and the paranormal (Flaxman is senior researcher with 15 years of experience at the Arkansas Paranormal and Anomalous Studies Team, a member of the T.A.P.S. group and "one of the nation's largest and most active paranormal research organizations"), they acknowledge that ghost hunters still don't know what a ghost is. Flaxman and Jones briefly describe about a half-dozen theories about what ghosts might be. The most popular idea is that ghosts are the earthbound spirits of the deceased. They admit that "this theory creates more questions than it answers" but nonetheless note that it is "the gold standard that guides most ghost hunters and paranormal researchers." But there are of course other theories, including:

> 1) Ghosts are "created by naturally occurring environmental conditions such as electricity and electromagnetic radiation"; evidence for this often comes in the form of EMF readings.

2) Ghosts are the "'playback' of energy or stored human emotion that was once present in the location and then somehow captured or 'recorded' into the environment"; evidence of this theory is often discussed in terms of "residual hauntings," for example. Flaxman and Jones note that if this theory is correct, it raises questions about the legitimacy of EVPs, which may in fact be "merely the thoughts and feelings of the investigators."

3) Ghosts "are very much alive and active, but present in alternate dimensions or realities," and "if a ghostly apparition is indeed coming to us from another dimension or parallel universe, it might not be a dead person at all but a real, live person whom we are merely glimpsing across the great divide of reality."

4) Ghosts may be either figments of our imaginations or products of temporary hallucinations (created, for example, by brain chemicals or low-level electromagnetic fields).

5) Ghosts "are sentient entities that enjoy vexing and even harming humans." This theory suggests that ghosts are similar to supposed demonic entities.

In the end Flaxman and Jones acknowledge that "The bottom line is...even when we appear to have some kind of direct communication from a ghost, we cannot know for sure that we are dealing with a spirit of the dead" (41). This refreshingly candid admission is exactly correct, and it fatally undermines virtually all of the other ghost hunters and paranormal researchers in the book and around the world. The fact that neither Flaxman and Jones—nor anyone else, for that matter—can conclusively rule out any of these competing explanations for ghosts demonstrates clearly that there are no proven facts about ghosts, no certain knowledge. It's all guesswork, speculation, and opinion that's often presented as self-evident truth ("our team helped the ghost to move on") or established fact ("through EVPs the spirit told us he was angry").

Those who might suggest that each of the different theories Flaxman and Jones present as plausible candidates for ghosts may simply be different aspects of the same phenomenon should note that many of the explanations are in fact mutually exclusive. A ghost cannot be both a sentient earthbound spirit *and* a hallucination; nor can a ghost be some sort of "stored environmental emotion" unknown to science *and* a malevolent, mischievous spirit or live human from another dimension. These theories must describe entirely different phenomena. If ghost experts don't have enough known, independently verifiable information about what they're studying to distinguish between a hallucination, a "time slip" from another reality, or a sentient spirit of the dead with verifiable knowledge of the past, the field is in far worse shape than anyone dared imagine.

If ghosts do exist and could be any or all of these things then why bother to have the categories at all? If a ghost can truly be anything you imagine it to be, and have any characteristics you can imagine it to have, how is that different from an imagined ghost? Unless the definitions and explanations for ghosts are anchored in verifiable reality and empirical evidence, it's all theory, speculation and guesswork.

This is why scientists do not accept "miracle" as an explanation for an experimental effect. Scientists do not, and cannot, simply paper over information they do not know with the label "paranormal" or "miracle" or "ghost" and carry on as if they've accomplished something. Saying "a ghost did it" does not promote investigation or inquiry but instead stops it cold—because once you accept a supernatural explanation for anything, you can accept a supernatural explanation for everything. In this worldview (which is prevalent in the ghost hunting community), even if no evidence is found for a ghost, that doesn't necessarily mean that no ghost is present; it simply means that any ghosts that might be there are carefully keeping their presence hidden and undetected.

This is a completely illogical and false point of view, and not how science operates: If, for example, a new drug is tested on 10,000 people and 80% of them improve beyond a placebo control, the logical and correct conclusion is that the drug is effective for most people—not that the drug is actually effective for 100% of the patients but that ghosts, demons, fairies, or some other supernatural entity intervened for unknown reasons to keep 20% of the patients from improving. Nor do scientists attribute the improvement to some unknown, mysterious, paranormal force instead of the active ingredients in the drug which have been tested and proven effective in carefully controlled, double-blind studies. That's simply not how the world works, and most people intuitively understand that—except when it comes to the paranormal, when ghost hunters carve out exceptions and try to introduce caveats in science and logic to accommodate their assumptions and worldviews.

This does not mean that ghosts do not or cannot exist; it simply means that serious researchers must be very careful to avoid falling into the common trap of using "ghost" as an explanation for some unknown light, sound, or experience. Calling something a ghost does not explain anything, nor does it provide any scientific basis upon which to investigate further. Specific phenomena *attributed* to ghosts, can be—and should be—thoroughly scientifically investigated, but a ghost hunter automatically calling anything he or she can't figure out a *ghost* is not merely wrong but counterproductive. *Ghost* is not a synonym for "something I don't understand."

Mysterious 'Flying Brick' photo taken at the Borley Rectory in the presence of Harry Price and other ghost investigators. Credit: David Scherman via Peter Underwood's collection, courtesy of Paul Adams.

The editors of *Ghosts, Spirits, and Hauntings*, Michael Pye and Kirsten Dalley, perhaps didn't realize (or were hoping readers didn't notice) that the book's contributors (including Loyd Auerbach, Joshua Warren, Nick Redfern, Andrew Nichols, and Raymond Buckland) often contradict each other on fundamental premises relating to ghosts. On and on the unnoticed contradictions go. These contributors are a microcosm of the ghost hunting community at large, populated by experts (Jason Hawes, Jeff Belanger, Katie Boyd, Deonna Kelli Sayed, Nick Groff, Zak Bagans, Von Braschler, Hans Holzer, Marcus Griffin, John Kachuba, and dozens of others) who claim literally centuries of collective ghost hunting experience among them, all who say they have found (what is to them) convincing evidence of ghosts, yet who can't even agree on the basic nature of what they all claim to be experts on. Dozens of new ghost hunting books (many of them self-published) by self-appointed experts come out every year, expanding on the cacophony of differing opinions.

I can't think of any field of human endeavor into which so much time and effort has gone, resulting in so little progress—and yet with adherents more convinced than ever that a breakthrough is near. In some ways there are parallels to the countless alchemists over the millennia who were sure they were on the path to finding a way to turn lead into gold, or the many UFO or Bigfoot investigators who keep searching year after year and decade after decade with faith that good evidence is just around the corner.

Many, if not most, of these writers and ghost hunters are sincere people who surely believe what they write and really think they are doing a public service by helping comfort scared homeowners and assisting confused or restless spirits "cross over" to the other side. In addition to the altruism, there's a very appealing populist element to this hobby, and ghost hunting offers a unique opportunity for the layperson to feel that they are working on the cutting edge of a new frontier. It's common to hear ghost hunters speak of their small but important role in pioneering the investigation of the afterlife. Unlike biology or medicine or physics, in which years of academic study and graduate degrees are required to amass enough knowledge to make great scientific discoveries (such as curing cancers or developing ultra-efficient solar cells), no university degree or even any background knowledge is needed to be an expert ghost hunter.

Of course another reason they do it is that there's a lot of money to be made in book sales, DVDs, and tours. As of early 2016 ex-*Ghost Adventures* costar Nick Groff was selling tickets to join his ghost tour of the haunted

Stanley Hotel for up to $245. Despite more than a decade of fruitless ghost hunting TV shows, the public's appetite for such programming shows no signs of waning. Promotion for a show on Destination America network in 2016 offered the following teaser: "In *Paranormal Lockdown*, Nick Groff and Katrina Weidman push the limits of paranormal investigations by living in known haunted locations for an unprecedented 72 hours. Their belief that the longer they stay in the locations the more spirits will be willing to communicate with them is a strategy that has led them to capture groundbreaking and chilling evidence of the supernatural. In the premiere episode, they captured terrifying footage of a slithering entity that manifested into a figure, and future episodes have them being attacked, capturing distinct intelligent spirit voices, and unexplainable visual anomalies that are exposing the paranormal community to evidence that has never been discovered."

Unfortunately, this description, like the show itself, is typical sensationalized nonsense trying to gloss over half-baked pseudoscientific investigation. For starters, Groff and Weidman cannot live in "known haunted locations" because in order for the locations to be "known" as haunted, ghosts must be proven to exist. Nor are the pair pushing "the limits of paranormal investigation" by living in a supposedly haunted home for three days. In fact many people live for months and years in homes claimed to be haunted. There is no incrementally increasing ghostly threat the longer an investigation goes on, so Groff and Weidman's brave posturing about "testing limits" is absurd. They are not free diving or running a grueling marathon; they are walking around a house with a camera crew, literally and figuratively in the dark. The only things they're testing are their video editor's endurance and the patience of their viewers.

I explain elsewhere why this "lockdown" technique is a badly flawed investigation method. There is also no logical basis for "their belief that the longer they stay in the locations the more spirits will be willing to communicate with them," because if that were the case then people who live and regularly work in supposedly haunted homes, hotels, and restaurants should be experiencing—and recording good evidence of—their resident ghosts all the time. This assumption also contradicts the experience of countless ghost hunters who have arrived at supposedly haunted locations (forts, sanitariums, battlefields, etc.) and within a few hours (apparently) contacted a ghost through EVP, a spirit box, on film, in person, and so on.

If Groff and Weidman are correct in their assumption—and there is indeed a positive correlation between how long a continuous single investigation at a specific location lasts and the quality of evidence gathered there (the longer the stay the better the evidence)—then they should presumably have gathered some of the best hard evidence to date, the promised "groundbreaking and chilling evidence of the supernatural." Instead they offer more of the same mundane ambiguous phenomena, vague shadows and odd feelings that somehow still elude all the cameras and gadgets the crew has. Nevertheless the show managed to bring in more than 1.3 million unique viewers.

I don't mean to single out Groff and Weidman for criticism and I understand that they have built careers on the TV ghost investigation business and need to earn a living. My real concern is that many of their viewers see these "reality" shows and are given a badly skewed idea of what a real ghost investigation looks like.

A Common Type of Shady Spirit: Ghost Hunting and Hoaxing

People have been faking ghostly phenomena for about as long as people have believed in ghosts. The techniques for phantasm fakery have improved over the centuries and decades, of course, but hoaxing remains common. For this reason—as well as the myraid ways people can fool themselves—skepticism is not only helpful but essential in ghost research.

Investigator Harry Price (discussed earlier) while surely sincerely seeking spirits much of the time, was not above fakery. As Andrew Clarke (2004), a historian with the Foxearth and District Local History Society, notes in his article "Price and a Flying Brick," the ghost hunter played fast and loose with the truth on occasion—always for his own benefit. In his book *The End of Borley Rectory,* Price included what he called "the first photograph ever taken of a Poltergeist projectile in flight." This famous photo, taken when Price and others visited the rectory (which at that point was being demolished), would become a famous and important image in the history of ghost investigation.

He described the circumstances of this extraordinary photo: "a brick, or part of a brick, suddenly shot up about four feet into the air in front of what remained of the kitchen passage, just below the bathroom passage. The three of us saw it, and, as I said, we were at least a hundred feet away from it. We all laughed and called it 'the last phenomenon,' and said the Poltergeists were 'demonstrating' in honour of our visit. We walked over to the passage, where there were many bricks lying about. I picked up several, and all appeared normal. No string or wire was attached to any of them, and we saw no workmen at all on that side of the Rectory" (Price 1946, 284). Price added that "If, indeed, this was a genuine paranormal phenomenon, then we have the first photograph ever taken of a Poltergeist projectile in flight."

In fact later evidence provided by Price's companions at the time clearly indicated that all of them were well aware of the origin of the "mysteriously flying" brick. It was not hurled by a poltergeist, as Price suggested, but instead "the brick was one of several thrown by a workman engaged in the demolition, who was concealed from the camera behind a wall, but who had been seen by all three of them, including Price, when they were walking around the Rectory," according to Mrs. Cynthia Thompson, who was with him at the time. Her account is backed up by the photographer himself, who told a correspondent in a 1956 letter that "To be quite frank, I saw the workman throwing stones out of the window of the Rectory as it was being wrecked and myself decided it would be fun if we put the camera in such a way so as not to see him, but only the stones he threw. Let me hasten to say that in so doing no attempt was being made to hoodwink our readers—as I recall the caption was jokingly written to imply that this was the sort of thing poltergeists were supposed to do, if poltergeists existed" (quoted in Clarke 2004).

Thus we see that one of the most famous ghost hunters of the early twentieth century was not above faking ghost photographs (Note 1); the most famous ghost hunters of the twenty-first century—TV's *Ghost Hunters*—have also presented hoaxed evidence to the public as well. Some of the photos and scenes on the long-running TV show were faked, including investigators being caught throwing objects and pretending that they suddenly and inexplicably jumped out of their hands, presumably due to an unseen force. One of the main investigators, Grant Wilson, was caught in an infamous and highly suspicious "jacket pull" sequence in 2008, in which he claimed that the collar of his jacket was violently tugged by an unseen force; search YouTube for various video analyses of the "mysterious" incident.

Fame and fortune are no impediment to fakery (and may in fact encourage it as audiences expect more and more dramatic photos and videos). The fact that so much ghost evidence is known to have been faked is a serious problem for ghost research. This problem has also plagued other areas of the unexplained as well; Bigfoot research, for example, is rife with hoaxes, bogus photos, and faked footprints. This creates huge problems for skeptics and believers alike—fraud only serves to taint the whole endeavor

Analysis of a "mysterious" jacket pull on the *Ghost Hunters* television show, seemingly evidence of ghosts but considered a likely hoax. Screen captures from "Jacket Pull Debunk," uploaded to YouTube on November 6, 2008, by "FORMERGH-FAN" and available at https://www.youtube.com/watch?v=ZIM-Uy8ODY.

and contaminates the body of evidence. Those who truly want to understand what ghosts are and if they exist should condemn hoaxers and frauds because they greatly complicate the search for the truth. As someone who has spent years of my life trying to understand ghost reports and analyze eyewitness accounts, I have no patience for hoaxers who waste my time and money. For that reason I give no credence to people known (or strongly suspected) of faking evidence who later offer new, "real" evidence of ghosts, Bigfoot, the paranormal, etc. As the saying goes, "Fool me once, shame on you; fool me twice, shame on me."

Ghost Hunter Ethics

U.K.-based ghost researcher Hayley Stevens, in a 2012 blog titled "The Ethics of Ghost Research," examines the thorny issue of ethical conduct among ghost hunters: "When investigating spontaneous phenomena you will come into contact with all sorts of people who are both involved in the case and not involved in it. As a researcher (whether professional or amateur) the welfare of those affected by your research is paramount. Being guided by your common sense or morality is often not enough to ensure you have considered all possible implications that your presence at a location as a researcher may have on those you come into contact with. This is why it is paramount that paranormal researcher organisations draw up a code of ethics to which organisation members are to abide by while on location." Stevens lists several categories of people who can be harmed by ghost hunters (and paranormal researchers more generally), including the recently bereaved, children, and vulnerable adults. She notes, "Adults who are not vulnerable can still be harmed by the actions of paranormal researchers...Many ghost researchers enter a location in the pursuit of 'evidence' that ghosts exist, this can not only misinform the people they come into contact with but it can scare them too and cause them to feel uncomfortable, unsafe or scared of their own home or place of work."

Most ghost hunters and ghost enthusiasts are, of course, law-abiding citizens, but some have committed crimes related to their activities. A group of ghost hunters set fire to a historic mansion in New Orleans in November 2013. Perhaps inspired by the television series *Ghost Hunters* and its many imitators, the men climbed through a hole in a fence and broke into the LeBeau Plantation house, near the Mississippi River. According to the St. Bernard Sheriff's Office, the men were looking for ghosts, legend tripping, and smoking marijuana.

The mansion, built in the 1850s, had survived many incarnations, including a boarding house, a hotel, and even an illegal gambling house. Though the mansion had been shuttered in recent years, its owners—the Arlene and Joseph Meraux Charitable Foundation—had plans to renovate the building. New Orleans has a rich history (happily promoted by its tourism board) of ghosts, voodoo, and mystery. LeBeau Plantation house was only one of dozens of gothic mansions and plantations rumored to be haunted. While some are more famous than others (the Myrtles Plantation, north of New Orleans in St. Francisville, is said to be one of America's most haunted homes and a prime destination for ghost hunters), it's hard to find a significant old plantation house in Louisiana that does not have at least one ghost story associated with it. Legends at LeBeau tell of a ghostly woman in a long white dress walking on the upstairs porch; other stories recount spooky lights in the hallways or the voices of long-dead slaves.

The fire broke out at about 2 a.m. Friday, November 21, and the building was almost completely destroyed by the time firefighters arrived. The ghost hunters had been trying to elicit a reaction from the spirits they assumed resided there by doing what TV ghost hunters call "provocation"— essentially making loud noises, yelling taunts at the ghosts, and banging on walls. Frustrated that their efforts failed to yield any spirits, the group decided to light a fire. Whether this was intended to smoke the spirits out or simply set in anger to burn the place down, the mansion was soon reduced to ashes and four brick chimneys.

While many ghost hunters engage in harmless (and fruitless) fun, as this case shows there can be a dark, dangerous side to it. In the wake of popular ghost-hunting TV shows, police across the country have seen a surge in people being arrested, injured, and even killed while looking for ghosts. In 2006, a woman was critically wounded looking for ghosts in a private house near a cemetery; she and a friend were trespassing and the house owner mistook them for vandals and shot them. In 2010, a North Carolina man went ghost hunting with a group of friends hoping to see ghosts from a train that had crashed years earlier. The ghost train did not appear—but a real train came around a bend and killed one man who couldn't get out of the way in time.

Luckily no one was hurt in the LeBeau blaze, which could have killed someone or spread to neighboring buildings. Seven men from Texas and Louisiana ranging in age from 17 to 31 were arrested on charges including arson, simple burglary, trespass, and criminal damage worth more than $50,000. In September 2014 all seven pleaded guilty to various crimes, with four of them receiving prison terms.

In September 2016 celebrity ghost hunter Ryan Buell was arrested on two felony charges including theft and stolen property, as well as a misdemeanor charge of theft of services. According to ABC News 11, "Buell claims to be a paranormal expert and appeared on the cable TV series *Paranormal State* that involved looking for ghosts or trying to prove that life after death is real. Buell has a pretty big fan base across the country... Buell had started a tour called 'Conversations with the Dead Tour.' Tickets were sold to shows in cities across the US and Canada, but the shows got postponed and then canceled and fans were left with no answers and looking for refunds. Fans were out hundreds of dollars and wanted their money back. Many of them never got a dime back. Some were able to get refunds by disputing the charge with their credit card company" (Wilson 2016).

Buell at one point claimed to have cancer, but as Catherine Townsend of Crimefeed.com wrote, "Ryan Buell's mother has seemingly confirmed many fans' suspicions that he did not have pancreatic cancer, according to a comment obtained by Crimefeed. Shelly Bonavita Lundburg recently reached out through social media and asked people not to enable her son, and responded to a comment posted by one fan who asked about his cancer diagnosis by writing: 'He's ill, but not from cancer. His family knows the REAL story. You all need to stop believing his lies and stop enabling him...PLEASE!' Her response was deleted, but a fan was able to capture a screenshot, which they forwarded to Crimefeed" (Townsend 2016).

There are other, less obvious ethical considerations as well, including respecting the dead and avoiding exploiting the living. I have encountered this several times over the years. In my investigation of the haunted KiMo theater in Albuquerque, New Mexico, I was contacted by a relative of the boy, Bobby Darnall, who died there. Stories of his ghost have haunted the Darnall family for decades. His sister and brother feel exploited by the story and do not appreciate the fictional claims that their beloved brother is a resident poltergeist ruining performances at the theater.

In my investigation into Jamaica's Rose Hall Plantation (the subject of Chapter 12 in my book *Scientific Paranormal Investigation* and the 2015 season premiere episode of the Travel Channel show *The Dead Files*) I revealed that the evil woman widely claimed to haunt the mansion—Annie Palmer, the so-called White Witch—was in fact based on an innocent historical person. I asked readers to consider the feelings of others: "Imagine if, a century from now, due to some strange mix of myth and circumstance, people describe you as a cruel, perverted, sadistic serial killer. Psychics and ghost hunters claim to contact your spirit, and relay your sensational confessions to the public." How would you feel to have your good name ruined by sensational, ill-informed ghost hunters who claim to contact your spirit and perhaps elicit a "confession" to murder, sexual abuse, or worse?

Zak Bagans, the ghost-hunting star of the popular Travel Channel series *Ghost Adventures*, released music that he claims includes the voice of a television actor's ghost. According to a press release issued on behalf of Bagans and reposted on several Web sites, "In 1999, actor David Strickland, best known for his role on the NBC sitcom *Suddenly Susan*, committed suicide in room 20 of the Oasis Motel in Las Vegas. More than a decade later, Zak Bagans, the host and lead investigator for the hit TV series *Ghost Adventures*, spent hours in that very room attempting to establish communication with Strickland's departed soul. The results of that investigation can be heard on the track Room 20 from NecroFusion, the upcoming album from Bagans and musical partner, The Lords of Acid's Praga Khan."

According to Bagans he went to the motel and "after hours of recording sessions... I began communication with mind-blowing responses. One of the responses I got was when I said 'hello' to David, and a male voice who I believe was his, replied 'Hi, Zak.' I asked if he could hear me and he said 'yea.'... I asked him if he knew where he was, and told me the name of the hotel... Oasis. This was one of the most powerful spirit communication sessions I have ever conducted."

Room at the Oasis motel in Las Vegas, Nevada, where David Strickland died; ghost hunter Zak Bagans claimed to record the voice of the actor's ghost and used it in his music. Photo by the author.

Bagans offered no scientific evidence for his claim. But assuming for a moment that Bagans did in fact contact a ghost, how does he know it was actor David Strickland? Several other people are known to have died violently in that Las Vegas hotel, including murderer Theodore Sean Widdowes in 1996 and professional poker player Stu Ungar in 1998. In fact given the sketchy area of Las Vegas where the Oasis is located, there might be dozens of people who died nearby by murder, accident, or suicide over the years—any or all of whom could presumably haunt the motel. Yet Bagans somehow positively identified a few short, muffled, ambiguous bits of words (what he hears as, "yea," "Hi Zak," "Oasis," etc.) as spoken by Strickland's ghost.

If what Bagans claims is true, he may have a unique opportunity to prove skeptics and scientists wrong, and show once and for all that EVP really are ghost voices instead of an auditory illusion. If the sounds that Bagans recorded are indeed the voice of deceased actor David Strickland, it should be easy enough for an audio expert to compare the EVP to voice samples taken from *Suddenly Susan* or any other of Strickland's television appearances. Either the sounds that Bagans recorded match Strickland's voice or they don't. Strangely, despite being "one of the most powerful spirit communications" Bagans has encountered, such a basic analysis was apparently never done. It's unclear how David Strickland's family felt about his tragic suicide (fueled by the actor's drug addiction and mental illness) being exploited as entertainment by Zak Bagans. For more on ethics in ghost investigations, see my article "Playing Witch Doctor: Hidden Ethics in Skeptical Ghost Investigation" in the Fall 2014 issue of the *Skeptical Briefs* newsletter.

It's important to note that people speaking with ghosts have at times led to serious consequences. Ghost communications—whether real or imagined—has even cost innocent lives, for example during the Salem Village witch trials beginning in 1692. More than 150 people were accused of witchcraft, with nineteen of them being put to death. Many of them were found guilty based in part on what was known as spectral evidence: communications or sensations from ghosts.

"While nobody was tried entirely on spectral evidence, it was what was initially brought against almost everyone at Salem, becoming a litmus test for discovering a witch," Emerson Baker notes in his book *A Storm of Witchcraft: The Salem Trials and the American Experience* (2015, 187). "Spectral evidence was not just drawn from written depositions made before the trial by the afflicted. It was also used in the courtroom, with high drama and to great effect. The climax of most trials occurred when the afflicted confronted the accused [witches]. When this happened, invariably the alleged witch's specter harmed the afflicted, who writhed and shrieked in pain in response to spectral attacks invisible to the jury and the rest of the court. This very public demonstration of spectral evidence could not help but have a strong impact on the jury, giving such evidence far more weight than it deserved. Not only did the judges allow this, but they ignored the many suggestions that such afflictions were being faked" (188-189).

Ghostly contact has not lost its ability to impress audiences over the centuries; though fortunately absent from modern courts, ghost hunters and psychic mediums reacting to unseen information, sensations, and even "attacks" are common. For those watching the reactions are vivid and compelling; something certainly *seems* to be causing the medium to speak in a strange voice or write out mysterious messages, and for many a ghostly presence seems more plausible than fakery, playacting, or the power of suggestion.

Everyone likes a good story, and ghost hunters especially love a creepy and compelling ghost story. Truth is often stranger than fiction, but ghost hunters must be sensitive to the people (with lives, loves, and families) behind their stories. Real people and reputations can be harmed—and the dead dishonored—by careless investigation. Ghost hunters have an obligation, to both the living and the dead, to act ethically and responsibly.

Note

Note 1. Some have attempted to defend Price by claiming that he never explicitly and definitively claimed the incident was unexplained or paranormal. While this is true, Price clearly and coyly led his readers to assume it was a complete mystery. No investigator of integrity should play coy with the facts, even pretending not to know. The credibility of any evidence of the paranormal—and photographs in particular—depend upon truthful, accurate, and complete information from those present. Pretending you don't know (or have some reason to doubt) that an event might have a normal, mundane explanation is not funny: it is dishonest and unethical. Investigation can be incredibly expensive, time-consuming, and difficult. There are few things more frustrating for a researcher than to spend hours, days, or weeks trying to solve a mystery under the assumption that the evidence and information given about it is at the very least believed to be truthful and accurate by those reporting it, only to find out later they were lied to. Anyone caught faking such images forfeits their right to be assumed honest on such matters.

CHAPTER 4

Applying Science—and Avoiding Pseudoscience—in Ghost Investigations

In a previous chapter I outlined scientific methods and explained why the importance of using good science is nearly universally acknowledged. The most famous ghost hunters in the world, Jason Hawes and Grant Wilson (co-founders of the Atlantic Paranormal Society—T.A.P.S.—and stars of the TV show *Ghost Hunters*), agree that science is the best way to approach investigations. They have always claimed to use good scientific methods and investigative procedures, for example writing, "T.A.P.S. uses scientific methods to determine whether or not someone's home might be haunted," and "We approach ghost hunting from a scientific point of view" (Hawes and Wilson 2007, 270).

Yet in their 2007 book *Ghost Hunting*, Jason Hawes dedicates a grand total of four paragraphs (out of 273 pages) to a chapter titled "The Scientific Approach." Hawes doesn't have much to say about science or the scientific methods—it's the shortest chapter in the book. As for his understanding of science, Hawes writes that "Scientific knowledge comes from systemic and objective observations, which help us make deductions we can trust. It also means we have to test those deductions through controlled experiments that can be repeated by others under those same conditions.... We're determined to come as close to scientific accuracy as we possibly can. That's the only way we're going to produce reliable evidence and advance the study of the paranormal" (13-14).

Hawes is correct, as far as that goes: only scientific investigation will shed light on ghostly phenomenon. But he is wrong in his belief that he and his T.A.P.S. crew are doing good scientific investigation. After watching episodes of *Ghost Hunters* and other similar programs it quickly becomes clear to anyone with a background in science that the methods used are both illogical and unscientific.

Science has been such a useful force in the world that it's hard to deny its usefulness. Researcher and creator of the Doubtful News website Sharon Hill has noted, however, that while many (if not most) paranormal and ghost hunting groups eagerly embrace and tout science, very few of them understand it. Most, in fact, only adopt the appearance of science because it lends them credibility and legitimacy; Hill (2012) calls these groups "sciencey" because to the layperson their methods can easily be mistaken for science. But to scientists—or nonscientists who have a basic understanding of science—it's often nonsense. An analogy would be two people having a conversation in front of a third person who doesn't speak their language; the two speakers could, as a prank, start saying gibberish words using the same sounds and accents, and the listener would never know the difference. In this case, however, the ghost hunters are speaking sciencey language and, unless the listener understands the scientific principles being discussed, it can seem very impressive.

Hill researched the characteristics of ghost hunting groups for her Master's thesis (and in an article for *Skeptical Inquirer* magazine) and noted that most lack the hallmarks of science: "Specialized skills and high standards characterize scientific work. However, hardly any amateur research and investigation groups (ARIG) lists formal scientific training as a desired qualification of its members. ARIG members generally do what appear to be respectable, convincing, and 'sciencey' things. The public mostly relies on heuristics, looking for cues that suggest a source of information is knowledgeable and sophisticated. Because much of the public has little understanding of the rigor and practices of science, it is easy for nonscientists to adopt a hollow likeness of science that misrepresents it. The average observer would not have the background knowledge to determine that ARIG portrayal of a 'high-tech' paranormal investigation is ineffectual and without a sound foundation in scientific principles. ARIGs deliver sham inquiry—a process that gives the impression of scientific inquiry but lacks substance and rigor" (Hill 2012).

Ironically, Hawes and Wilson formed T.A.P.S. because they were dissatisfied with the lack of good investigation methods they saw among ghost hunters. According to Jason Hawes, "Finally I said, 'Screw the rest of what's out there,'" referring to other ghost hunters and their methods. "'Let's do it our own way'" (5). Unfortunately, when the T.A.P.S. team developed their "own way" of ghost investigation, they started from scratch and did not consult professionals from relevant fields. Had their procedures been developed by scientists or investigators, their research methods would be much more scientific. Some of the T.A.P.S. crews' methods are slightly better than other groups' (for example, they were among the first to dismiss "orbs" as dust mistaken for ghosts), but are not much more scientific. They lacked good science to begin with, and their methods have not become more scientific (nor effective).

The goal of conducting research is to collect data; scientists use a variety of tools and techniques to collect valid information. But information, alas, does not interpret itself; it's up to people to understand what the data mean—and the more objectively the better. To a scientist, a ghost sighting in and of itself is not proof of ghosts, and it's probably not even evidence of ghosts; it is instead a data point—one of many that must be collected to establish a large enough sample to adequately form or test a hypothesis.

As discussed previously, most ghost hunters grossly underestimate the amount of data that need to be collected to establish a valid baseline reading for environmental conditions. This is crucial because if you don't know what's normal for the area then it's difficult to know what's abnormal (or even paranormal). Let's say that a diligent ghost hunter conducts a monthslong experiment in a reputedly haunted location and collects 120 pieces of data about the weather, wind conditions, EMF fields, lunar phases, geomagnetic soil properties or whatever else he or she thinks might potentially be relevant to a haunting experience. If a quick look at the data reveals that ghosts are seen statistically more often on full moon nights, does that mean that ghosts are somehow more common on full moons? (Surely a creative ghost hunter could come up with some suitably gothic-sounding explanation, such as that ghosts are drawn to moonlight energy from their nether dimension.) Maybe, maybe not. It could just be a function of when people are looking for ghosts; for example, a local ghost tour may be especially popular on full moon nights (for added spooky ambiance), and thus there are more potential people who are hoping (or expecting) to see ghosts on those nights than on moonless nights. An apparent increase in sightings may be caused by that; or it could be that ghosts are rarely seen on especially cold nights—not due to the nature of any spirit-retarding chills but instead the reluctance of their warm-blooded seekers to spend frigid, dark hours in unfamiliar surroundings. Ghost hunters must think like scientists, carefully evaluating alternative explanations, and conclusively ruling them out if possible.

Ghost investigators must understand standard distributions; as well must positive and negative correlations. They must understand control groups and the difference between dependent and independent variables; they must identify possible confounding variables and explain how they have been accounted for in the results. They must understand why correlation does not prove causation.

Of course investigators need not have a Ph.D in mathematics or statistics. The in-depth and arcane formulas are intimidating and unnecessary. Those who wish to understand whether they have found a real effect must understand at least basic statistics, the kind that can be found in introductory books and college-level courses.

A full discussion of valid experimental methodologies and good research design is beyond the scope of this book, but there are some excellent, easy-to-understand resources available. *Research Design: Qualitative & Quantitative Approaches*, by John Creswell, is a very useful and accessible introduction. I highly recommend *Essentials of Research Design and Methodology*, by Geoffrey Marczyk, David DeMatteo, and David Festinger, especially chapter 6, "Validity." The sections on the different types of validity (construct validity, statistical conclusion validity, internal validity, and external validity) should

Ghost hunter Dave Considine and his crew set up their extensive equipment to investigate California's Wolfe Manor for a taping of the *MysteryQuest* television show "Return of the Amityville Horror." Photo by the author.

be required reading for anyone wishing to use the right tools and methods to understand the phenomenon in question. The failure to understand or achieve construct validity (specifically, ruling out alternative explanations) is one of the most fundamental ghost hunting mistakes.

By far the biggest misunderstanding in ghost investigation is what constitutes *good* evidence. There is plenty of evidence for ghosts—but what matters in science is not the quantity but the quality of the evidence. A dozen flawed studies are no better than one flawed study, and one well-designed study can be strong indeed. Just as many cups of weak coffee cannot be combined into one cup of strong coffee, hundreds of ambiguous ghost recordings do not add up to strong evidence of anything.

Ghost hunters share "evidence" and teach others (through books, seminars, and talks) how to find their own "evidence" in the form of EVP, photos, and other recordings. For many novices this provides powerful confirmation—not merely of a ghostly presence but more importantly of the validity of their investigation techniques. I have spoken to many amateur ghost hunters who vividly recount the first time they personally collected an EVP, orb, shadow figure, or other ghostly evidence: They were shaking with astonishment, excited (and sometimes feeling "honored") to have finally had a first-hand experience with something they had seen on television or read about in books. Such an experience can be incredibly powerful and compelling, and because of that it's little wonder that they are extremely reluctant to acknowledge that their "evidence" is not evidence at all, but instead a misunderstanding or a misinterpretation. Admitting that the orb or ghost voice triumphantly shared with colleagues, friends, and family—and perhaps the Internet as well—is merely a flash reflection or an ordinary noise is very difficult to do. Yet it is precisely those things we most *want* to believe that we should question most. It's easy to challenge or dismiss evidence that we disagree with and overlook the flaws in the arguments and evidence we like.

Typical Ghost Investigations

There are some variations, but most ghost investigations follow a similar pattern. First the group hears about a claim and goes to the location to interview one or more people who reported some unusual event. Next, armed with reports and speculation about what might be going on, the team spends hours hauling out and setting up high-tech gear (cameras, audio recorders, EMF detectors, infrared cameras, etc.) around the reputedly haunted location.

Then the group does a stakeout that lasts anywhere from a few hours to overnight. During this time they walk around taking photos, temperature readings, recording audio and video footage, and so on. The lights are turned off, and sometimes psychic mediums, dowsing rods, pendulums, and the like are used to try to communicate with a spirit. Other times a test or "control" object (such as a teddy bear, ball bearings, a toy, a candle, etc.) will be placed in a conspicuous place, and the ghost is asked to affect or move it.

Usually as the investigators, individually or as a team, walk around the darkened place they may hear noises or bump into things. Often any "strange" sounds, smells, lights, or other experiences will be considered potential ghost activity. Sometimes the ghost hunters will find an explanation for this (and the original claimed) phenomenon, other times they won't. Nothing terribly dramatic happens, and at the end of the specific time, the investigators have some phenomena (recorded sounds, video, etc.) to be analyzed at a later time; the stakeout ends and everyone gets some sleep.

Later, the investigators spend hours going over every bit of audio and video that they recorded, combing through it for anything that anyone thinks might be strange or unusual. Depending on how much recording they did, they may have dozens or hundreds of hours, and usually they are able to find a few faint "unexplained" noises (that might be EVPs, or ghost voices) or lights or odd electromagnetic field readings. If the team uses psychics, they will give their impressions. Usually at this point the team has found at least a few pieces of evidence that they can associate with a human presence. For example, a psychic may say she sensed an older male presence in one area; or a faint sound recorded at some location might be thought to resemble a child's voice; or one of the investigators might suggest that a shadow on a wall looks like a tall, thin woman.

Typically the investigators research (or further research) the history of the house, poring over early records and newspaper archives, perhaps interviewing previous owners, looking for anything having to do with the house, its previous occupants, or even the nearby land and houses. Once they have a rough history of the place, they will look for similarities: Is there anything in the location's history that can support or confirm the "evidence" they gathered during their investigation?

Often the answer is yes: If it turns out that an elderly man lived in the house at any point since it was built (and especially if he died there— or even *might* have died there), that "confirms" the psychic's impressions. If a young girl lived there at some point (especially many years ago, and therefore might have since died), then the sound that could be a girl's voice is probably her. And so on. In this way, the investigators believe they are being successful when they find a correlation. They congratulate themselves on a good ghost investigation, explain their findings to the location's owner, and then call the local news media or write up a report for their website, listing the phenomena they couldn't explain.

While this is standard operating procedure for many ghost hunting groups and paranormal investigators, there's a whole catalog of errors, logical fallacies, and investigative mistakes in this scenario, from start to finish. Most of these mistakes fall into two categories: They create false evidence (red herrings, or what in science are known as false-positives, or Type I errors) or the practice is illogical and violates basic scientific methods.

Before discussing the ghost hunting mistakes, I want to be very clear about a basic premise. I've touched on this before but it merits repeating: The goal of ghost hunting is to solve the mystery, to understand what is causing the unexplained phenomena. If a ghost hunter's purpose is simply to have fun with friends (or try to land a TV show) instead of real investigation, then this book will be of no benefit. People thinking they will be exploring the edges of reality during a spooky overnight stay in a haunted location will find themselves bored stiff by sober investigation.

It's important to note that ghost hunters and paranormal investigators often call themselves skeptics, claiming (and sincerely believing) that they are employing science and scientific methods. Whether they claim to be scientific is irrelevant. As the common saying from Matthew (7:16) goes, "Ye shall know them by their fruits." If you want to know whether an investigator or group is scientific or not, examine their methods and results. Do they use the pseudoscientific methods described here? What is their track record of solved cases? Do their investigations end up with inconclusive and ambiguous results, or solved mysteries?

From my nearly two decades of investigation experience, reading books and reports, and talking with ghost hunters and seeing their methods and case studies, it is clear to me that their understanding of science is poor at best. This is not surprising, since virtually all ghost hunters and paranormal enthusiasts are ordinary folks: college students, homemakers, plumbers, and so on. They are not scientists, and studies have repeatedly found that the general public has a very poor understanding of science. Indeed, there's no reason to expect the average person to understand the basic principles of science any more than the average person would be expected to understand the basics of economic theory, dentistry, or accounting. Most ghost investigators are intelligent, sincere people who have simply never been exposed to the real scientific side of ghost hunting, and so instead take their cues and methods from what they see on TV shows.

This is not to suggest that ghost investigators must be scientists. A few of them are—Dr. Steven Novella, a clinical neurologist at Yale University—is one example. But most first-rate paranormal investigators are not scientists; I am not a working scientist, and neither are James Randi, Joe Nickell, Massimo Polidoro, and others. What we share is a solid understanding of the fundamentals of science and its methods. It is often helpful to understand how investigations can go wrong, and to that end I have compiled a list of the most common errors in ghost hunting and haunting investigations.

1. Assuming that no specialized knowledge or expertise is needed to effectively investigate ghosts.

One of the most common assumptions among ghost investigators is that in the paranormal field "there are no experts." If there are no experts, then of course anyone can effectively investigate ghosts. Almost all ghost hunters are amateur, part-time hobbyists from all walks of life, and thousands of them investigate ghosts. On the hit TV show *Ghost Hunters* two ordinary guys who work as plumbers during the daytime are touted as experts on ghost investigations, though none of the team has any background or training in science, investigation, forensics, or any other field that might help solve mysteries.

Why it's a mistake:

Paranormal investigation requires no certificate; anyone can do it with no training, knowledge, or expertise whatsoever. Whether they are effective or not—actually solve any mysteries—is another matter entirely.

It is certainly true that ghosts have never been proven real, and that a person cannot be a true authority on something not known to exist. However, this argument misinterprets the nature of investigation. Anyone can go search for a ghost. That takes no specialized knowledge at all. Despite their name, *ghost investigators do not investigate ghosts*; rather, they investigate various phenomena that might (or might not) be related to a ghost. Effectively investigating claims and solving mysteries, on the other hand, does require some experience and expertise—specifically in logic, critical thinking, psychology, science, forensics, and other areas. And there certainly are experts on that subject, people who have researched and investigated phenomena claimed to be evidence for ghosts.

This shouldn't surprise anyone. Ordinary people hire specialists all the time to explain or handle things that seem too arcane or mysterious for us layfolk. We hire mechanics to investigate and solve (fix) that strange clanking sound under the hood. We hire lawyers to investigate ways to get us out of legal trouble (or avoid it in the first place). We hire doctors to investigate pains and diseases, identify the underlying problem, and suggest how to treat it. And when confronted with mysteries that are also crimes, we hire people who are specifically trained in investigation and scientific methods (such as police detectives) to research the phenomenon.

People don't assume that a person without training can be a good mechanic, doctor, or athlete, yet when it comes to the supposedly "unexplained" mysteries like ghosts, people often assume that no expertise or specialized knowledge is needed to successfully investigate the phenomenon.

One thing that distinguishes an expert from an amateur is that experts get better with experience. They improve their tools and refine their techniques as they gain knowledge and apply their experience to future investigations. Many ghost hunters, on the other hand, repeat the same mistakes over and over, investigation after investigation, year after year. The ghost hunting tools and techniques used in the first season of *Ghost Hunters*, for example, are pretty much the same as those used in the most recent season.

The results speak for themselves: Experts who use scientific methods have conducted—and, more importantly, solved—dozens of ghost cases, while most amateur ghost hunters solve relatively few haunting cases.

2. Considering subjective feelings and emotions as evidence of ghostly encounters.

Members of ghost hunting groups (and TV shows such as *Ghost Hunters*) often report descriptions of personal feelings and experiences, like "I felt a heavy, sad presence and wanted to cry," or "I felt like something didn't want me there," and so on. They also describe in detail how, for example, they had goose bumps upon entering a room, or grew panicked at some unseen presence, assuming they were reacting to a hidden ghost.

Why it's a mistake:

Subjective experiences are essentially stories and anecdotes. There's nothing wrong with personal experiences, but by themselves they are not proof or evidence of anything. Most people who report such experiences are sincere in their belief that a ghost caused their panic, but that belief does not necessarily make it true.

The problem, of course, is that there is not necessarily any connection between any real danger or a ghostly presence and how a person feels. Many people suffer from irrational phobias and panic attacks, terrified of any number of things such as insects, airplane travel, and crossing bridges. Their fears and panic are very real—they truly are sweating and terrified—but it's all psychological; it has nothing to do with the outside world. In the same way, the power of suggestion can be very strong, and a suggestible ghost hunter can easily convince herself—and others—that something weird is going on.

There is no objective, scientific way to test these sorts of claims, no test for fear, uneasiness, panic, a sense of dread, a "spooky" feeling, or other subjective sensations. Even if a person is sweating, or his skin feels clammy, there could be any number of things causing it. Most ghost hunters recognize that their personal feelings can't be considered good evidence, yet they often report these experiences along with the rest of their evidence. Investigators should make an effort to learn about psychology (especially perceptual processes) and human behavior so that their investigations aren't sidetracked by these distractions.

3. Failing to consider alternative explanations for anomalous or "unexplained" phenomena.

Ghost hunters often overinterpret evidence and fail to adequately consider alternative explanations—including assuming that "orbs" are ghosts, EVPs are ghost voices, and so on.

Why it's a mistake:

The designation of "unexplained" or paranormal must only be accepted when all other normal, natural explanations have been ruled out through careful analysis. The explanation for orbs as flash reflections of dust, insects, mist, etc., has been widely discussed for years. Many ghost-hunting groups, to their credit, accept this and flatly reject orbs, though some claim, without evidence, to be able to distinguish "normal" orbs from unexplained ones. Yet many ghost hunters who accept the scientific, skeptical explanation for orbs continue to record EVPs as ghost voices, despite the fact that the scientific evidence for the validity of EVPs is as poor as it is for orbs. Not a single orb has ever been proven to be a ghost, and not a single EVP has been proven to be the voice of a dead person.

Another common error is overinterpreting supposedly anomalous phenomenon. Ghost reports are filled with phrases like "one investigator heard a young girl singing softly" or "the shadow of an old man appeared in a hallway." How, exactly, does the ghost hunter know for a fact it was a young girl's voice or an old man's silhouette? I know adult women who could convincingly mimic the soft singing of a young girl, and cast a shadow that might look exactly like an old man's. It is of course possible that the sound and shadow is of a young girl and old man, respectively, but an investigator must be careful not to go beyond the established facts and assume that their interpretation is the correct one. Once you have made a specific, declarative statement like "a young girl singing softly," you have locked onto that interpretation and not kept an open mind about other interpretations. This also brings up another basic problem that plagues ghost hunters: how do they know that whatever is causing the mysterious phenomenon is necessarily the disembodied spirit of a dead person? Why couldn't it be an invisible gremlin, or a miraculous act of God, or anything else? A ghost is only one of many possible interpretations, and "explaining" a phenomenon by saying "a ghost caused it" is really no explanation at all.

One excellent example appeared in *Mysteries* magazine (Fall/Winter 2006), in which the writers state very matter-of-factly that an inn in Ontario, Canada, is reputedly haunted by the ghost of a woman who "one tragic night fell down the stairs, killing both herself and her unborn child." As proof, the authors offer this chilling account: One night a female guest reported hearing "the nighttime pacing of a pregnant woman" in the hallway above. The woman thought nothing more of it until the next morning when the woman casually inquired at the front desk about the pregnant woman she had heard upstairs the night before. Yet she was assured that there were no other guests staying there—she must have heard the poor woman's ghost, re-enacting that tragic night!

It seems spooky until you ask a simple and obvious question and realize that something is not quite right about this story and the ear-witness. Why would the woman interpret footsteps as necessarily being made specifically by a pregnant woman? What do a pregnant woman's footsteps sound like, and how would they be any different than a large woman's or man's footsteps? Assuming for a moment that the story is true (and not just folklore), there's no way to know what—footsteps, or anything else—the woman heard. Effective investigators must recognize that assuming that the sounds were made by a pregnant ghost is a huge logical leap. (Note that the woman's ability to actually tell the difference between a pregnant and a non-pregnant woman just by her footsteps might be a scientifically testable claim.)

It's important not to overinterpret the claims and go beyond the evidence. Unfortunately this is a very common mistake among beginning ghost hunters. In his book *How to Hunt Ghosts: A Practical Guide*, Joshua Warren writes that "I once investigated a haunted New Orleans mansion where heavy footsteps could be heard thumping up and down the wooden stairs at night. The owner of the home, a sweet, silver-haired woman, wasn't bothered by the activity. 'You may call them a ghost but to me they're just footsteps,' she said. Indeed, she was right" (6). Warren uses this anecdote to illustrate how different people can interpret the same (presumably mysterious) phenomenon, but he manages to completely miss the important lesson in his story: that he *didn't* hear footsteps, he heard "thumping" coming from stairs which he interpreted—perhaps correctly, perhaps not—as footsteps. All that glitters is not gold, and not everything that sounds like something familiar is that thing. Human expectations are incredibly powerful and guide our experiences and interpretations; if we believe the place is haunted and we've heard reports of ghostly footsteps on a staircase and we hear what seems to be thumping from the stairs it's perfectly natural to assume it's footsteps—but to do so is badly flawed investigation (more on this in later chapters).

I don't know what the thumping sound was—neither do you, and obviously neither does Joshua Warren. It could be footsteps coming from another part of the house, or it could be a radiator coming on, or it could be something else; there are many things that could make a thump in a house. I'm not saying Warren didn't hear footsteps; I'm saying it is scientifically impossible for him to conclude—as he clearly did—that what he heard must have been (and could not have been anything other than) footsteps. This sort of basic error is rampant in ghost investigations.

Unless a person verifies the source of a sound, it is logically impossible to identify with any certainty what created that sound. An (alive) adult, an animal, a breeze whistling through an unseen passage, or something else might sound like a child's voice. These sorts of reports are very common and cannot be accepted at face value. They are ambiguous at best and provide no explanation.

4. Using unproven tools and equipment.

There are two basic types of equipment and tools that ghost hunters use: metaphysical ones (psychics, dowsing rods, pendulums, séances, etc.) and scientific ones (electromagnetic field detectors, thermometers, FLIR cameras, etc.). These devices are commonly used (and sold as) ghost hunting equipment. This will be discussed in greater detail in the next chapter.

Why it's a mistake:

In their work, scientists and investigators only use equipment that has been proven effective and is designed for the purpose for which it is used. Police detectives don't use dowsing rods to identify suspects, and doctors don't use EMF detectors to test for genetic diseases. It's not that EMF detectors aren't useful—they very much are, in certain fields—but they have nothing to do with what the doctor is investigating. The same holds true for these unproven tools in the ghost hunting field.

Some investigators claim that they don't use the equipment to detect ghosts; instead they use it to rule out natural explanations for a ghostly phenomenon. The problem is that the naturalistic "explanations" they claim to be ruling out often have nothing to do with the original ghost claims.

For example, let's say that a person believes his house is haunted because he hears faint voices at night, an odd glowing form appeared in a photograph of the house, and small items have inexplicably fallen off a kitchen shelf. Ion counters, FLIR cameras, and EMF detectors are of no benefit in addressing these claims. They cannot reveal the true identity of a glow in a photograph, nor will they explain the origin of the voicelike sounds or what caused an item to mysteriously fall off a shelf. The ghost investigators are not "ruling out" any natural explanations with this equipment, because the gear has nothing to do with the claims. Establishing the location of an electromagnetic field is of no value; it doesn't "explain" anything.

Many ghost hunters consider themselves scientific if they use high-tech measuring equipment such as Geiger counters, Electromagnetic Field (EMF) detectors, ion detectors, infrared cameras, sensitive microphones, and so on. Yet the equipment is only as scientific as the person using it; you may own the world's most sophisticated thermometer, but if you are using it as a barometer, your measurements are worthless. Using a calculator doesn't make you a mathematician, and using a scientific instrument doesn't make you a scientist.

The use of these devices rests upon nothing more than assumptions and pure speculation. For any of these pieces of equipment to be useful there must be some proven connection to ghosts. If ghosts were known to emit electromagnetic fields, then a device that measures such fields would be useful. If ghosts were known to cause temperature drops, then a sensitive thermometer would be useful. If ghosts were known to emit ions, then a device that measures such ions would be useful. And so on.

The problem is that there is no body of research that shows that any of the things these devices are measuring have anything to do with ghosts. Many things are known to emit electromagnetic fields and cause temperature drops; ghosts are not among them. There has not been a single study showing that these tools can detect a ghostly presence. Until someone can reliably demonstrate that ghosts have certain measurable characteristics, devices that measure those characteristics remain irrelevant.

The problem lies not with the devices but instead with the investigators' overinterpretation and extrapolation of their findings. Every single reading, whether a fluctuation in a field or a drop in temperature or anything else, can always be attributed to something other than a ghost: even if an investigator gets an "anomalous" reading, there's simply no way to prove it was caused by a ghost. The evidence gathered by these devices will be inconclusive at best—and always has been.

There is no reason for any scientific investigator to possess or use these devices, since there is no evidence that they detect ghosts. Using a tool or device without being certain it works to find what you're searching for is illogical and unscientific. What's the point in using a tool that—even if it works as you think it does—can't prove anything one way or the other?

Is it theoretically possible that, if ghosts exist, EMF detectors might find a sign of them? Of course it is; anything is possible, but there's no evidence for that. There are hundreds or thousands of other devices or tools that could possibly do the same thing. Without knowing what specific characteristics define a ghost experience, the assumption is based on nothing more than guesses. There's no logical reason to think that an EMF detector would be any more useful in detecting ghosts than a snow globe, a broken inkjet printer, or a fuel gauge from a 1983 Buick. I don't use EMF detectors to find ghosts for the same reason I don't use a toaster to clean my laundry.

This is not to say that cameras and other recording gear cannot be useful in an investigation. They can, but it all depends on the purpose—that is, what the investigator is using them for. A camera set to record an entrance might be very useful in making sure that no one enters unnoticed to pull a hoax or prank. If there is a specific claimed phenomenon that is said to occur, the camera may be a useful tool to record the event if it happens. But simply setting a camera up to record for hours on end with no particular purpose is an easy way to collect bogus evidence. I'm often asked for advice on what sort of equipment is best to use for ghost hunting, and it's difficult to answer the question because of the wide variety of phenomenon. It really depends on what exactly you're trying to record. However, for reasons I explain throughout this chapter, the best gear is often standard old-school video cameras and audio recorders—not EMF detectors or infrared, or other "ghost gear" that is often as expensive as it is useless. Think of it this way: ghostly forms are seen by humans in visible light, so therefore they can be seen by cameras in visible light; ghostly sounds are heard by humans, so therefore good-quality microphones can record them.

5. Using improper and unscientific investigation methods.

In addition to misusing scientific equipment, ghost hunters often misuse (or ignore) good scientific research methods.

Investigating with the lights off

Nearly every ghost-themed TV show has several scenes in which the investigators walk around a darkened place, usually at night, looking for ghosts. Purposely conducting an investigation in the dark is the equivalent of tying an anvil to a marathon runner's foot. It intentionally hobbles the investigation and is completely counterproductive. It also violates common sense and logic. Think about it for a second: if you are trying to identify an unknown object, is it better to look for it under bright lights, or in a darkened room? There are no other objects or entities in the world that anyone would think are better observed in darkness instead of light; why would ghosts be any different? Humans are visual creatures, and our eyes need light to see—the more light the better. Darkness, by definition, severely limits the amount of information available. Searching at night in the dark puts investigators at an immediate and obvious disadvantage in trying to identify and understand what's going on around them. If limiting the investigators' ability to detect things around them helps find ghosts, why not take it a step further and use blindfolds and earplugs on the ghost hunters?

Furthermore, this strategy fails on its own terms. While some report seeing ghosts as glowing figures, many people report them as shadows or dark entities. Searching a dark room for a shadowy figure is an exercise in futility. If it was an established fact that ghosts emit light, there would be some logic to looking for them in a dark room. Unless a ghost or entity has been specifically and repeatedly reported or photographed emitting light, there's no valid, logical reason that ghost investigators would work figuratively (and literally) in the dark.

Some ghost hunters believe that darkness helps to draw out ghostly entities. Yet even a casual review of ghost reports shows that this is not true: most sightings do not occur in darkness. People have reported seeing ghosts in broad daylight, in the morning, and at all times of the day. It is true that people are more likely to report seeing a ghost in the evening hours, but it does not logically follow that ghosts must be more active after sunset.

There are several non-supernatural reasons why ghost reports would occur more often at night, especially in homes. For one thing, there's a sampling bias: most people are not at home during the daytime, and most of their waking hours while at home occur in the evening. Obviously, people are more likely to report potential ghostly activity at night in their homes instead of during the day at an office job or assembly plant. Furthermore, people are more likely to be in psychological states that can induce misperceptions (and even mild hallucinations) in the evening. The evening hours—which of course coincide with the darkness hours—are when people get off work to relax; sometimes they drink alcohol or use recreational drugs. Even those who don't indulge in these substances still succumb to another mental state that has been clinically proven to greatly increase misperceptions and hallucinations: ordinary fatigue.

This does not mean that everyone who is tired after a long day will necessarily see or hear things that aren't there, but fatigue is a real and significant factor that cannot be dismissed. Ghost hunters who are quick to attribute hallucinations to EMF fields often overlook fatigue as a far more obvious (and proven) cause. Ironically, ghosts are almost never reported under the conditions in which most ghost hunters search for them: late at night, in near-total darkness with flashlights and EMF detectors.

Much of the reason that modern ghost hunters look for their quarry in the dark has nothing to do with science or investigation but is instead rooted in fraud and fakery—specifically the conditions under which hoaxing would be least likely to be detected and visitors would be most open to misperception and psychological suggestion. In her book on the spiritualist town of Lily Dale, Christine Wicker notes that "mediums so disliked light that they nailed planks over the windows of their séance rooms... The mediums further improved their chances by constructing so-called spirit cabinets—curtained-off portions of the room from which the spirits emerged once all the lights were extinguished. Spirits demanded such conditions, the mediums said" (65).

The darkness helped mediums and people who claimed to communicate with the dead to hide hoaxing and trickery. It's the same reason that magicians carefully control where their audience sits; they are keenly aware of the angles from which they can be observed and use that to their advantage in presenting their illusions. While it's an unspoken rule that inquisitive audience members are not allowed backstage, or onstage behind the magician while he or she performs, the mediums offering a ghostly experience would give clear instructions about what their sitters could and could not do.

When people were caught faking ghostly phenomena it was often because the investigators did not follow the rules carefully set for them but instead took steps to get a clearer view of what was going on by bringing out hidden flashlights, or whisking off a dark cloth hiding trickery they'd been told not to touch. Keep in mind of course that this would only reveal fakery and not true ghosts; if the writings really did magically appear on slates caused by ghostly hands, or the spirit trumpets really did float in the air from otherworldly forces, there's no reason these things couldn't happen in a brightly lit room. The same holds true today.

There is no logical or scientific reason that ghosts would not (or could not) manifest themselves in bright light and under well-observed conditions. In fact while many ghost reports are liminal, others have been claimed to be very clear and obvious, such as in poltergeist cases in which dishes, telephones, and other large items are said to suddenly fly off tables and shelves. Some ghosts have even been claimed to move and rearrange furniture including chairs and tables. These are not faint, brief sounds or light arguably best perceived in the dark, but instead large and loud obvious ghostly displays which presumably should and could occur in bright daylight and while cameras are recording—yet do not.

This quest for minimal light creates an amusing paradox in which ghost hunters' desire for ghost-friendly (not to mention error- and suggestion-prone) darkness must be weighed against the fact that ghost hunters must be able to see *something* in order to sustain the pretense of investigation. So a compromise is often reached in which ghost hunters use flashlights. That's right: after choosing to remove a bright, fixed light from the investigation area the ghost hunters then reintroduce small amounts of light, thus clearly illuminating only what is directly in front of the flashlight whose light constantly moves along with the ghost hunters, thus introducing moving shadows into an area in which moving shadows are easily mistaken for ghosts. If a ghost hunter has reason to believe—based, for example, on multiple eyewitness reports or videos—that ghosts emit light, then the investigation to find those entities should be done in complete darkness; if not, then it should be done in bright lights. But removing the primary light from an investigation area and then turning smaller lights back on is illogical and a very poor investigative strategy virtually guaranteed to fail.

It's like trying to record auditory evidence for ghosts by turning off stereos and devices generating ambient noise—but then putting on headphones to listen to music while investigating. It's as if the ghost hunters are unwittingly doing everything they can to introduce false-positive evidence of ghosts and make it as difficult as possible to determine whether something paranormal is truly occurring or not.

As Thomas Paine wrote, "It is error only, and not truth, that shrinks from inquiry." Ghost hunters should not sabotage their own research by turning the lights off or otherwise impeding their ability to investigate and identify the source of any anomalies, whether natural or supernatural. The reason it's often done for television shows is obvious: it makes for dramatic footage. It's spookier and more visually interesting to film the ghost investigators with infrared cameras. If the purpose of the investigation is to get spooky footage, turn the lights off. If the purpose is to scientifically search for evidence of ghosts, leave the lights on.

Sampling and statistical errors in ghost hunting

Elsewhere I explain why a ghost stakeout or overnight investigation is a bad idea, but there's another, less obvious basic scientific mistake. Usually ghost hunters will begin their stakeout by taking readings from their high-tech equipment. While a thorough investigation into specific claims or phenomena (such as why a door opens on its own, or the source of a strange noise) can be conducted in a matter of hours, a complete investigation into a haunted location can't be done in such a short time, or even during an overnight stay. The reason is very simple: a few hours or overnight is not enough time to gather enough information to establish a valid set of baseline (or control) measurements for what "normal" (i.e., presumably ghost-free) conditions are at the location.

To know what is extraordinary for the area, an investigator must first determine what is ordinary. Many ghost hunters understand this general principle but greatly underestimate the importance of valid sampling. In environmental science, measurement sampling (for example checking for water or air contaminants), is a very complex process: choosing how to sample, where to sample, what to sample, how often, with what tools, etc., is critical to getting useful measurements. This is why for valid experiments scientists must take dozens—sometimes hundreds—of independent measurements, and analyze the results to derive a statistical average (along with a range of normal variation), which can be used as a basis for research. The timeframes and number of samples that ghost hunters use are far too scant to yield any scientifically meaningful baseline numbers.

There's also the logical problem of comparing readings (EMFs, temperatures, etc.) taken at different times. As any scientist or statistician can tell you, two data points are meaningless. All you can tell from two sets of readings is that either the number has changed or it hasn't. How can the investigator know that the baseline readings taken "before" the investigation started were not detecting ghosts? Think of it this way: Just because Measurement A was taken a few hours before Measurement B does not mean that Measurement A is the "normal" one (the control) and Measurement B represents an anomaly. Maybe Measurement A was the anomaly; or maybe Measurement B was the anomaly; or maybe both Measurements A and B were within the ordinary range of variation and if the investigators took Measurement C they would find *that* to be the anomaly. There's no way to tell which of these interpretations is correct without many more samples (data points).

This sparse data set gives no information on correlation or causation (such as noting that a higher temperature reading was taken in a room that had just been occupied by a dozen warm-bodied investigators). It gives no information about anything, yet it is a standard procedure among many ghost hunter groups who have convinced themselves and others they are doing good science.

A scientific ghost investigator would have to make at least a dozen—and probably many dozens or hundreds of—separate visits to the location (at different times of the day and under different conditions) to carefully measure and record whatever variables (temperature, humidity, light, vibrations, sounds, electromagnetic fields, etc.) will be measured during the stakeout. The more times an investigator samples the location, the more complete and more accurate the information will be.

It's easy to understand why ghost hunters don't follow scientifically valid sampling methods. First, it requires learning about basic scientific and sampling methodologies. This doesn't require a college education; there are plenty of books that can help investigators learn about this. But ghost hunters need to know what it is they don't know and be willing to study and use correct procedures.

Second, there is the time commitment and "fun factor." From my experience, most ghost hunters aren't really interested in the science; they want the fun. Taking measurements and creating a data set in preparation for an investigation is neither interesting nor spooky; it is boring, tedious, mathematical drudgery. Why bother spending weeks with equipment and silly old numbers and textbooks when you can be walking around an abandoned hospital with flashlights, spooking your friends and jumping at shadows?

Third, if the haunted location is a private residence, the homeowners are unlikely to agree to such an intrusive investigation. It's one thing to allow a group of ghost hunters into one's house for an overnight vigil or stakeout to seek spirits; it's quite another to commit a week or more to allowing investigators access for an hour or more at a time—20, 50, or more times, at varying hours—so they can carefully record their observations and gather a valid set of baseline recordings. Even a place of business angling for a ghost tourism boost is likely to object to a disruptive long-term sampling effort.

Anomaly hunting

Much of what passes for ghost investigation, both on television and in ghost hunting groups across the country, is what's called anomaly hunting, or basically looking for anything weird or unusual. Ghost hunters often search for spirits by walking around a supposedly haunted location for hours and setting up tests (or "trigger items"), waiting for anything they consider unusual to happen.

To see the difference between investigation and anomaly hunting, consider the following example. At one famously haunted location in New Mexico, the Albuquerque Press Club, the ghost of a woman—Cliffy McCallum (better known as "Mrs. M")—is said to often appear at the small downstairs bar. As Mrs. M is said to have a taste for gin, a glass of it is left for her on the bar at closing time, and is said to mysteriously "always be found empty the next morning."

This is of course an eminently scientifically testable claim; it would be a simple matter to leave a full shot glass on the bar every night with a high-definition camera trained on it to see whether the gin does in fact mysterious disappear from the glass, and if so, how (Emma, the resident cat, was at first suspected but later cleared as a suspect when a breathalyzer revealed only tuna and mouse).

Why would testing this claim be investigation instead of anomaly hunting? There are two key reasons. The first is that the "test" is based on—and attempts to duplicate (or understand the conditions of)—an original claim from one or more independent eyewitnesses occurring under normal conditions and in a naturalistic setting. In other words, normal people seemingly experiencing ghosts in their normal environments and everyday lives—not staying up all night walking around in the dark with EMF detectors. The second difference is specificity of the claim: under X circumstances (during a moonless night, or in a bar overnight when certain conditions are met, etc.), then specific strange effect Y is seen, heard, or otherwise experienced—not, notably, that *something* odd might happen.

A glass of gin left overnight as an offering for the ghostly "Mrs. M" at the Albuquerque Press Club bar in New Mexico. Photo by the author.

Most amateur ghost hunter groups rely largely on anomaly hunting instead of investigation. Historically, writer Charles Fort (author of several book on historical oddities including *The Book of the Damned*) perhaps best personifies anomaly hunting, doing little or no actual investigation but instead scouring published clippings for anomalies and strange accounts. But reports of anomalies, absent rigorous investigation, are merely anecdotes and are not proof of the paranormal.

Anomaly hunting is a very poor investigation technique; it is not particularly useful in solving mysteries and is in fact usually counterproductive. That's because scientific paranormal investigation begins with a specific claim (e.g., "A ghost in my house throws plates at me," or "My Elvis statue is weeping bloody tears"), which is then closely analyzed. Anomaly hunting reverses this process, essentially putting the investigator in the position of needlessly generating spurious new claims.

It's the classic paranormal fallacy of arguing from ignorance (or personal incredulity): "I don't understand X, therefore it's an anomaly." We see this in everything from UFO reports to ghost and Bigfoot sightings, where people experience something they believe is weird and assume it's paranormal (or at least an "anomaly"). In science, if what you're observing contradicts known facts or the accepted body of knowledge, the first assumption should be that the experiment (or the assumptions behind it) might be flawed in some way—not that you have discovered some new phenomenon.

But isn't anomaly hunting scientific? The answer is no. Scientists, as a rule, do not spend their time searching for anomalies. Geologists don't spend their careers sampling soils around the world looking for anything unusual, and epidemiologists don't randomly screen the public hoping to find some unknown disease. Instead, anomalies appear in the course of their ordinary work and are usually easily distinguished as anomalies. For example, conjoined twins are an anomaly, but it would be pointless for a researcher to spend his time visiting one hospital after another around the world looking for such an anomaly; instead, the anomaly will appear, and *then* be investigated. That's how science works.

It's also important to realize that scientists, unlike ghost hunters, have an idea of how to identify a true anomaly. Scientists educate themselves with reliable knowledge about the characteristics of what they're studying; ghost hunters cannot. Alleged ghostly phenomena is very poorly defined and includes an impossibly wide variety of "signs" including cold, heat, noise, silence, fear, and so on.

To see the problem that anomaly hunting poses, consider the following example. A college student reads that water freezes at 32 degrees Fahrenheit. Being a naturally skeptical and inquisitive fellow, he decides to try it for himself. He fills a cup with water and puts it, along with a thermometer, in a freezer and sets the freezer's temperature. The next day he opens the freezer door and finds that the water is very cold but not frozen. This information—this anomaly—contradicts widely accepted knowledge about the freezing temperature of water. The thermometer reads below 32 degrees, yet the water is not frozen. Science was wrong!

Before he sends an e-mail to the Nobel Committee notifying them of his breakthrough, he should read the fine print for a better understanding of what he was looking for. *Pure* water freezes at 32 degrees Fahrenheit *at sea level*. If the water was not pure, or if the thermometer was not exact enough for scientific purposes, or if he's not at sea level, or if there was a bit of oil or another contaminant in the cup—or any number of other factors he didn't think of—then he will not necessarily get an accurate reading. What he perceives as an anomaly is in fact nothing of the sort. The error is not with accepted science but with his procedures and/or understanding of the phenomenon. Ghost hunters often go through an identical procedure, not understanding what they are looking for and mistaking normal variations in a room's temperature, or ambient sounds, or electromagnetic fields, or any other measure, as mysterious anomalies.

But, one might object, what about something completely unknown to science, as ghosts are said to be? How could a scientist or investigator even begin to determine what qualities it would have? The answer is that many of those (alleged) qualities *are* known; ghosts are said to have been photographed, therefore by definition they exist in the visible spectrum; they are said to make sounds, therefore they are material. The fact that ghosts are said to be heard, felt, seen, smelled, or otherwise sensed means that, if they exist, they can, by definition, be detected through scientific means.

Ineffectively using recording devices

As we have seen, devices such as EMF detectors and ion counters have no use in ghost investigations. Ordinary cameras and audio recorders, however, can be helpful if used correctly. Unfortunately, many ghost hunters (including the *Ghost Hunters*) don't know how to use the equipment effectively.

For example, in episode 401 (airdate March 5, 2008), the T.A.P.S. crew investigated Philadelphia's Fort Mifflin. While there, lead investigator

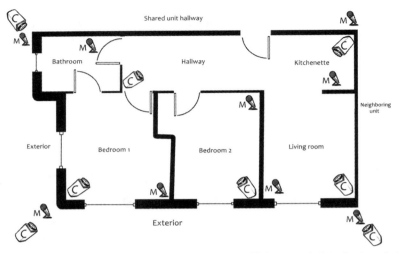

Example of where to place microphones (M) and cameras (C) in a sample floorplan to optimize results and minimize false reports. Illustration by Celestia Ward of Two Heads Studios.

Grant Wilson acted startled on camera while looking through a crawlspace (in near-darkness, of course). He claimed he saw a human face staring back at him only a few feet away, but predictably the television crew trailing him didn't capture it on video. This type of incident has happened dozens of times over the course of the *Ghost Hunters* television show: One or another ghost hunter claims to have seen or heard something just off camera, and therefore without any proof. Was it real, a hoax, an illusion, or hallucination? Without some recorded evidence, it's just another personal story. The solution is obvious: head-mounted wireless digital cameras. They were finally used in a few later episodes (though not consistently by all the crew); it's odd that it took five years for the high-tech T.A.P.S. crew to realize they were a good idea.

Another example is the use of voice recorders. Most ghost hunters, including the T.A.P.S. team, use handheld voice recorders in an attempt to capture a ghost voice or EVP. Often the ghost hunter holds it while standing in the middle of a room while addressing the supposed spirit, or while walking around. Sometimes a voicelike sound will be heard at the time; if so, the ghost hunter(s) will ask more questions, and even if no sound was apparent, the recording or EVP will be saved for later analysis. (For more on EVPs, see chapter 7 in this book.)

Unfortunately, this is not an effective protocol. To identify the nature of the sound (human, ghost, cat, furnace, etc.), an investigator must first determine its source, and that in turn involves locating the sound's origin. This can be very difficult for a ghost hunter to do, especially in a darkened room. If the sound came from an open window, that would suggest one explanation, while if the sound's origin could be traced to the middle of an empty room, that might be more mysterious. Locating the source of a sound is nearly impossible using only one recording device.

The way to scientifically determine the source location of a sound is with more than one microphone—at least three, and the more the better. By placing sensitive microphones throughout the location (and certainly in the four corners of a room and outside), the signal strength of the sound can be measured at each microphone.

Sound is created by longitudinal compression waves in the air, moving away from the source of the sound. Furthermore, soundwaves have several measurable characteristics, including frequency, amplitude, speed, and wavelength. Armed with a basic knowledge of acoustics and math, these characteristics allow a careful investigator to triangulate within a few feet where the sound came from. Ideally this should be done in real time so that the ghost hunters can immediately investigate. Methods of triangulation have been used by engineers and sailors for hundreds of years, but are apparently unknown to the T.A.P.S. crew.

6. Focusing on the history of a haunted location instead of the specific phenomenon reported at it.

Ghost hunters often spend considerable time and effort researching the history of a house or building, scouring local records and newspapers to determine when the place was built, by whom, who may have lived or died there, stories, legends, lists of past owners, tragedies, and so on. This is a staple of many ghost investigations, in which the first hour or so is spent listening to (real or fictional) stories about the history of the place.

Why it's a mistake:

While the history of the location is interesting, it almost always has little or nothing to do with the current haunting claims or phenomena. This becomes clearer if you think of a haunted house as analogous to a crime scene. To a police detective investigating a homicide, the important evidence at hand for solving the mystery may be the dead body, the fingerprints on a door, and gunpowder marks—not when the house was built, who the previous owners were, or who may have died there in a fire during World War II.

If a ghostly figure is reported in a stairwell, a spooky face is photographed in a bedroom, or mysterious noise is reported coming from the attic, knowing who built the place in 1928 (or the name of the little girl who died there ten years ago, or whether two or 200 people died there) is completely irrelevant. It has nothing to do with the face or noises, which must be investigated independently. Sometimes ghost hunters will hear or record what they believe is the sound of a voice and *assume* it must be a ghost, then get so wrapped up in researching the house's history trying to "identify" the ghost that they neglect to fully investigate the source of the sound. If one's goal is to tell a spooky story, then the backstory is essential. For investigations, however, it is usually a distraction.

Time spent researching the location's history is usually wasted unless there's some reason to think that a building's structure may be related to some specific unexplained phenomenon. For example, knowing when a house was built might give you an idea of its construction materials and architecture. This knowledge could help identify odd sounds resulting from a bygone era's plumbing and heating systems. For more on blending historical research with ghost investigation, see *Lone Star Spooks* by Nate Riddle (2011) and *Piercing the Veil* by Charles Spratley (2012).

7. Doing a stakeout or "lockdown."

This is typically an overnight "investigation" into a haunted location, usually with a half dozen or more people wandering around, setting up cameras and other gear, etc. This is one of the most common and basic mistakes made by amateur ghost investigators. Nearly every ghost-themed "reality" television show features this, and it's a staple of most ghost-hunting groups and a particular favorite of the cast of *Ghost Adventures* and *Paranormal Lockdown*. It's also a huge red flag, warning of bad science and amateur investigation.

Why it's a mistake:

As an investigative procedure in ghost hunting, the stakeout (or "lockdown," as it's sometimes melodramatically called) has a 100% track record of failure; out of the hundreds of stakeouts conducted by ghost hunters, not a single one has yielded any significant proof of ghosts. (As I noted, they might have better success if they left the lights on.)

Every stakeout gets more or less the same results: a few ambiguous—yet supposedly mysterious—noises or lights or shadows, but never anything scientifically useful or definitive. Scientists and investigators abandon tools and techniques that don't work, help solve mysteries or explain phenomenon. Instead of recognizing that their evidence never gets any better using this technique, amateur ghost hunters keep doing it. They keep doing it for a variety of reasons, including that they see it on TV and assume that's how ghost investigation is done by the "professionals," and it's something interesting and active. There's a certain entertainment value in walking around a supposedly haunted location and scaring each other silly.

A stakeout is essentially a scientific experiment without the science. Scientific experiments are carefully controlled by the investigator or experimenter: he or she controls some variables or conditions, and measures the variation. To use a basic example, if a botanist wants to see if one potting soil helps plants grow better than another potting soil, she can set up a simple experiment to test this. But she would need to establish careful controls over the experiment to make sure that the results she gets are valid. She would take two identical plants (ideally cuttings from the same parent plant to control for genetics) and expose them to identical sunlight, water, temperature, and so on— essentially controlling a dozen or more variables, so that she can be sure that any difference in growth between the two plants is a result of the dependent variable, the different potting soil. This careful control of the environments is absolutely critical to conducting a valid experiment. If one of the plants was given more sunlight or more water, then that could be the reason it grew better, regardless of which soil it was planted in. Without careful control over the variables and conditions, the experiment is invalid and any results from that experiment are worthless.

Some ghost hunters and paranormal investigators believe they are using good science and controls when they conduct tests, such as setting out "trigger" or "control" objects (teddy bears, balls set on tables or chairs, and so on) that ghosts are invited to move to demonstrate their presence. The problem is that there is no scientific control group to compare any result to. For example, let's say that a child's ball is placed in the center of a table in a reputedly haunted room and recorded on camera overnight. Even if the ball begins to move or roll for some reason, it is not a valid experiment. The investigator would need to have a control condition—one or more identical balls set up in comparable conditions and locations that are supposedly not haunted. It might be, for example, that slight vibrations from a passing train a few blocks away are enough to move the ball, and that any ball placed on any comparable table anywhere in the neighborhood would act the same way. If the investigator only tests that one ball on that one specific table in the suspected haunted location, it's impossible to know if any movement was caused by a circumstance unique to that place. Without a control group, there is nothing to compare any result to. It is classic pseudoscience.

This is directly relevant to ghost investigations, because in a stakeout the experimenter by definition cannot control all, or even the most, of the variables and conditions in the experiment he's conducting. In an issue of *Haunted Times* magazine, ghost experts Christopher Mancuso and Brian J. Cano suggest searching for ghosts in urban areas such as abandoned hospitals, institutions, and factories. This, of course, is a textbook example of a completely uncontrolled location with an untenable signal-to-noise ratio. It's difficult to understand why Mancuso and Cano would think that their "urban exploration" would be a productive setting for an investigation. A serious investigator wants fewer variables and distractions, not more.

You might as well try to record EVPs during a rock concert. How, exactly, is an investigator supposed to discern the typically subtle signs of a ghost in a place that is not only decaying (and likely infested with rodents, insects, and other animals) but also surrounded by the typical lights, smells, and noises of an urban area? There are likely to be ordinary sounds and drafts all over the place that would duplicate or mask any supposed ghostly phenomena. (Not to mention the potential problems of running into vagrants, drug users, and police enforcing trespassing laws.) It's hard to think of a worse place for ghost investigation—or one that would be more likely to create false-positive evidence. An investigator's inability to reliably distinguish between ordinary and extraordinary phenomena renders these investigations a farce.

Making the problem worse, ghost hunters often have little or no training in proper investigation procedures and usually create as much "evidence" as they uncover during the stakeout. I have witnessed many cases where ghost-hunting groups waste time investigating "evidence" that they themselves created because of sloppy technique and carelessness. It's very much like a dog chasing its own tail, and it would be funny if it wasn't such a serious problem.

It's important to remember that nearly anything anyone thinks is odd for any reason can be offered as evidence of a ghost. There is an impossibly broad spectrum of phenomena that have been claimed as signs of ghosts, including lights, shadows, noises, silence, heat, cold, moving objects, smells, uneasiness, and so on. If the presence of a ghost could be narrowed down to a specific phenomenon—for example, if everyone agreed (or it had been proven) that ghosts give off red light, or a certain high-pitched sound—then the problem of not having a controlled location would be greatly reduced. An investigator wouldn't need to rule out every possible source of sound, smell, light, etc., but instead focus on any sources of red light or high-pitched sound. But because just about any phenomenon can be attributed to ghosts, there is no way to rule out or control for the conditions—making ghost stakeouts or lockdowns an unscientific waste of time.

There is one limited exception when a stakeout is warranted: if there is some claim or specific reason to believe that the ghostly phenomena will appear at a certain time, or under certain conditions. This can help establish or refute a cause-and-effect link. For example, if a mysterious sound or light is claimed to happen at a specific time (say, around midnight), or under certain conditions (such as a full moon or the anniversary of a death), then it is reasonable to be present and ready to investigate should the phenomenon present itself. However, simply sitting around waiting for some unspecified event to happen is non-scientific and almost guaranteed to create false positive evidence.

8. Doing a post-mortem evaluation of evidence gathered during a stakeout or lockdown.

During the above-mentioned overnight investigation ghost hunters typically record dozens or hundreds of hours of audio and videotape to be painstakingly reviewed at a later time in a search for any anomalies that were not noticed at the time of recording. This is another standard pseudoscientific procedure seen *Ghost Hunters*, *Ghost Adventures*, and other television shows.

Why it's a mistake:

As noted above, the stakeout is inherently unscientific, and therefore any evidence gathered during that investigation is of little value. If the procedure for collecting data is flawed, then any results from that procedure will be flawed: garbage in, garbage out. Beyond that, it's a mistake for other reasons.

Except in rare cases, reviewing evidence after an investigation concludes is of very limited value. Even if something strange or unusual is recorded, the chance to meaningfully investigate the phenomenon (say, a noise, light, or moving object) has passed. Good investigators must fully investigate any unexplained phenomenon *at the time it is occurring*; noticing something strange on an audio or video playback days or weeks later is pointless.

In statistical analysis, this process—which is discouraged because it often finds evidence where none exists—is called retrospective substratification, also known as data mining. It happens when an experimenter collects a lot of data but doesn't find the effect they were looking for. Instead of accepting that their experiment found no results, they look closer and closer at the data, combing through the data (and sometimes analyzing it in different ways), searching for some effect—even if it's not what the experiment was originally designed to find. Often, with a large enough data set the experimenter will finally find some anomalies or trends whose significance is ambiguous and then claim that as evidence supporting their original theory or hypothesis.

A very similar process happens with after-the-fact reviews of ghost evidence. Let's say, for example, a ghost hunter sets a camera to record a so-called trigger item. The item is videotaped from dusk until dawn, and later during the "evidence review" the ghost hunter watches hours and hours of footage of a completely stationary object doing absolutely nothing. The test's hypothesis that the ghost would make the object move (maybe float in the air, spin around, or emit green slime) has been falsified: it did not happen. But if at any point during the many hours there seems to be a faint light or sound or movement, the experimenter may decide that *that* occurence might be the ghost. (Or, of course, it might have been a flying insect, an unnoticed headlight or flashlight, a video glitch, or any number of other things.) The point is that the ghost hunter did not accept that the original intended effect was not found and instead kept looking and lowering the bar of evidence until some apparently minor, likely mundane, event was considered ghostly evidence. Everyone would agree that a teddy bear suddenly floating in the air could be considered strong evidence of the paranormal, but no scientific investigator would agree that a faint sound is good evidence.

9. Lack of any systematic scientific testing of hypotheses.

In chapter 2 I discussed the basic principles of the scientific process. Despite a lack of hard evidence about the nature of ghosts, there are many popular claims and theories about them; almost none have been tested.

Why it's a mistake:

Many theories about ghosts make testable claims and predictions, yet few good scientific tests have been conducted. For example, if an investigator believes that ghosts inhabit a building, and also that ghosts give off electromagnetic fields, then logically a "haunted" building should have higher levels of electromagnetic fields than a comparable control building that the investigator believes is not haunted. If an investigator believes that a device (such as a "Frank's Box," see chapter 7) can actually communicate with the dead, there are ways to test that theory. And so on.

To address one common claim, batteries are said to become mysteriously drained by ghosts in haunted locations. Some think it's because ghosts are primarily energy and feed off the batteries to manifest themselves. There's plenty of speculation—but little experimentation. Yet this is an easily testable, verifiable claim: Either batteries in a supposedly haunted location lose their charge more quickly than identical batteries in a control location, or they do not. I personally conducted just such a test at "The Haunted" Wolfe Manor (aka Andleberry Estates) in Clovis, California, in 2009. I purchased four sets of identical batteries (two each of "C" and "D" cells), and sealed them in Ziploc bags and used high-strength plastic tape to wrap them tightly, which I signed to prevent tampering. I then placed half of them in Wolfe Manor and the other half at another location offsite.

Twenty-four hours later I used a battery meter to check the cells' charges; my experiment showed no electricity drainage at all in the "haunted" location batteries or anywhere else. This was a simple, basic scientific experiment that just about anyone could do, yet as far as I know this was the first time that any ghost hunter had tested this claim.

Why is there so little actual scientific experimentation of ghost claims? I think there are several reasons. First, conducting scientifically valid experiments is not easy; it requires knowledge of basic experimental design (such as controls, control groups, single- and double-blind testing protocols, etc.). These ideas are not difficult to grasp, but they do require a greater understanding of science and its methods than the average person possesses. Most people have never done a scientific experiment in their lives, outside of

Testing the hypothesis that batteries mysteriously lose their charge inside a haunted house for a taping of the *MysteryQuest* television show "Return of the Amityville Horror." Photos by the author.

THERE ARE NO WRONG ANSWERS IN GHOST HUNTING!

Illustration by Celestia Ward of Two Heads Studios.

a few in high school biology class.

Second, controlled experiments are not nearly as much fun as wandering around a haunted house at night with friends looking for ghosts. Not doing the necessary research is also a big mistake because it is exactly this type of experimentation that *could* prove that ghosts exist. All other types of evidence—all the anecdotes, stories, legends, orb photos, EVPs, and so on—have been (and likely will remain) inconclusive and ambiguous at best. But if a ghost investigator conducted a series of well-designed experiments proving that there was some measurable difference between a haunted location and a nonhaunted one, that would be valid, scientific evidence to build on and that discovery might change the world.

Some claims are impossible to test and are therefore unscientific. One of the hallmarks of good scientific methodology is that a claim, proposition, or hypothesis must be falsifiable; that is, there must be some way to determine whether an event occurred or it didn't, or whether a phenomenon exists or it doesn't. If I claim that an invisible, undetectable polar bear is living in my garage, that may be true but is not a testable, falsifiable claim, because if an investigator searches for evidence and finds none at all, I can just say, "Of course you couldn't find evidence for it, the polar bear is undetectable."

Thus it is an untestable, scientifically worthless claim. (Carl Sagan first wrote about this analogy in his book *The Demon-Haunted World*.)

Pseudoscientific ghost hunters are essentially operating on the premise that what they are looking for can choose whether or not to exist (or at least be detected). This renders their investigation unfalsifiable and inherently unscientific, because even if there's not a shred of evidence, the ghost hunter can claim that there are many ghosts present but they choose not to make themselves known. Ghosts are the only things in the universe that are said to be able to exist at will; nothing else that has ever been studied is claimed to have this ability. It's the equivalent of explaining something by saying, "God did it," and it's a logical fallacy called special pleading. Such a claim can't be proven or disproven, and reduces ghosts to a mere brainteaser.

Many ghost hunters frame their investigations in exactly the same unscientific, untestable way. In the world of ghost hunting, the fact that the ghost hunters cannot explain a phenomenon is taken as a sign of their expertise. That is, they will confidently proclaim a location haunted if they could not find an explanation for some (apparently) strange phenomenon or other; that is, if they couldn't figure it out, couldn't solve the mystery.

Unscientific ghost hunters set up a no-lose situation for themselves: If they are able to debunk or find ordinary explanations for ghostly phenomenon, then that shows what good investigators they are because they cleverly figured it out. On the other hand, if they *can't* figure out an explanation for some phenomenon, then that also demonstrates what good investigators they are, because they claim it is evidence of ghosts! And if they don't find any evidence of ghosts, that of course does not prove that ghosts don't exist. It can just be interpreted to mean that there were no ghosts active there at the time the ghost hunters were there, or the ghosts simply chose not to show a sign of their presence. The door is left wide open for later investigations which are likely to find some "anomaly," especially given the lax standards of evidence. For other suggestions on bringing scientific rigor to ghost investigations see Michaeleen Maher's chapter "Ghosts and Poltergeists" in *Parapsychology: A Handbook for the 21st Century*.

Imagine if other investigative professions operated the same way, claiming success when they were unable to solve a problem: Police detectives unable to solve crimes would be promoted; doctors unable to correctly diagnose diseases would be congratulated and receive awards; mechanics who couldn't explain and fix automotive problems would be successful. Usually, inability to accomplish a goal (such as explaining a mystery) is seen as an obvious failure; for ghost hunters it's a sign of success.

Serious paranormal investigators should see skeptical and scientific researchers as allies, not opponents. I respect and support anyone who makes a sincere and serious effort to u nderstand these phenomena, I have made a sincere and sustained effort to raise the level of scientific rigor of investigation into these topics.

CHAPTER 5

Ghost Hunting Gear and Equipment

Over the years I've often been asked by viewers of television ghost hunting shows whose cast runs around with thermal imaging cameras, EMF detectors, and digital thermometers, jumping up and down when something beeps or lights up—whether their gadgets actually do anything. In 2003, while I was investigating a haunted house in Buffalo, New York, the owner of the house asked me what sort of equipment I was going to use. He had glanced in my duffel bag, which contained two cameras, a tape recorder, notebooks, a tape measure, a flashlight, and a few other items. Perhaps he was expecting to see a Negative Ionizer Ghost Containment backpack like the kind Bill Murray wore in *Ghostbusters*.

Ghost hunters use a wide variety of cameras, detectors, and recorders in supposedly haunted locations in search of evidence of the afterlife. Photo by the author.

When it comes to searching for ghosts, you'd think that only the most reliable equipment would be used in an attempt to get solid evidence for something as mysterious and elusive as a spirit. Yet, in ghost hunting, often the *less* scientific the methods and equipment, the *more* likely a researcher is to find "evidence" for ghosts. As Mary Roach notes in her book *Spook: Science Tackles the Afterlife*, "The lure of the gizmo remains strong among modern-day paranormal hobbyists" (199).

EMF, Infrasound, and Other Detectors

In a bid for scientific prestige, ghost hunters often use scientific equipment such as Geiger counters, Electromagnetic Field (EMF) detectors, ion detectors, and the like. Yet the equipment is only as scientific as the person using it.

According to many ghost hunters I've met (and the website Prairieghosts. com), an EMF meter is "the most common device used by ghost hunters today and is considered the most reliable." The group also recommends dowsing rods, which "are said to sway in the direction of an energy field. When the ghost is discovered, they are said to cross."

To find out more about the devices I contacted Tom Cook, of TomsGadgets. com, a British purveyor of "scientific" paranormal kits for the enterprising (and gullible) investigator. Starter kits began at about $180 and reach up to $1,000 for a custom ghost-hunting kit (Negative Ionizer Ghost Containment packs were not listed). By e-mail, I asked him what, exactly, was the scientific rationale behind the ghost-detecting equipment he sold.

He replied, "At a haunted location, strong, erratic fluctuating EMFs are commonly found. It seems these energy fields have some definite connection to the presence of ghosts. The exact nature of that connection is still a mystery. However, the anomalous fields are easy to find. Whenever you locate one, a ghost might be present, although the environmental conditions will not allow the specter to appear to the naked human senses….The Gauss meter serves as an excellent introduction to ghost detection equipment. It will easily allow you to pick up the fields from household appliances and other artificial sources. The first thing you want to do is rule them out. Then, any erratic EMF fluctuations you may detect may indicate ghostly activity. Currently, there exists no device that can conclusively detect ghosts."

I gave him credit for admitting that last bit, but I also recognized that the logic is fatally flawed: If one area of a home is colder than another, that may indicate a ghost; if an EMF meter detects a field, that too may be a ghost; if dowsing rods

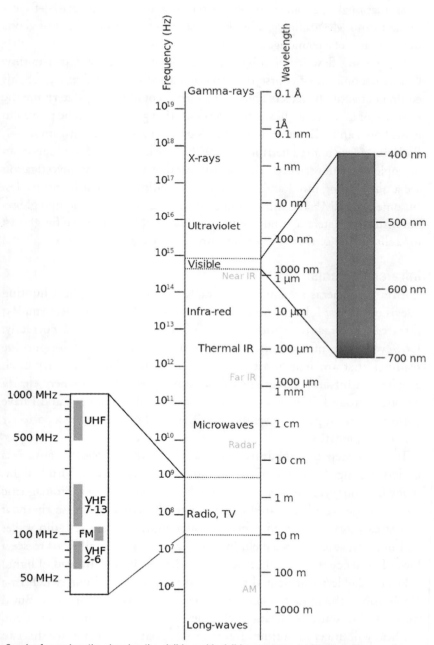

Graph of wavelengths showing the visible and invisible spectrum; technology allows us to access information beyond the range of our senses. Courtesy of Kenny Biddle.

cross, that might be a ghost. In other words just about any anomaly—from a sound to an EMF reading to a headache, can be considered evidence of ghosts in the context of a haunting.

The glaring flaw in all this—the big, skeptical elephant in the tiny, haunted room—is of course that no one has ever shown that any of this equipment actually detects ghosts. If a device could reliably determine the presence or absence of ghosts, then by definition ghosts would be proven to exist. I own an EMF meter, but since it's useless for ghost investigations—it finds not spirits but red herrings—I use it in my lectures and seminars as an example of pseudoscience. The most important tools in any investigation are a questioning mind and a solid understanding of scientific principles. In some cases EMF and infrasound detectors are not claimed to find ghosts but instead to detect natural phenomena that could be mistaken for ghosts; for a discussion of those devices in those contexts see chapter 8.

Infrared Cameras

Infrared cameras are among the staple devices used on ghost hunting television shows. Like the other scientific gear that ghost hunters employ, infrared cameras are valid and useful devices when used correctly. However more often than not infrared cameras create false-positive readings that amateur ghost hunters mistake for ghostly activity, such as when an infrared camera reveals a human-shaped form where clearly no one is around. This can seem very spooky and mysterious, and I have witnessed this in person several times. There is, however, often a perfectly rational explanation.

The first step to explaining the nature of these "ghostly auras" is understanding the nature of the electromagnetic spectrum. Visible light, that which our eyes can see, makes up only a fraction of the electromagnetic waves in the world. Infrared electromagnetic waves comprise the next lowest category of frequency below visible light (and above radio waves and microwaves). In a nutshell, infrared cameras simply allow us to see a lower frequency wavelength, detecting variations in heat instead of light.

Heat is far less transient than light; if we turn off a light switch in a closed room, the bulb dies and the area goes dark almost instantly. But if we turn off a source of heat—including body heat—to an area or room, the heat will linger for a time after the source has been removed. This can seem mysterious to amateur ghost hunters.

At an investigation I did in 2009 for an episode of the *MysteryQuest* television show titled "Return of the Amityville Horror," one of the ghost hunters used a FLIR camera to detect a foot-long vertical warm spot on a pillar. No one in the room could explain what caused it; one person suggested it was a sign that a ghost had been watching them. In fact I had seen one of the ghost hunters leaning against the pillar a few minutes earlier, and the warm spot matched exactly the height and shape of the man's upper arm. All the ghost hunters swore that none of them had leaned against the pole, and when I suggested they review a videotape, they saw I was correct. If they had not been recording that area (or if I hadn't seen the investigator create the warm spot), it likely would have remained mysterious. This is quite common in TV ghost hunting shows, and is the explanation for many of the anomalies.

Verifying Environmental Anomalies

The scientific equipment ghost hunters use—like all scientific equipment—must be accurately calibrated and, even when calibrated, has a normal margin of error. This is important to remember when interpreting "anomalous" readings; for instance if you measure the electromagnetic radiation or temperature in the same spot twice over a short period of time, small fluctuations will appear under normal conditions.

Let's say that a ghost hunter uses a thermography device to record the temperature in a room at 7 PM and gets a reading of 74.25 degrees Fahrenheit. She returns ten minutes later (perhaps after hearing a noise or "sensing" something in the area) and takes another reading. She is shocked to discover that the temperature is now 68.85 degrees! She is unable to explain how the room could have dropped five and a half degrees over the course of just ten minutes. However, before interpreting that as signifying a ghostly presence, there are a few factors she should keep in mind.

One thing she should be aware of is that a room is rarely a single, uniform temperature throughout; the floor will usually be a different temperature than the ceiling, and different walls may have slightly different temperatures as well—especially if one of them is an exterior wall, which can gain or lose significant heat due simply to sunlight exposure and exterior temperature. Thus it's important to make sure that the readings are comparable and taken at the same spot.

Take, for example, a given infrared device that has a margin of error of 1.8 degrees. This range is perfectly acceptable for most household purposes, but ghost hunters who look for any fluctuation must be careful not to

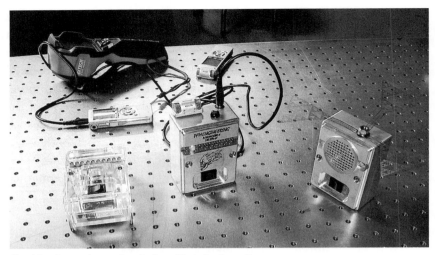

Ghost hunting and recording devices. Photo by the author.

over-interpret the readings. That 1.8 margin of error means that a nearly four degree range difference can be expected in normal use, so an object that is 70 degrees might read 68.2 or 71.8, or anything in between in consecutive readings (of course electronic devices don't always work at optimal performance, so that 1.8 range could in fact be even greater). If the ghost hunter measured an exterior wall while the sun was setting (or shade covered that wall from a tree, for example), the temperature of that wall could very easily drop a few degrees in the ten minutes between the first and second readings. Obviously if the temperature drop is dramatic (say, 15 or 20 degrees as confirmed by a second device to rule out a device malfunction) over a short period of time with no plausible explanation that's another matter. But many variations in temperature of five or ten degrees are perfectly explainable and the results of measurement error.

Some ghost hunters have sought to explain ghost reports (and poltergeist reports specifically) as caused by some unknown geological force: Could some odd mix of magnetic soil (high in iron?) or weather pattern (high in ozone?) somehow combine in just the right circumstances to create unexplained disturbances like dishes flying across the room or cupboard doors opening and closing? There seems to be no evidence for this; in fact when two researchers "studied the forces required to produce classical poltergeist phenomena and conducted experiments in a house about to be demolished, they concluded that 'ordinary houses could not withstand geophysical forces of a magnitude which would throw objects around within them.' In short, the structural damage would be so severe that occupants would flee in terror before they had a chance to witness any poltergeist-like phenomena" (Maher 2015, 338).

Ghost Detection Technology

In 2014 a man who believed he developed a scientific way to detect ghosts and other paranormal entities in everyday photos and videos launched a crowdfunding program to raise money for further development. According to a press release by ghost hunter Joe DiMare, "Many people believe in ghosts, but not many people have evidence to support their belief. Now with Hidden Intelligence Tracking (HIT), anyone can shoot a 30-second video and submit it to have minor changes in light and motion amplified to reveal evidence of the paranormal. The creator of HIT has launched a crowdfunding campaign to raise $49,999 by August 5 to expand computer capabilities so that more videos can be processed quicker. Taking a whole new approach to ghost chasing, HIT works like a microscope for video, revealing minute changes in motion and light." That "amplified video" is *guaranteed* to contain a ghost, according to DiMare's 'Ghost Guarantee: We promise to find a ghost on your video if you follow our instruction video.'" The HIT program, according to DiMare, "redefines the paranormal in our everyday lives" and is "perfect not only for paranormal enthusiasts, but also videographers, private detectives, students, educators, and anyone interested in seeing a greater truth."

I contacted DiMare seeking a better understanding of his technology and specifically what, exactly, the claimed connection was between video flickers and ghosts. I asked, "Does the technology have a way to distinguish between ordinary changes in light and motion in a video (for example, a flickering light source, or someone walking in front of a light) from paranormal changes?" DiMare responded by email that "Ghosts are made of light.... I think they can take any form they want. This technology detects motion. The ghosts are vibrating and will make an imprint on the video. Amplifying the movement lets us see it better." He did acknowledge that the program "does not know the difference between a candle or a person walking by. It just amplifies the changes that happen from one frame of video to the next. The user has to look at the amplified video he or she takes and determine if something paranormal is present." (How the user should determine what is paranormal and what isn't remained a key unresolved question.)

In other words, DiMare's program simply amplifies both signal *and* noise in the video, which in turn amplifies existing video artifacts and creates new ones. DiMare's "ghost-hunting" technology is essentially putting back the very noise and image distortions the camera technology has worked to correct and filter out of the image in the first place. When closely examined, some of those video glitches and anomalies may resemble faces, human forms, or other figures, just by random chance and due to pareidolia.

On his crowdfunding site DiMare gave an example of a seemingly ordinary video frame that had been enhanced with his computer technology to reveal what he describes as "a frog standing waving back at the camera. He is standing in front of and under the tree. About 2 feet tall, he looks like he has a bow tie on, and he is waving with his left arm." I asked DiMare to clarify whether he was claiming that his photo actually revealed a two-foot tall, bowtie-wearing frog waving at him. "The frog is what I see in the footage," he responded. "Some people say they see an owl... this phenomenon is quick, that is why it is invisible to most people. Viewing the footage frame by frame and amplifying the changes makes all the difference. I'm not sure if it is real or an illusion."

This remarkably candid admission demonstrates that the answer to this phenomenon lies in psychology, not the paranormal. The ghosts and other "weird" images captured on video and made visible by his technical process look exactly like ordinary camera artifacts. The most likely explanation for these apparently paranormal images is an optical and technological one, not a paranormal or supernatural one. Other similar computer programs and technologies that claim to reveal ghosts have the same problem. DiMare's fundraiser ended having raised exactly three dollars.

Dowsing for Ghosts

Many ghost hunters employ not only dubious technology but decidedly unscientific items in their attempts to communicate with the dead. Jeff Belanger, author of several books on ghosts and founder of Ghostvillage. com ("the Internet's largest supernatural community"), describes a variety of divination methods he claims can be used to receive ghostly information in his book *Communicating with the Dead: Reach beyond the Grave.* These include Ouija boards, tarot cards, casting runes, mirror gazing, dowsing, and EVP. He mentions the "spirit rapping" Fox sisters in the introduction, yet he seems unaware of the fact that the sisters admitted that they faked

A young girl is introduced to dowsing rods at an event organized by a ghost hunting group in Albuquerque, New Mexico. Photo by the author.

these ghostly communications. This is a curious oversight for such a self-professed expert on ghostly communications; either he doesn't know about their hoaxing confession or he doesn't want his readers to know about it lest it undermine his point (though to his credit he does acknowledge the fakery of spirit photography pioneer William Mumler; see chapter 6).

The problem is that there is no credible scientific evidence that Tarot cards, runes, or any of the other devices and techniques Belanger offers have any powers of prophecy or spiritual communication. The dowsing that most people are familiar with is water dowsing (also known as water witching or rhabdomancy) in which a person holds a Y-shaped branch (or two L-shaped wire rods) and walks around until they feel a pull on the branch, or the wire rods cross, at which point water is allegedly below. Sometimes a pendulum is held over a map until it swings (or stops swinging) over a spot where the desired object may be found. Dowsing is said to find anything and everything, including missing persons, buried pipes, oil deposits, and of course ghosts.

According to many books and dowsing experts, the practice has a robust history and its success has been known for centuries. In the book *Divining the Future: Prognostication from Astrology to Zoomancy*, Eva Shaw writes, "In 1556, *De Re Metallica*, a book on metallurgy and mining written by George [*sic*] Agricola, discussed dowsing as an acceptable method of locating rich mineral sources." This reference to *De Re Metallica* is widely cited among dowsers as proof of its validity, though there are two problems.

The first is that the argument is a transparent example of a logical fallacy called the "appeal to tradition" ("it must work because people have done it for centuries"); just because a practice has endured for hundreds of years does not mean it is valid. Furthermore, it seems that the dowsing advocates didn't actually read the book, because it says exactly the opposite of what they claim: Instead of endorsing dowsing, Agricola states that those seeking minerals "should *not* make use of an enchanted twig, because if he is prudent and skilled in the natural signs, he understands that a forked stick is of no use to him."

The second problem is one of mechanics: If dowsing could be proven to work, what could the mechanism be? How could a twig or two metal wires know what the dowser is looking for (water, ghosts, a lost item, etc.), much less where it could be found? The proposed mechanisms are as varied as the dowsers themselves. Some sources claim that strong psychic energy is radiated by the object and detected by the dowser; others believe that ghosts, spirits, or mysterious Earth energies direct the dowser to their targets.

My colleague James "The Amazing" Randi, in his *Encyclopedia of Claims, Frauds, and Hoaxes of the Occult and Supernatural*, notes that dowsers often cannot agree on even the basics of their profession: "Some instructions tell learners never to try dowsing with rubber footwear, while others insist that it helps immeasurably. Some practitioners say that when rods cross, that specifically indicates water; others say that water makes the rods diverge to 180 degrees."

Though some people swear by dowsing's effectiveness, dowsers have been subjected to many tests over the years and have performed no better than chance under controlled conditions. It's not surprising that water can often be found with dowsing rods, since if you dig deep enough you'll find water just about anywhere. If missing objects (and even missing people) could be reliably and accurately located using dowsing techniques, it would be a great benefit: If you lose your keys or cell phone, you should be able to just pull out your pendulum and find it; if a person goes missing or is abducted, police should be able to locate them with dowsing rods. If dowsing worked, it could presumably help the estimated ten people each day—four of them children—who are killed or maimed by land mines in rural areas around the world.

Fortean Times writer Alan Murdie, in his "Ghostwatch" column, explains why "Many sincerely believe divining rods and pendulums may be used for spirit detection and communication, readily identifying gyrations and movements as proof of contact."

Though Murdie (2011) believes in the validity of dowsing in general (for water, minerals, etc.), he is clear that the practice is worthless in ghost hunting: "anyone with the slightest knowledge understands that such movements are not those of the rods themselves; they do not 'move of their own accord'. ... Whereas dowsing for water, a mineral deposit or a dead body is open to verification (either you find it or you don't), there is no way of objectively confirming any claim by a psychic or medium that says a ghost is moving a dowsing rod."

As Murdie notes, it gets even worse for ghost dowsers, since there is no universal agreement on what the rods' movement means; one ghost hunter may think that if the rods cross, that is evidence of ghosts, whereas another ghost hunter may insist that rods separating is proof of a ghost. Any given movement by dowsing rods or pendulums can be interpreted in completely contradictory ways. Murdie sums up: "Beliefs that pendulums and rods can be used for contacting the spirit world are not founded upon any controlled and reported experiments (despite many ghost-hunting groups claiming to be 'scientific')."

Flashlights as Spirit telegraphs

Some investigators use flashlights to try to communicate with ghosts, setting them up so their batteries or switches are only loosely engaged and may cause the light to blink on or off with a slight pressure. Emily Christoff-Flowers, in her ebook *The Ghost Journal: Memoirs of a Ghost Tour Guide in Williamsburg, Virginia*, describes a man who "asked [a ghost named] Eliza to turn off the flashlight if she really existed. As he sat on the pew with his arms crossed and a smirk on his face, the flashlight turned off. It had to be a coincidence so he asked her to turn it back on. It turned back on. He said he still didn't believe it, and so it flashed on and off repeatedly. This is the part where he screamed."

This method remained popular for a few years, until several experiments showed that the blinking light was merely the result of physics. As skeptic "Verklagekasper" noted on the JREF (James Randi Educational Foundation) forums, "Typically, the performing ghost hunter turns the flashlight's head to a position where the lamp easily goes on or off by the slightest touch. Then the ghost hunter puts it on a table or on the ground and starts asking questions. Eventually, the flashlight seems to respond by going on or off. The questioning goes on, and the flashlight keeps going on and off without any noticeable force affecting it. The ghost hunters claim that the flashlight is operated by a spirit. But there is a physical explanation for the flashlight repeatedly going on and off by itself."

As a 2012 video debunking this effect explained, "This video presents experiments with the Mini Maglite 2-Cell AA (Xenon), which happens to be the model used in the TV show *Ghost Hunters* that made the trick popular. Experimental results and considerations of contact physics reveal that the trick is actually caused by a heat cycle" ("Verklagekasper" 2012).

Many ghost hunters have since abandoned this technique, though some still insist that it works, having seemingly gotten intelligent responses to questions.

For those who still believe in the validity of this technique, there is a simple way to help determine whether the flashlight is being externally manipulated: use two or more flashlights. There is an old nugget of wisdom that "A man with one watch knows what time it is; a man with two watches is never sure." It reflects what in psychology is called an anchoring bias: if we only have one source of information we tend to assume it is correct, since there are no alternatives to choose from. However if we have two or more sources of information we can better determine what is true and valid. Instead of having a single flashlight—which may or may not be reliable depending on its age, quality, batteries, and so on—it would be much more powerful evidence if three or more flashlights were turned on and then a spirit was able to turn them off. The chance of a given single flashlight blinking on or off randomly at any given moment (seemingly in response to a question) may or may not be significant, but the chance of three different flashlights doing it at the same time when requested is exponentially less likely and would therefore be much stronger potential evidence of a ghostly presence. If a ghost can move objects, materialize, and cause a partially-connected flashlight to blink, there's no reason it couldn't make two of them blink in synchrony.

Ouija Boards

Ouija boards are known worldwide as both a game and a supposed tool for communicating with the spirit world. The game is simple and consists of two parts: the board itself—printed with letters and numbers, and a hand-sized, roughly heart-shaped device called a planchette, designed to slide smoothly over the board (using small wheels or felt pads) when two or more pairs of hands are upon it. Many believe that something other than the human sitters controls the planchette as it moves across the board answering questions and spelling out answers.

There are many varieties of Ouija boards, decorated with a wide variety of symbols including the sun, moon, stars, and other embellishments, but the basic elements are the letters of the alphabet, numerals 1 through 0, "yes" and "no," and "goodbye." (Of course non-English Ouija boards use their own alphabets and language.) Some even have answers that can be found in another pseudomystical children's divination tool, the Magic 8 Ball.

Though some sources claim that the Ouija dates back to ancient Greece, it is in fact of much more recent vintage. The Ouija is only one of countless divination tools used for millennia, from reading tea leaves to astrology. The

Ouija boards, originally designed and advertised as a party game, are widely believed to have occult powers and the ability to communicate with ghosts. Photo and ghostly hands courtesy of Kenny Biddle.

game was invented in the early 1890s by a man named Elijah Bond, who soon sold his patent to a William Fuld, who recognized its moneymaking potential and in turn sold the game to Parker Brothers (now Hasbro) in 1966.

Folklorist Eric Eliason, writing in the *American Folklore* encyclopedia, notes that for much of its early existence the Ouija board was not considered anything other than an amusing pastime "unrelated to the occult until Pearl Curran, a prominent figure during the World War I-era Spiritualism revival, began touting Ouija as a tool for divining the future, finding lost objects, seeking daily advice, and contacting spirits. Soon thousands of Americans were using Ouija to check up on their loved ones fighting in Europe." Curran is largely responsible for the Ouija board's modern reputation as a "real" tool of prophecy and spirit communication.

Ouija boards are universally recognized as a conduit to the spirit world, but are they real? Do they really do what Curran believed they can do? Many people certainly believe so; in fact many Evangelical Christians believe that occult divination tools such as Tarot cards, pendulums, and Ouija boards can connect with, and even summon, evil spirits including Satan. Not only is using the Ouija board asking for trouble because it might summon evil spirits, but the board is believed to actually invite full demonic possession. This is related to Christian concerns of temptation and the notion that genuine Satanic evil can come in the form of otherwise silly and benign games (similar concerns are often expressed about children's participation in Halloween activities). Other "occult" activities viewed with suspicion include forms of divination such as astrology, dowsing, tarot, and even hypnosis. All are considered forms of witchcraft, which is explicitly condemned in the Christian Bible. There were of course many skeptics—including Thomas Edison, who wrote in his diary, "Why should personalities in another existence or sphere waste their time... play[ing] pranks with a table?"

Because of its prominent place in pop culture as a conduit to spirits and demons, the Ouija board has been a staple of horror films for decades. Hundreds of films, including *The Uninvited* (1944); *The Exorcist* (1973); *The Changeling* (1980); *Witchboard* (1986); and *Paranormal Activity* (2007) have featured the boards as a plot device through which spirits, ghosts, and demons communicate. Parker Brothers, not wishing to alienate large segments of the Christian family board game market, has always promoted the Ouija board as it was originally created and intended: as a harmless parlor game instead of a telephone to the dead.

How Ouija Boards Work

There is no doubt that Ouija boards can be used to spell out names and other words. The question is how the planchette is controlled: by humans or spirits? Of course logic and common sense suggests that Ouija boards do not actually communicate with the dead; if it did surely there would be no unsolved homicides, since police detectives would merely need to pull out the Ouija board to contact the murdered victims and ask how they were killed and under what circumstances.

If the movement of the planchette across the Ouija board is truly controlled by spirits independently of any human contact, then the game should answer questions without anyone touching it. The human participants should be able to sit back with a drink in their hands, ask questions of the board, and have the planchette magically and mystically scoot around to answer whatever questions anyone has. Of course, that doesn't happen, because it is *human* movements that create the answers.

We know exactly how the Ouija board works: it relies on something called the ideomotor effect. The participants unconsciously move the planchette across the board, though because they are unaware of what's going on, they attribute the movement to some external influence or supernatural intelligence. The movements of the planchette across the Ouija board can seem very mysterious to the participants, all of whom swear that they are not intentionally moving anything (though now and then a playful prankster consciously helps spell out a message).

Testing the Ouija board is very simple and can be done by anyone in a few minutes. All it takes are a couple of blindfolds (or a tablecloth or piece of cardboard held just above the board to block the participants' views) and a third person to watch the board and take notes on what it says. The idea is to make it so that the participants themselves can't see where the letters are; after all, if ghosts or spirits truly are guiding the planchette instead of the people, then it shouldn't matter whether those touching the oracle can see the board or not. Invariably the result is gibberish, a string of random letters and numbers that carry no message at all. The Ouija board is a game based on self-deception. There's nothing wrong with that—in fact it can be fun and frightening to pretend that it's connecting to the dead—but there's nothing mysterious about it.

A modern version of the Ouija board is the so-called spirit box, one version of which is known as "Frank's Box," also known as the "broken radio." Because these devices essentially produce EVP, they are discussed in depth in chapter 7.

Infrasound as Ghost Doppelgänger

Many paranormal researchers have long believed that infrasound (specifically that of a 19 Hz frequency) may be responsible for some reported hauntings. Infrasound can be produced by anything that creates vibrations—typically machinery (such as a fan, washing machine, or printing press) but also the weather, or even ocean waves. Results from exposure to infrasound vary greatly (depending on the person, the duration, proximity to the source, etc.) and can range from breathing difficulties to nausea and even minor visual misperceptions—many of which have been reported at supposedly haunted locations and taken as evidence of a ghostly influence. The idea (first proposed by engineer Vic Tandy in the 1980s, as reported in the *Journal for Psychical Research* in 1988 and 2005) is that some people may be unknowingly exposed to infrasounds and wrongly attribute their seemingly unexplained symptoms to a spirit's presence.

Though referenced in countless ghost and paranormal books for many years, recent investigation has cast doubt on the link between infrasounds and ghost reports. Researcher Steve Parsons reviewed Tandy's work and found that many of the more dramatic claims about the effects of infrasound were exaggerated and unsubstantiated. According to Parsons, "There seems to be a generally poor understanding of the original work done by Tandy, and of the technical constraints in making infrasound measurements, and this has led to misunderstanding of any actual relationship between infrasound and paranormal experiences and accounts" (quoted in Rutter 2013).

Parsons conducted original research and found that some of Tandy's key conclusions were based in part on calculation errors. In the end, "Looking at his data, and that from several other studies, Parsons concluded that infrasound at 19 Hz is not the ghost inducer we had been led to believe. Infrasound is around us all the time, and whilst it may well be a factor in leading us to believe a location is haunted, it is not the overriding one and by itself does not produce such an effect" (Rutter 2013, 53).

High-Resolution Recording Gear

With the introduction over the past decade of small body-mounted cameras, such as those worn by police officers and sports enthusiasts, recording an event is easier than ever before. The popular GoPro brand cameras, for example, offer the public affordable, rugged, high definition recording capability. Some camera models offer continual recording; for example the type used in law enforcement "is constantly recording what it sees. But most of its images are kept in a 30-second buffer, after which they're discarded. The unit begins saving longer segments of video—and begins capturing audio—only when an officer double-taps a control switch. The 30-second buffer is a way of allowing officers to essentially record events that began in the past" (Manjoo 2014). This would be a tremendous boon to ghost hunters, who obviously can't know exactly when a ghost may choose to make itself known. This technology, properly used, should help eliminate the perpetual ghost hunter complaint that something paranormal happened just moments before he turned his recording equipment on, or just after she turned it off. There should be no excuses, since the camera records everything and the past half-minute can be saved and examined at any time.

Another piece of cutting-edge technology that could be employed by ghost hunters is the 3-D camera. An early model called the Lynx A was developed in 2012; writer Jenny Blair explains how it works: "When the user holds it up to an object or space, it computes a 3-D image within seconds. Architects can turn its scan of a room into a CAD file, making tape measures unnecessary... The Lynx A uses a standard color camera lens combined with an infrared-light projector, which lays a pattern over whatever it is looking at. A receiver then observes the way the pattern warps. The graphics processing unit make billions of calculations per second to put together the visual and IR data. Together, they build a detailed, instantly updated representation of what the camera sees" (Blair 2013).

The application of 3-D cameras to ghost investigations is obvious: Because ghost photographs (of orbs, streaks, shadows, etc.) only depict the anomaly in two dimensions, they are indistinguishable from mundane phenomenon. There is no way to determine their depth (if any): an orb created by a flash reflection would have no discernible depth because it's merely the light from the surface of a speck or shiny surface. However a 3-D photo would allow the ghost hunter to triangulate the location of an anomaly, whether three millimeters from the camera or three meters. This in turn would presumably provide the size, shape, and other characteristics of ghosts. If used properly, the 3-D cameras should help eliminate "ghosts" that are merely photographic artifacts or insects on camera lenses.

Smelling Spirits: Gathering Olfactory Evidence

In addition to audio and video recordings, it may also be possible to capture and record otherwise elusive olfactory phenomena. Many ghost sightings are claimed to be accompanied by a distinctive scent, often suggesting the presence of a specific spirit.

One study found that 8% of ghost witnesses claimed that specific odors accompanied their ghost experiences. I have encountered this many times; for example while investigating Santa Fe's famously haunted La Posada hotel (described in chapter 13 of *Mysterious New Mexico*), I was told at least two resident ghosts are associated with spectral smells: lady of the house Julia Staab, who loved flowers, and one known only as the Cigar Man, whose presence is said to be signified by cigar smoke. Many miracles are also associated with smells; for instance the heavenly scent of violets, lilies, roses, or even fresh tobacco were said to accompany famous stigmatic Padre Pio.

It may seem strange that something as ephemeral as a smell could be recorded, but it's not surprising from a physics point of view. As Marilyn vos Savant notes, "Odor is the name of the phenomenon produced by airborne particles (and the name of the particles themselves) actually coming into contact with areas inside the nasal passages. Even though their number is relatively minute, smelling an odor is like inhaling an infinitesimal amount of whatever is generating it" (vos Savant 1994). Odor has mass, and therefore that weight can, with the right equipment, be captured, measured, and recorded.

A device designed by Amy Radcliffe can capture smells. *Wired* reports, "the technology behind it has actually been used by scientists and fragrance houses for decades. Headspace technology is the process that allows perfumers to bottle the notes of a rose or a scientist to analyze the scents of a rainforest. To capture any smell, an object is placed inside a hollow glass dome that is hooked up to an odor trap via an air hose. As air is sucked from the dome, it's absorbed by the trap, which is essentially a small glass tube filled with an absorbent polymer resin. Depending on the concentration of the smell, it can take minutes or days to adequately capture a scent, with Radcliffe noting that citrus fruit would take only minutes to document, while something more subtle, like a general environment or the smell of a person's skin would take a bit longer" (Stinson 2013).

Ghost investigators could use these devices in a number of ways, including verifying that a person does indeed smell what they think they smell and are not mistaken or imagining the scent (some ghost hunters have theorized that smells associated with hauntings are actually olfactory illusions created by ghosts). Researchers could also record and compare audio, visual, tactile, and olfactory data. If a specific scent signature could be reliably correlated with the appearance of an alleged ghost, it might open new lines of investigation. If, for example, a ghost hunter established an air sample baseline for a given location whose air currents could be controlled and monitored, a sudden or inexplicable appearance of a smell might offer tangible evidence of paranormal activity. After all, scent molecules cannot suddenly appear out of thin air; the smell of roses (that is, molecules of rose) cannot appear in a vacuum, and the smell of lemons (that is, molecules of lemon) cannot appear where there are no lemons; it is simply not possible under the known laws of physics. Thus the sudden appearance of flowers, perfume, cigars, or any other scent claimed to be associated with a ghost would be a genuine mystery if verified.

Furthermore, if—as some ghost hunters claim—spirits manifest themselves as mists that can be seen, felt, and photographed, then it's possible that "aroma cameras" might even be able to capture spirits themselves, something like the proton packs seen in *Ghostbusters*. None of this equipment or analysis is cheap, but ghost hunters could pool their money to invest in the technology and share it.

It's important when analyzing ghost reports to keep in mind that our noses are just as fallible, if not moreseo, as our other senses. Just as things we see and hear can be mistaken for other things, so can the things we smell. A notable high-profile example of this occurred in 2013 when many consumers who had bought a new Dell computer model Latitude 6430u complained that their laptop smelled exactly like cat urine. Initially cats were blamed for peeing on the computers, but eventually users realized that unless an incontinent cat was in charge of quality control at the Dell factory, it must be something else. The feline urine smell was traced to a stinky—though allegedly nonhazardous—manufacturing chemical which was quickly changed.

Some reports of ghost smells may be the result of misperceptions. *Fortean Times* writer Joshua Cutchin (2017) notes that "there are a variety of olfactory disorders, mostly of neurological origin. Anosmia is the inability to smell; dysnomia, a distortion of smell; cacosmia, the unpleasant interpretation of pleasant smells [as well as] phantosmia, the hallucination of odors in the absence of notable smells. These phantom scents are often unpleasant and are frequently caused by brain damage or seizures in the temporal lobe.... phantosmia is a neurologically generated medical condition that is entirely internal. It is individual-based and not location-based, though it may provide an explanation for odors in single-witness sightings and accounts of clairscent (psychic smells). It is possible for the power of suggestion to create imagined scents" (p. 35) as well. Any of these disorders may come or go at different times and under different circumstances, and it's quite possible that a person might be unaware they have such a condition. After all, smell is a weak and often ambiguous sense, and if a person happens to hallucinate a floral scent while walking through a park or an office building, for example, it might easily go unremarked or chalked up to perfume or unseen flowers nearby. It's likely that one or more of these conditions might be responsible for at least some reports of specter-associated scents. Humans are not very good at distinguishing different smells (especially at low concentrations), so this equipment would be a step toward better evidence.

Conclusion

In a chapter on ghosts and poltergeists in *Parapsychology*, Michaeleen Maher laments the recent fascination with ghost-detecting gadgets, noting that "amassing technological data is no substitute for thorough research, and in some ways the technology boon has proved to be a distraction from the real issues underlying the study of ghostly phenomena.... There is often no real scientific consensus on what all of the accumulating data actually mean. Until all of this gets sorted out, researchers' interpretations of their technology-driven data should be regarded as provisional at best.... Until replicable evidence resolves conflicting hypotheses, it is left to the enterprise and industry of the beleaguered ghost investigator to attempt to rule out all known sources of potential error before concluding that something paranormal has occurred" (Maher 2015, 332-34).

In 2016, journalist Jennings Brown researched the scientific validity of ghost hunting gadgets for *Popular Mechanics* magazine, and his results surprised many amateur ghost hunters. Brown notes that "one of the most popular [devices] among amateur ghost hunters [is] the Ovilus series. When the Ovilus is triggered by variations of electromagnetic fields, the mechanism spits out words from a pre-programmed dictionary. Like a demonic Speak & Spell, the phrases often sound like they were cherry picked from a John Carpenter flick....The developer of the Ovilus and founder of Digital Dowsing, Bill Chappell, also supplies most of the gadgets for the Travel Channel's popular paranormal reality show, *Ghost Adventures*. He is one of the most prolific developers in the paranormal field, and because of his close association with *Ghost Adventures* he is respected within the community. Chappell declined an interview request.... However [he] did explain his view on the paranormal in a blunt email saying, 'I do not believe in Ghosts or Spirits.' The inventor says he's built hundreds of devices and performed countless experiments over the last decade trying to understand the phenomena of EVPs and instrumental transcommunication. 'The unmistakable conclusion,' he wrote. 'It is us, we are the ghosts'" (Brown 2016).

That's right: one of the world's top creators of ghost hunting devices admits that he doesn't believe that ghosts exist. He didn't elaborate on why he builds and sells devices advertised as detecting ghosts if he doesn't think that ghosts are real, but as Sharon Hill (2016) commented on the *Doubtful News* page, "Chappell tried, it didn't work. Good on him for admitting it. Yet, the Ovilus 5 still sells for $335 in the online store. Ghost hunters continue to be played by promoters of these ghost tech gadgets. Regardless of the admission by Chappell that we create the ghosts, believers will continue to use the device because it's dramatic and provides results, albeit worthless. Those blips, blinks and snippets of words are interpreted as something greater, a giant unwarranted wishful leap in conclusions. They enhance the belief in communication beyond death. It's a dream, it's not real. And Chappell just admitted it."

There are too many ghost hunting gadgets to cover in depth, and new ones are being developed all the time. Regardless of any minor tweaks, most fall into one of two categories, either measuring ambient environmental conditions (light, heat, etc.) or generating supposed ghostly information (such as Frank's Box and the Ovilus). For more information on specific devices beyond what is covered here (including the K2 meter, Dr. Gauss EMF meter, Mel-Meter, Vortex Dome, REM pod, Laser grid, IR temperature guns, and full spectrum cameras) I recommend blogs and articles by Kenny Biddle.

It would be impossible for me to discuss all environmental sampling devices that could possibly be used in ghost hunting. At the end of the day, understanding what your equipment does and does not do is far more important than what specific gear you use. It is crucial to understand what a given device is measuring and to recognize that any connection between observed anomalies and ghosts must be proven, not assumed. Success in ghost hunting depends far more on skills of observation, critical thinking, and scientific analysis than what environmental measurement devices are used.

In a 2016 interview TAPS cofounder Jason Hawes said that "I think with the advancement of equipment we have been able to better prove the existence of the paranormal. What we've done throughout the last two decades has helped to push the idea there are these things out there. But now, we're trying to figure out what they are" (quoted in Brown 2016). Hawes is simply—and obviously—wrong. The paranormal is no better proven today than it was in

1980 or 1880; despite enormous time, expense, and effort by professional and amateur ghost hunters alike for decades, real evidence for ghosts remains elusive. What Hawes, Bagans, and countless others have tried has clearly not worked, and if ghosts exist then finding them will be the result of improving research methods.

PART II
ANALYZING
EVIDENCE

CHAPTER 6

Ghosts on Film and Video

Amateur ghost hunters are often eager to jump right into investigations, snapping away with cameras to take dozens of photos of their location. Cameras, both still and video, are very good for documenting the environment—but sooner or later those photographs and videos will need to be interpreted and carefully reviewed to determine whether they reveal anything extraordinary. Distinguishing between what can and cannot be explained is not an easy task, and it's helpful to understand the history of ghost photography when analyzing ghostly images.

A Brief History of Ghost Photography

When did the first ghost photos appear? Photographs said to be of ghosts are all over the Internet and cable television and published in countless books and magazines. These days amateur ghost hunters offer thousands of photographs of things they believe are (or suspect might be) ghosts. The phenomenon of people claiming to photograph the spirits of the dead is relatively new. Though much about ghosts is shrouded in mystery, we know precisely who the first person was to claim to have photographed a ghost. His name William H. Mumler, a Boston photographer who produced the first "spirit photographs" in 1861 and created dozens more over the next decade.

These ghosts were not the orbs or shadowy figures often held up as paranormal today. Instead these were clearly images of real people, though faint and ghostly. John Harvey, author of *Photography and Spirit* (2007), notes that "In Mumler's photographs, the disincarnate spirits look pallid, like a watermark on the backcloth, dressed in either a bleached version of their customary attire or in a white smock reminiscent of an angel's dress." Ghosts dressed up in those days, reflecting popular notions of the spirit world of the era. Mumler was the first person to produce such ghostly images (though his success spawned many imitators), and he convinced many people that he and his camera had some sort of special connection to the other side. Mumler's most famous subject was Mary Todd Lincoln, Abraham Lincoln's widow.

Mumler published his first spirit photograph in 1862, which he claimed was an image of a young cousin who had died twelve years earlier. When he did, "the media sensation it provoked inspired him to give up engraving and set himself up as a 'Spirit Photographic Medium.' In Boston and New York, he prospered by servicing a clientele desperate for comforting confirmation that the spirits of their deceased loved ones hovered around them as guardian angels. But Mumler's thriving career was interrupted in 1869 when he was charged with fraud. He was acquitted due to lack of evidence, despite it being proven that one of the supposed spirits photographed was actually alive. His defense was predicated on the supposition that the spirits of the dead did appear to the living, and therefore there was no reason for Mumler to fake his photographs" (Davies 2007, 201). (It's difficult to imagine that argument being made by a suspected ghost photo faker today: "How dare you accuse me of hoaxing this image! Why would I do that, since anyone with an Internet connection can easily find thousands of ghost photos online! Why would I need to fake them, when they are so common?")

William Mumler's famous 1872 photograph of Mary Todd Lincoln— along with
an "extra" allegedly of her dead husband
Abraham. Author's collection.

Celebrated ghost investigator Harry Price with a "spirit extra" in a photograph made by William Hope. Originally published in Harry Houdini's book *A Magician Among the Spirits*, courtesy of Tim Binga and the Center for Inquiry libraries, from the author's collection.

Reprint of a ghostly double exposure photograph ca. 1905. From the author's collection.

The "ghosts" Mumler captured were, as you have likely surmised, merely double exposures of previous clients whose images he had not completely wiped clean from his glass plates. Many spirit photographs at the time were investigated and ruled "authentic," by which was meant that no obvious tampering was found. That was the case with Mumler's images: they were not mechanical fakes, nor hand-drawn images. But neither were they real; the double exposure might be recognized by fellow photographers familiar with the process but not the average portrait sitter. Investigator Joe Nickell describes "a well known technique for producing such fakes that does not require any tampering with the negative or other darkroom deception. It was used by some spirit photographers: while the sitter remained motionless for the lengthy exposure, a confederate—suitably attired— simply appeared briefly behind the unwitting person, the result being a photo with a semi-transparent 'spirit'" (Nickell 2012, 302). Many ghost hunters of the era experimented with "ghost" photographs and successfully created their own "spirit photos," including Harry Price.

Mumler's photos weren't images of the dead, and he knew it. Thus the first ghost photographs were an outright hoax, and many remain so to this day (for a look at other early ghost photo fakers including Frederick Hudson, see chapter 7 in Owen Davies's book *The Haunted*). A century and a half later, despite ever-increasing technology, real proof of ghost photos remains elusive. For a review of several famous ghost photos included in the book *Ghosts Caught on Film* by Melvyn Willin, see Nickell 2012, p. 297-305.

Modern Ghost Photos

If the earliest ghost photos don't depict ghosts—since they have been proven, admitted, or suspected as fake—where does that leave modern ghost photos? The quantity and variety of alleged spirit images has exploded over the years, but the quality of the evidence remains as disappointingly ambiguous as ever. Some are shadowy, humanlike figures; others are flash reflections of light appearing as round white spots dubbed "orbs" (discussed later). Some ghosts are reported to look and act exactly like living, real people, suddenly revealing their true nature only when they suddenly vanish or walk through a wall. If those accounts are to be credited, then it should follow that there could be tens of millions of ghost photos that are not recognized as such—strangers in crowds or backgrounds in public areas could presumably include ghosts. If these spirits are visually indistinguishable from ordinary people, as some eyewitnesses claim, then any photo containing one or more people whose identity (and therefore status as alive or dead) is not conclusively known *could* include a ghost. I'm not suggesting this is the case, of course, but merely noting the practical complications that this view of ghosts implies.

As writer Alan Murdie laments in *Fortean Times*, "illusory, spurious, and downright hopeless ghost photographs abound" (2014). Describing an example of a "'real' ghost caught on camera in Clophill church ruins," and "a pattern of light and shadow which, when viewed in slow motion," looks like a human figure turning its head and then vanishing. Murdie correctly notes that "Unfortunately, this apparition is in no way obvious—the film was actually recorded in 2012 with no one noticing any figure until after a clip was placed on the Internet. This late identification is not encouraging; could one really remember precise camera positions and exact levels of illumination at a nighttime vigil 18 months earlier?"

Think of all the ghost hunters in all the groups investigating the thousands of supposedly haunted locations in the United States and around the world, month after month and year after year, in places both locally and internationally known. Groups of ghost hunters book rooms and do tours every night throughout the year at dozens of famously haunted hotels and buildings, places like the Myrtles Plantation, the Whaley House, the St. James Hotel, the Stanley Hotel, the Queen Mary, and so on. Despite those decades—or perhaps centuries—of collective person-hours spent trying to record evidence of ghosts, the inescapable fact is that the evidence collected by the current generation of ghost hunters has been ambiguous at best and a complete failure at worst.

This conspicuous lack of solid evidence gathered during ghost investigations was noted by Alan Murdie: "Although earlier generations of ghost hunters reported seeing materialized apparitions at séances, they seldom saw anything when investigating haunted houses... The best apparition reports come from people not on ghost hunts but simply going about their normal business and not thinking about ghosts at the time. In contrast, today's investigators, whilst admitting they don't usually see anything on a vigil, nonetheless and almost routinely believe they have captured phantoms on film, despite the fact their anomalous images scarcely looking like anything at all" (Murdie 2014).

Indeed, images that "scarcely look like anything at all" (and audio recordings that scarcely sound like anything at all) are disappointingly the rule rather than the exception. Unfortunately this cornucopia of nonevidence is rarely recognized as the false-positive ghostly fool's gold that it is; instead, as Murdie notes, it is usually mistaken for substantive proof by ghost hunters eager to make something of their experience. There is a very real, if implicit, psychological incentive to make the best of an otherwise uneventful ghost hunt; if a group has collectively spent many hundreds of dollars (and days of time) planning the trip, traveling to the location, setting up gear, investigating, reviewing evidence, and so on, even weak evidence that might otherwise be dismissed under other conditions will often be showcased as potentially significant. Even if the fruits of their investigation only amounts to an anecdote about a weird feeling in a hallway or an unknown sound recording, no one is eager to admit their time and effort came to nothing.

High Definition Cameras and Ghosts

The public's idea of what a ghost photo is (or would look like) is at least partly influenced by entertainment media. Most ghost hunters today are introduced to orbs, streaks, and other possible photographic anomalies though movies, TV shows, magazines, and books.

It's not that ordinary people haven't photographed such anomalies before; indeed they have. But the images weren't considered indicative of anything unusual (and certainly not paranormal) until the 1990s, when TV shows such as *Ghost Hunters* offered tens of millions of viewers what were claimed to be mysterious examples of photographic proof of the afterlife. In other words, the mass media (with help from experts and self-styled ghost hunters) offered a script or template—a ready-made, public-friendly definition and depiction— of "ghost photos" and videos.

Paranormal Activity is a series of successful low-budget horror films about amateur ghost hunters who document video evidence of the supernatural. The first film, released in 2007, was a surprise indie hit around the world. The films are shot in a "found footage" style, in which what the audience sees is meant to appear as footage taken in real life through home videos and security cameras. This technique, often involving handheld cameras and actors addressing the camera, has been around for years but was widely popularized in the 1999 paranormal-themed film *The Blair Witch Project*.

The grainy, low-budget look of the films is no accident; it was done partly because the films actually *are* low-budget, and partly for added realism. The fact that the low-quality picture skips and jitters adds to the suspense, and Horror Filmmaking 101 teaches that a dark, partly seen monster is much scarier than one that's seen clearly in bright light.

It's been effective in the films, scaring up hundreds of millions of dollars at the box office, and it's also true in real-life ghost hunting. High-quality video cameras in the real world never manage to capture good images of the paranormal. Virtually all of the evidence for ghosts appears in the form of brief, ambiguous anomalies recorded with low-quality cameras (or good-quality cameras sabotaged by low-light conditions).

Ghost hunters, both on TV and their real-life counterparts, face a drought of evidence caused by modern technology. People have long reported weird, ghostly, and paranormal activity, but perhaps the strangest mystery is why the evidence—especially the photographic evidence—hasn't improved along with technology. If ghosts exist, it stands to reason that the photographic evidence for them should improve dramatically as more and more people look for them with better and better equipment.

There are more people actively trying to document paranormal activity than ever; at no time in history have so many people had high-quality cameras on them virtually all the time. Today there's no excuse for anyone to capture ambiguous photos or video images of anything, whether it's your aunt in a horrid floral hat, Bigfoot in the woods, or paranormal activity in your hallway. As of this writing the latest ubiquitous Apple iPhones currently have built-in 8 megapixel cameras featuring state of the art optics, image stabilization, automatic lighting adjustment, and other features that rival cameras used by Hollywood videographers only a few years ago.

High definition provides more image information, which helps identify things often mistaken for ghosts—random shadows, unnoticed reflections, video artifacts. With those ghost impostors more easily dismissed, any real ghostly images should be sharper and clearer than ever before. Logic suggests that the age of poor-quality video evidence of the paranormal should be coming to an end. High definition video technology will likely progress to the point in which the only real-life ghost hunters who capture paranormal activity are intentionally using cameras that produce low-quality images. After all, that's where the ghosts are most likely to appear.

Panorama Phantoms

As cameras become more versatile the possibility of capturing accidental ghostly images increases. This is partly because there are more functions than ever before (and thus more ways to capture images), and partly because most people have only passing familiarity with their camera's operations. Most people get perfectly acceptable, even impressive, results from just letting the camera's technology take care of most of the important functions, with automatic point-and-shoot simplicity provided by auto focus and so on. Most of the time it works fine, but on occasion a glitch or camera artifact can be mistaken for something supernatural.

In April 2016 a visitor to a famous—and famously haunted—hotel in Colorado claimed to have captured a ghostly image. According to an April 18 news piece on CNN, "Tourist Henry Yau recently took a picture at the Stanley Hotel in Estes Park, Colorado, which appears to show two ghostly apparitions standing on a staircase. In the photo, a woman can be seen at the top of the stairs in a period outfit with a child beside her."

Predictably, several amateur ghost hunters weighed in suggesting it was unexplainable. Others, however, have a pretty good idea of what it is. Researcher Kenny Biddle of the Geeks & Ghosts podcast examined the photo and noted that Yau had used the panoramic feature on his iPhone to capture a full view of the grand stairwell. This is important because in panorama mode the camera doesn't just take one photo but instead scans across the scene rapidly. As Biddle noted, "Panoramic images are not taken in the same fraction of a second as normal images are. They take several seconds...which would allow Yau to start taking his panoramic image at one end of the room, and another guest or two to hit the halfway point down the stairs, turn the corner, and begin the second set of stairs to the floor as Yau ends his panoramic image on the other side of the room."

Odd glitches using the panorama function on cameras are common, and many websites display hundreds of bizarre and double images (see, for example, a Tumblr account titled "Panorama Fail"). Biddle notes that "when looking at a close up of the alleged ghost and second ghost (to the left of the more solid looking figure), we see that the features of both figures match up: the hair, the spaghetti-strap top, the height of the head, shoulders, and the top of the dress. This is a double image of the same person, not someone else. This effect was caused by the low light environment, slower scanning speed due to the camera trying to take in more light, and the movement of this person as they rounded the corner."

Yau claimed that he doesn't remember seeing anyone at the top of the staircase when he took the photo, but it's quite possible that he simply didn't notice the woman as she appeared and turned at the top of the stairs, as he was trying to hold the camera steady and take the photo. Upon closer inspection there is nothing remarkable in the image; it's a perfectly ordinary blurry, double image common in long exposure and panoramic iPhone photographs. Had it been taken in any number of other locations, it would not likely have attracted such attention. Most people routinely take photos that are flawed in some way, or that have unusual images in them, including flash reflected orbs, odd shadows, blurry body parts, double exposures, objects behind a person seemingly coming out of their heads, and so on. Usually they are ignored or deleted, unless the photographer (or someone else) decides that there's some reason why the photo might be of something supernatural.

The photo was taken at a doubly famous hotel—not only did it inspire the Stanley Kubrick-directed horror classic *The Shining*, but it's also claimed to be one of the most haunted hotels in the country and promotes itself as a ghost hunting destination. To some degree we see what we want or expect to see—and that can include ghosts. People who are aware of a building's haunted reputation are more likely to take many photos, and

A mysterious orb photographed at Canada's most haunted place, Fort. George (see chapters 11 and 12), is revealed after investigation to be a tiny piece of dust caught in a long spider web strand. Photos by the author.

Orb streaks. Photo by Kenny Biddle.

anything odd or even potentially mysterious in those photos is likely to be considered evidence of ghosts. A person could take an equal number of similarly strange photos at a location not assumed to be haunted, and the odd photographic artifact would not be as closely examined or interpreted as anything mysterious. As Biddle notes, panoramic photos must be subjected to additional scrutiny.

Ghost-Adding Apps

Examination of ghost photos has become more complicated over the past few years partly due to pranksters and ghost-generating apps. Several smartphone apps allow their users to easily tweak photos to make them look strange or mysterious, adding quasi-transparent ghostly images in the background. Up until recently, it took at least a little bit of effort or Photoshop experience to create an even halfway convincing snapshot of your recently departed grandmother's spirit appearing in an otherwise ordinary photo. These days it just takes a few taps on a screen to add faint figures of spooky little girls, Confederate soldiers, outlaws, monks, or any other historical (or horror film) caricature you can think of.

With so many fakes, how can you tell which photos (if any) really show something possibly paranormal? One group in the United Kingdom that has raised concerns over the rise in fake ghost photos is the Association for the Scientific Study of Anomalous Phenomena (ASSAP). Carrie Searley of ASSAP told me in an interview, "fake ghost photography is in the minority, however, it does occur. Here at ASSAP we like to turn it into a positive... one of our aims is to offer a scientific explanation as to the methodology used in creating a fake ghost photograph."

Before digital photography replaced film, investigators could examine the photograph's negative for evidence of fraud. Searley noted, "In the digital age of photography, being able to authenticate a photo can be tricky, as no negative is made. It is purely down to us to educate ourselves with the up and coming new photo apps that are being offered on the market." To that end, ASSAP requested the public's help in cataloging known fakes created by sneaky smartphone apps. It will be a never-ending project, since new apps are being created (and old apps tweaked) to keep ahead of the fake-photo ghost busters. Information on the various ghost apps can be found at http://www.assap.ac.uk.

Types of Photographic Anomalies

Most alleged ghosts in photographs and videos fall into four basic categories: orbs, wisps or shadows, figures, and faces. There is some overlap between these categories; it's not unusual, for example, for faces to be seen in orbs upon magnification on a computer screen.

Wisps and shadows are blurry, elongated forms seen in photos or video; wisps are usually white or yellow, while shadows are—as the name implies—dark or black. Shadows are often vertical (roughly mimicking a standing human silhouette), while wisps may be horizontal or vertical and may appear as anything from an extended orb to a streak. There are many things that can create these wisps or shadows, including dust in the air, cigarette or vape smoke, breath in cold air, moving a camera while the shutter engages at slow speed, and so on. Each type is discussed below, and though their causes vary there is little difference in how each is investigated.

I asked two experienced ghost investigator/photographers, Patrick Burns (professional photographer and former star of several shows including Tru TV's *Haunting Evidence*) and Kenny Biddle (author of *Orbs or Dust?* and co-host of the Geeks and Ghosts show) to contribute short sections on photographic anomalies that can be—and have been—interpreted as evidence for the paranormal.

Photographic Artifacts: Orbs, Streaks, and Mists
Kenny Biddle
Orbs

Dust particles are by far the most common cause of orbs in both still photography and video. These particles are so small that they usually go unnoticed. However, when a strong enough light falls upon them—such as a sunbeam, flashlight, or camera flash—these tiny particles suddenly appear in view. When these particles float within a few inches of the lens, they're much too small for the camera's optical sensors to detect and thus focus on. Because most ghost hunts take place in low light or near-darkness environments, the camera's default setting usually causes the flash to fire. This illuminates the out-of-focus dust particle(s), resulting in the classic "orb": a transparent, white circle. The perceived size of an orb—from baseball to basketball—can change depending on a reflected particle's distance from the lens, which may change with a difference of just a few inches.

Whether inside or outside, flying insects can also cause this effect—not just large, easily seen ones such as bees but also smaller insects such as gnats, mosquitoes, and flies (in his chapter on orbs in *The Other Side*, Patrick Burns wryly jokes that "Perhaps Raid insect killer might be renamed 'Orb Be Gone'!"). While walking around a cemetery or abandoned site, these pesky bugs sometimes fly in front of the lens unnoticed and create an orb just like dust particles. It is a different situation when bugs land on the lens of a video surveillance camera. With the camera prefocused on an area much further away, a bug crawling across the lens will appear to be a semi-transparent blob moving around. The bug-blob will appear as if it's floating around the area being monitored. Security footage starring these insects have been shared on social media with sensational, mysterious titles such as "Phantom in Junk Yard," and "Specter at Gas Station."

Another common cause of orbs is lens flare, which is caused by a bright light source directly hitting the lens. This light causes internal reflections within the camera as the light bounces around the lens elements and reflects off the sensor. The light source doesn't even have to be within the scene to effect the image; the light just has to reach the lens. This flaring can cause a foglike haze, rainbow colored streaks, and both polygon-shaped and round orbs. Often a series of orbs are created by this process, appearing in a straight line leading back to the light source.

Misunderstanding focus has also tripped up many ghost hunters over the years. I've covered how small objects will appear out of focus if they are too close to the lens. On the other side of the coin, objects can also appear out-of-focus if they are too far from the lens. Distant background lights—such as street lights, porch lamps, flashlights, LEDs on ghost hunting gadgets, and even the glow off reflective surfaces—will appear out of focus when the camera is focused on a subject only a few yards away.

Light Streaks

Streaks of light can be any elongated light anomaly on an image. They are caused by a combination of long exposures and motion—either by the subject or the camera. In low light situations, or when the flash of the camera is turned off, the camera defaults to a slower shutter speed (also referred to as longer exposure time)—basically, the camera takes longer to take a picture because it needs more time to get enough light to make a coherent photo from the dark scene. When done unintentionally, it will produce distorted and often unrecognizable images.

Motion blur occurs when one or more objects in a scene are in motion, such as a car on a highway, while a camera takes a long exposure image. The car will be a blurred streak, while the rest of the scene appears normal. *Camera shake* occurs when the camera is set (or defaults), to a long exposure, but is not on a stable surface such as a tripod. Any tiny movement by the camera during a long exposure will cause the resulting image to contain streaks or blurs as well as causing sharp edges to become fuzzy. For example, if an insect flies through the scene as the flash goes off, it will reflect light (both from the flash and any ambient light) for the entire exposure. This can easily create a streak of light that appears to be several inches to several feet long in the final image.

Hair is another common cause of light streaks. When unnoticed strands of long hair make their way in front of the camera lens and are illuminated by the flash at such a close range, they appear as blurry, washed-out streaks. Similar objects, such as spider webs and camera straps, will also produce light streaks when photographed closeup. In addition, when the end of a strand of hair is within the frame, it will often appear as an orb.

Light Mists

Whether you're walking through a cemetery on a cold night or in historical buildings that lack heat, your breath can easily become a ghostly mist. In the dark—which is of course when most ghost hunts take place—it's difficult to notice when your own breath frosts up (much less that of other people). Generally, ghost hunters—like most photographers—hold their camera a few inches in front of their faces, which allows exhaled

With only a slight bit of camera movement—such as can result from not using a tripod—and a lack of flash can result in light streaks. Photos by and courtesy of Kenny Biddle.

breath to frost over and float up in front of the lens and the flash. When we inhale, the air goes into our lungs, where it warms and picks up moisture. As we exhale into ambient air that is cooler, the moisture condenses into a vapor. Depending on humidity and temperature, the vapor cloud can last up to ten seconds, either hanging nearby or floating away—possibly towards another ghost hunter taking pictures. While we most often see our breath on crisp, cold winter mornings, breath vapor can also form under warmer-than-expected conditions.

When ghosts hunters present a ghostly mist photo with a caption asserting that there was "no smoke" when a picture was taken, they're generally referring to cigarette smoke. However, smoke can get in front of the lens from other sources, such as pipes, e-cigarettes, campfires, torches, and candles. It may seem silly to think that such sources would be captured and misinterpreted as paranormal, but candlelight ghost tours with guests that smoke pipes, cigarettes, and vaporizers (like e-cigs) are common. Ghost tours generally aren't especially concerned with accuracy or tracking legitimate causes of a strange anomaly as long as it brings them attention and promotes their tour. Thus images of dust particles, long exposures, and cigarette smoke are often used to sell tickets even if the tour guides or other photographers have a pretty good idea what the image is.

Explaining (and Avoiding) Photographic Anomalies
Patrick Burns

When taking photographs, often we find our images get "photobombed"—not by a cheeky bystander trying to be funny, but by a portion of the photographer's own body. A stray strand of hair or a wayward finger can accidentally slip into frame and mistakenly be interpreted as a ghostly anomaly.

When the intense burst of light from the camera strobe / flash fires, even something as minuscule as a few strands of hair—if close enough to the light source—can cast an impressively large shadow on an adjacent wall that appears in frame. After the photo has been taken (and the camera moved away from the photographer's face) the culprit responsible—the photographer's own hair—has likely moved off the flash or fallen by the wayside. The resulting image showing a mysterious dark, looming shadow or "mist" may appear at first glance to have no logical source or explanation.

This can seem all the more mysterious because inspection of the camera will reveal that there is (now) nothing obscuring the flash, and subsequent images taken in the same location (and of the same subject) may fail to recreate the anomaly. With no obvious cause for the strange image, it may be attributed to possible paranormal activity, when in fact there may be a perfectly rational explanation.

One way to safeguard against such "hair shadows" is to ensure that if the photographer has long hair it is either tied back or secured under a hat, away from the face. It's also prudent to inspect the camera flash itself before taking photos to ensure that there is nothing stuck on its lens.

If the photographer has short hair (or longer hair that is restrained), that does not necessarily rule out the possibility of a natural explanation for a seeming supernatural anomaly, because other factors may be at play. I've observed many photographers (and I'm guilty of this as well) sometimes holding their cameras in awkward, unconventional grips, for example in an effort to capture a specific image from a specific perspective that wouldn't be otherwise possible. It may also be out of ignorance, laziness, or just the photographer's poor understanding of how to properly hold the camera. Sometimes the photographer's own hand may unknowingly cover part of the flash. If a single strand of hair can cast a looming shadow in the flash burst, you can imagine what sort of shadow a finger or edge of a palm can cast. This can appear as a large, ominous black mass enveloping a large portion of the room, while other areas of the room are normally lit. Once again this is nothing paranormal but might appear so to the layperson.

A stray strand of hair can cause problems if it gets in front of the camera's optical lens. Depending on various technical specifications (including the depth of field of the image and the focal length of the lens), that stray hair may or may not be visible in the resulting image. If it is visible it can take on a variety of mysterious characteristics; for example if the hair happens to be illuminated by the flash it might appear as a bright "rod" or streak. If it is closer to the lens of the camera it might be within the shadow of the flash and thus appear as a dark streak.

When gathering any type of data, a scientist will tell you that a single data point is meaningless. In a typical experiment the results hinge on having a broad range of data points to compare against one another over time, to be able to spot trends and also to recognize sources of error in the data. For the same reason I would argue that a single photograph in a paranormal investigation is meaningless. You need multiple photos—or data points—to compare against one another: Does an anomaly appear in previous and subsequent frames? If yes, then why? If no, then why not?

Studying multiple "burst" frames that are taken in rapid succession can often reveal the true source of an anomaly based on how it moves in concert with the camera movement, or how it does *not* move—even when the camera *does* move.

Finding and Interpreting Faces and Figures

While these sections provide a good overview of the basic forms in which ghosts are said to appear, more discussion is in order about interpreting human forms. More humanlike in silhouette than wisps or shadows, figures tend to be seen as head and shoulders, often in full frontal exposure instead of in profile. Note that an indistinct figure standing in profile or at a three-quarter turn may look more or less like a post, since the distinctively human head, neck, and shoulders are viewed from an angle that obscures depth. Most of the semidistinctive figures in photos turn out to be hoaxes; if a figure dressed in period costume is fairly clear, it's likely an intentional double exposure or an app addition.

I discussed this in a previous chapter, but this section is a good place to briefly revisit the issue of psychology. One of the most important things to understand about ghost photos is the way that they conform to our expectations. Indeed, what we think is plausible within a given context—what we expect or hope to see or hear—strongly influences our interpretations.

Let's say that you are presented with a photograph taken in an infamous Old West town or hotel that has a reputation for being haunted. Our social and pop cultural knowledge, gleaned from television shows and movies set in the Old West, subconsciously fills in details for us when we see ambiguous forms in photos. People will see Confederate soldiers in photos taken at Gettysburg for the same reason they will see gunslingers in cowboy hats in Deadwood. These stereotypes fit our expectations, but that doesn't make them real.

Like book authors and screenwriters, ghost hunters often populate their investigations with these stock characters (jealous lovers, slaves, soldiers, etc.) and tell stories about them. These dramatic and sensational themes of murders and bloody revenge are what we expect to encounter, and it's what the ghost hunters' audiences expect to hear. There's a reason why those who tell ghosts' stories (such as psychic mediums and ghost hunters seemingly piecing together a ghost's biography) rarely relate communications from a spirit whose life story can be summed up with, "I spent most of my life farming wheat; I had a long, happy, and boring life and the most dramatic thing I experienced was a cow stuck in a fence. Boy was she mad!"

It's telling, from an investigative and folkloric point of view, that genres rarely mix or stray far from stereotyped narratives linked to a specific location. It's presumably perfectly possible, for example, for the ghostly image of a flowery sundress-clad hippie girl to appear on a Gettysburg field or a 1970s disco glam dancer straight out of an ABBA video to appear on a supposedly haunted military ship such as the Queen Mary (hippies who have since died have visited Gettysburg, and disco dancers who have since died have visited military ships—who's to say they could not have returned to haunt places they visited?).

Because there are no known or verified "rules" for ghosts, it's all assumptions and speculation—and being aware of your assumptions and unconscious biases is important for investigations so you can guard against them. If we see what appears to be a humanlike figure holding something in a photo, it's very easy to assume we know what it is based on the context and latch onto that as an obvious explanation: If it's an Old West setting, it's probably a gun.

Of course even if it is a ghost, we have no way of knowing what that person's profession was. There are countless assumptions and expectations that ghost hunters bring to what they see in photos and videos, including that whatever a ghost is apparently doing, holding, or wearing necessarily reflects their profession. In this stereotype, cooks are assumed to hold spoons, gunfighters are assumed to hold guns, and so on. Except, of course, like everyone else, cooks, gunfighters, preachers, blacksmiths, soldiers, and others held or used thousands of common objects at some point in their lives, from pencils to cups to shoes. (Keep in mind that over the past decade thousands of teenagers and young adults have been killed or died suddenly, and presumably some of their spirits may be seen; if their ghosts are seen with the items important to them they're probably holding smartphones and Playstation game controllers.)

These may seem like silly examples, but they demonstrate how much we bring our own expectations and stereotypes to shapes and forms in photos and videos. It's very easy to do—many people often confuse their opinions with assumptions and facts—but it's important not to go beyond the evidence and to make as clear a distinction as possible between what you can independently prove and what you're assuming or guessing. Scientific ghost hunters must recognize and guard against overinterpretation of ghostly evidence, whether in the form of a human-shaped blur in a photo or an indistinct sound in an EVP recording.

Finding Faces

Faces are very common in the ghost photos I've analyzed; when I ask the person who sees the ghostly face to outline it for me, the images they find often resemble not human faces but caricatures or cartoons of human faces, with distorted features such as long chins, elaborate mustaches, hats, and so on. The problem is that this leaves enormous room for wild interpretation and often goes far beyond an objective analysis of what's there.

Any obvious discrepancies between what a human face looks like and what the ghostly face in the photograph looks like can be easily rationalized away. If the apparent "head" is the wrong shape, then the person doesn't revise their original conclusion (deciding it's not a ghost after all), but instead assumes that the ghost must be wearing a hat; if the eyes are slightly in the wrong place (or if the face is missing a feature such as a mouth), then the ghost must still be materializing; and so on. The problem is that once you abandon realistic human faces as the anchor or reference point by which to judge whether something in a photo is humanlike or not, then anything goes. Any random splotch or fragment of light or shadow might conceivably be part of a ghostly face, or an ear, or a cheekbone from an odd angle, or a ghost's spleen, or anything else. Is it a face, or isn't it? Who knows? It might be a genuine ghostly face—or it might not.

The discussion often subtly moves from scientific, testable analysis to subjective interpretation. It's like two people being given a Rorschach ink blot test, and one of them saying the ambiguous form looks like a running elephant, and another saying it clearly looks like a burning house. There is no right or wrong answer because there is no independently objective correct answer; one answer is as good as the next. This issue—essentially an investigative red herring—is a common and rarely recognized problem in ghost photo and video analysis.

Even if the photo truly is an actual image of a ghost, from an investigative standpoint, without some sort of corroborative evidence, photos tend to be fruitless. The images are not explanations nor, really, evidence of anything; they are two-dimensional representations of a three-dimensional space which may range from completely accurate to wildly misleading. In this regard ghost photographs are similar to Bigfoot or UFO photos: if of good quality, they are potentially interesting but not enough to prove or disprove existence. Photographic and video evidence, by itself, cannot prove or disprove the existence of ghosts. If authentic, what such evidence can do is potentially provide researchers and investigators with information to form hypotheses about ghost characteristics for further study. Let's say, for example, that a videocamera records objects moving by themselves in a demonstrably empty house and fraud can be conclusively ruled out. The condition under which that occurred can be recorded and theoretically duplicated to see if it happens again.

Another line of investigation might be opened if the ghostly image is clear and distinct enough to be compared to an independent, third-party photograph or image of a dead person who lived there or died there. See, for example, Blake Smith's excellent April 2010 *Fortean Times* investigation into the famous *SS Watertown* ghost photo, where the faces of two dead sailors were claimed to have been photographed off the side of their ship in 1925. Smith showed that the ghostly faces would have had to be nearly ten feet high to appear as they did in the photo. Though that photograph was faked, if a ghost photo showed a clear likeness to a specific dead person, that might be worth a closer look. In my years of investigating ghosts and haunted locations I've never seen, nor heard of, any such authentic image clear enough to be credibly matched with an old photograph, but it's possible one might appear.

I have encountered many very similar ghost faces in my investigations. After orbs (white spots), faces are by far the most common feature in ghost photos, though some people see torsos or human-shaped figures. People see faces in clouds, ink stains, reflections, tree trunks, even in tortillas and other food (including the Virgin Mary in a grilled cheese sandwich). The scientific word for this psychological process is *pareidolia*, and there is even a state quarter that shows this: "The Old Man of the Mountain" in New Hampshire, a group of rocks that looks like a human face.

But why faces, specifically? People almost never report seeing a ghost's elbow, or thigh, or foot. There are very good psychological reasons for why we see faces in things, sometimes even when they do not actually exist. The human brain is hard-wired to recognize faces; faces are the first things that babies learn to recognize, and parts of the brain are specialized for finding and recognizing faces. And it's not just human faces; virtually all animal faces—from dolphins to cats to horses—are similarly recognizable because faces contain so much information about an animal's state, expressing contentment, fear, pain, and so on. It's no wonder that, evolutionarily speaking, faces are the first things that humans look for: Our ancestors, when meeting a stranger for the first time, didn't look at the other person's feet or elbows or chest to determine if he or she was friend or foe; a smile or a scowl conveys enormous information instantly.

It's important to remember that people who see faces and ghostly images in photos and videos are not stupid, gullible, or crazy. It is a perfectly normal and natural thing to do, and it's how our human brains work. Just as anyone can see faces in clouds, anyone can see faces in photographs that include ambiguous forms and patterns. The role of the investigator should be to offer an objective and knowledgeable opinion based on experience, critical thinking, and scientific principles.

CHAPTER 7

Ghosts on Audio: Voices and Electronic Voice Phenomena

"The single biggest problem in communication is the illusion that it has taken place." — *George Bernard Shaw*

Electronic voice phenomena (EVP), the supposed attempts of the dead to contact the living through recorded audio media, has enjoyed a new burst of popularity over the past decade among ghost hunting groups.

A full history of the link between "unexplained" sounds and ghosts is beyond the scope of this chapter, but a brief survey helps to provide context for understanding the phenomena. The interpretation of specific noises, raps, and taps as communication by spirits is very old. Claude Lecouteux, in his credulous but historically fascinating book *The Secret History of Poltergeists and Haunted Houses*, notes that "we can find knocking spirits under the entry for 'spirits' in the *Grand Robert* of 1974, with the following definition: 'Souls of the dead who manifest their presence by rapping on the furniture, etc. Spirit, are you there?'.... Claude Auge's *Dictionnaire universal encyclopedique*, published in 1897, defines the term as 'Knocking spirits: souls of the dead who manifest their presence by knocking against walls, the furniture, or who express their thoughts by knocking a number of times equivalent of the letter of the alphabet they wish to designate'" (Lecouteux 2012, 8).

This notion of spirits rapping out communication in Morse code or in telegraphic style dates back to at least the mid-1800s. Perhaps the most famous case occurred in the early 1840s in Hydesville, New York, when a young peddler arrived at the home of a Mr. and Mrs. Bell to sell his housewares. He was invited into the home by the Bells' housekeeper and stayed for some days. The maid was shortly dismissed from service but abruptly rehired a week later. She found the peddler was gone, but many of his items were now in use in the Bells' kitchen. The maid thought little of it until she began experiencing strange, ghostly phenomenon, only to find out from the peddler's ghost that he had in fact been murdered in her absence.

At least that was the story told by two sisters named Maggie and Katie Fox, who claimed to communicate with the peddler's ghost through taps and knocks. The Fox sisters became famous across the country and in Europe for their ability to communicate with spirits of the dead, drawing enthusiastic crowds for decades. Years later, however, the sisters admitted it had all been a hoax; there was no murdered peddler, and the spirit communications they offered had been faked. The confession notwithstanding, many continued to believe, and the sisters inadvertently ended up founding a religion called Spiritualism, which is still practiced today.

Rapping and knocking communication from spirits has its origins in fakery and hoaxing, and for several decades afterward many self-proclaimed psychic mediums would continue the practice, pretending that knocks in darkened séance rooms came from the spirit world instead of from the medium (or her assistants). The ghosts graduated far beyond mere taps and raps with the advent of spirit writing (also called automatic writing), in which sentences, paragraphs, and even small books were dictated by the dead to and through mediums. The ghosts, often using chalk and slates or pencil and paper, would pass along long, effusive letters of love and reassurance to their still-living relatives. The ghosts never gave any important or useful information from the other side (for example directing relatives to important missing documents like wills or unknown bank accounts), but instead limited themselves mostly to messages of love.

Unfortunately—and predictably—these too were fraudulent. Psychic mediums (usually purposely faking but surely sometimes sincere) were generating the messages, not spirits of the dead. The psychics would take money from grieving families and offer faked messages from the dead in return. The practice largely fell out of favor in ghost hunting circles by the 1950s, though in the 1960s and 1970s many books were published that were claimed to have been written by spirits through channelers such as Jane Roberts, J.Z. Knight, and others.

Automatic writing is still done today by some ghost hunters and psychic mediums but it has never been proven accurate or valid. (For a history of investigations into psychic mediums from the 1860s through the 1940s, see books such as *A History of Ghosts*, by Peter Aykroyd; *The Science of Ghosts*, by Joe Nickell; and *Secrets of the Psychics,* by Massimo Polidoro.)

Ironically, ghost and spirit communication has come full circle, and today's ghost hunters are looking for the same types of evidence that Spiritualists sought 150 years ago: knocks, taps, raps, and faint voices.

Despite vast advances in technology, ghost hunters are in many ways stuck in the last millennium, and they have no more information about what ghosts are than their forefathers did when Martin Van Buren was president and the telegraph was cutting-edge technology.

Writer Mary Roach explains that the early fascination with ghost voices was largely a product of the era: "The heyday of Spiritualism—with its séances and spirit communications zinging through the ether—coincided with the dawn of the electric age. The generation that so readily embraced Spiritualism was the same generation that had been asked to accept such seeming witchery as electricity, telegraphy, radio waves, and telephonic communications—disembodied voices mysteriously traveling through space and emerging from a 'receiver' hundreds of miles distant.... Viewed in this context, the one unfathomable phenomenon must have seemed no more unbelievable than the other" (Roach 2005, 201).

While the modern age has brought technology into virtually all our lives—most people walk around with, and routinely use, powerful personal computers the size of their palm that can access nearly unlimited information and allow instant, real-time contact with people on the other side of the world—many people don't understand how the technology works. It's not that they're stupid, or that how the devices work is a secret, but instead that for the most part they don't care exactly *how* their cell phone or computer works. As long as it works that's what's important and if something's wrong they pay computer experts to fix it. This situation is understandable and normal, but it also suggests that even at the dawn of the twenty-first century, technology remains fundamentally unknown and mysterious in some ways to the average person.

EVPs: Best Evidence of Ghosts?

After surveying the efforts and results of ghost hunters over the years it's clear that, in their opinion, by far the strongest evidence for ghosts they have found has been in the form of EVPs. Perhaps the biggest reason that EVP is so widely embraced is that (unlike static and impersonal ghost photos) it promises a real-world (or otherworldly) personal interaction. Most other ghostly evidence is inherently ambiguous—things that could have ordinary explanations—but virtually all the ghost hunters I've met were impressed most by the ghost voices they discovered.

In her book *I Think My House Is Haunted!*, Joanne Emmons, founder of a ghost hunting group in New Jersey, claims to know for a fact that ghosts

Parapsychologist Konstantin Raudive, a pioneer in developing a theory of recording ghost voices, or Electronic Voice Phenomenon. Credit: Mary Evans Picture Library / Manfred Cassirer.

are real ("I simply know that they exist," she writes on page 15, though a few pages later she admits "When it comes right down to it, we just aren't 100% sure about much of anything when it comes to the paranormal"). Emmons's reasons for why she is absolutely convinced that ghosts exist—despite an obvious lack of scientific evidence—is typical of most ghost believers. Most importantly, she writes, "there are my own personal experiences," and "the other evidence that has left me without any doubts whatsoever includes the many EVPs that my fellow investigators and I have recorded" (Emmons 2012, 15-17).

Note that the EVPs are especially convincing to Emmons and many others because they actually fall into two categories of "evidence": they are believed to be an audio recording of the dead, but—perhaps more importantly— they are also a form of *personal experience* for the gathering ghost hunter. In other words, an EVP offered by another ghost hunting group may or may not be taken as evidence of ghosts, but an EVP captured during an investigation can be very powerful and convincing to a ghost hunter because they have a strong personal investment in its authenticity, a cognitive bias toward believing that the EVP must be real.

They were there, they insist defiantly, when the many hours of preparation and ghost hunting finally paid off and a disembodied spirit finally responded and interacted with them, no matter how briefly or ambiguously. It's difficult to underestimate how persuasive, chilling, and thrilling it must be for a ghost hunter to listen to a recording of themselves and hear what they think is a spirit from another world interacting with them. As Emmons writes, "When you hear EVPs presented as evidence on television shows, it's certainly intriguing, but when you record the voice of someone not present on your own recorder... well it's nothing short of amazing" (17).

Because EVP is so common (and widely regarded as legitimate among amateur ghost hunters and the public) it's important to take a close look at this technique and evidence. My goal in this chapter is to provide the most comprehensive scientific examination of EVP techniques and evidence to date.

In their simplest form, EVP are heard as voices and bits of speech hidden amongst the background noise and static from audio recordings, radios, televisions, and other devices. Ghost hunters claim that such interference is created (or modified) by spirits trying to speak to us from the afterlife.

According to Mary Roach, "The EVP movement got its start in 1959, when a Swedish opera singer turned painter named Friedrich Jurgenson set up a microphone on the windowsill of his country home outside Stockholm, intent on recording bird songs. As Jurgenson tells it, a titmouse was suddenly and mysteriously drowned out by a male voice saying something about 'bird songs at night.'" Puzzled by this apparent appearance by an unknown voice (a voice not necessarily assumed to be from the dead), Jurgenson recorded more and more, coming to believe that he was hearing short messages and voices directed at him from extraterrestrials. "Jurgenson wrote a book, and the book caught the eye of a Latvian-speaking psychologist named Konstantin Raudive. Raudive picked up the EVP ball and ran with it," eventually recording 70,000 snippets of "extra voices" and sounds he became convinced were voices of the dead.

Jurgenson's work was sloppy and unscientific ("considered today to contain rather flimsy research"; Aykroyd 2009, 116), and much of Raudive's EVP research was eventually discredited as well; the voices and sounds were not coming from aliens or the dead but from more earthly sources. For example, "Raudive's recorded voices had been identified by others as having been part of [radio] broadcasts. What he interpreted as 'I follow you tonight,' for example, turned out to be a Radio Luxembourg announcer saying, 'It's all for you tonight!'" (Roach 2005, 184). Indeed, "In the midst of the excitement over EVP, the Society for Psychical Research commissioned an electronics expert by the name of D.J. Ellis to investigate some of the EVP findings. Ellis concluded that the voices heard were likely due to natural phenomena (dust on the tape, ambient sound, atmospheric electrical interference) and cautioned that the interpretation of such sounds was highly subjective, susceptible as it was to imagination" (Aykroyd 2009, 116). That the SPR—not always known as a bastion of hard-nosed skepticism—reached such a conclusion is noteworthy.

Nonetheless, decades later ghost hunters revived Raudive's work and decided that they could apply it to modern ghost investigations; by 2005 the validity of EVPs was widely accepted among ghost hunting enthusiasts—and even among many in the public, thanks to science fiction films like *White Noise*. Some writers have claimed that Thomas Edison tried to invent a kind of "Telephone to the Dead," a so-called "Psycho-Phone," but this is false. As Mary Roach notes in her book *Spook*, the Psycho-Phone "did indeed exist, but it wasn't designed for paranormal communications. It was an early, phonographic precursor to the modern-day subliminal self-improvement tape" (205).

There are several ways that ghost hunters collect EVP samples; often it simply involves setting up a recorder in an empty room and leaving, returning hours later. Other times investigators will have handheld recorders as they walk through a supposedly haunted area. Sometimes ghost hunters will try to talk or communicate with any spirits that they think might be present, asking questions of the empty room (such as "Is there a spirit here? Do you want to communicate with us? Can you give us a sign?") and waiting for a reply—any sort of "reply" at all will do, any noise or action from a creak to a tap.

The ghost hunters usually later carefully review the tapes or audio files, turning the volume up high and increasing the contrast so that even faint background noises are made more noticeable. Many of the sounds are indistinct at best; it may require repeated listenings or extensive computer filtering to discern any faint words. If the person listening to the recording hears anything that he or she thinks might be strange for whatever reason, it will often be interpreted as a ghost voice. For reasons I'll soon cover, scientific investigators never use this technique.

The Psychology of EVP

There is little mystery about what causes EVPs, and it has nothing to do with ghost voices. Psychological research shows clearly that our brains naturally look for meanings and patterns in the world around us; we are very good at finding patterns—so good in fact that we sometimes recognize patterns that do not exist. One common example of this, mentioned in the last chapter, is when people see faces in random shapes like clouds. The faces are not really there, of course, but our brains unconsciously seek out dots that could look like eyes, an opening that could look like a mouth, and even sometimes noses and ears. People who see faces in clouds aren't stupid or deluded; exactly the same phenomenon happens with EVP, except the process is auditory instead of visual.

EVP are created by a well-understood psychological process called apophenia, which causes people to "hear" distinct sounds in random white noise patterns such as the background static in an audio recording (similar to mistakenly hearing the doorbell or the telephone while one is in the shower). James Alcock, professor of psychology at York University in Toronto, notes that EVP can be simulated in a laboratory setting: If the test subject is given an expectation of what they will "hear," and if the cadence of those words matches the cadence of the white noise, "then the brain will turn those sounds into those—now clearly discernible—words." EVPs are created in our brains and influenced by our expectations. If a ghost hunter is expecting (or hoping) to hear words or phrases in faint sounds—especially in a place thought to be haunted—he or she just might.

Laboratory tests have proven that EVPs can be artificially created; famous psychologist "B.F. Skinner once played nonsense sequences of vowels to subjects and asked them to tell him when they heard something with meaning. Not only did they hear words (with consonants), they were quite solidly convinced that their interpretations were correct. The human mind is also adept at turning nothing at all into intelligible sounds. C. Maxwell Cede, an honorary secretary of London's Society for Psychical Research, described... an experiment in which a group of people were handed paper and pencil and asked to help transcribe what they were told was a faint, poor-quality recording of a lecture. The subjects offered dozens of phrases and even whole sentences they'd managed to make out—though the tape contained nothing but white noise" (Roach 186). Other scientific experiments have reached similar conclusions; many more examples can be found in Joe Banks's book *Rorschach Audio*.

Doubt about the validity of EVPs goes far beyond skeptics and psychologists; despite the popularity of EVP, there are some who are convinced that ghosts exist but doubt that EVPs have anything to do with spirits. As noted psychical investigator and ghost proponent Dean Radin notes, "EVP researchers may be genuinely sincere, but insufficiently critical to assess their own results" (Roach, 193); researcher Jurgen Heinzerling, writing in *Fortean Times* magazine, described the EVP research field as "often hampered by a remarkable lack of critical judgement" (quoted in Banks 2012, 48). These conclusions echo my own years of experience with ghost hunters and EVPs: They are often found by sincere, well-intentioned investigators who simply have not done the necessary research to understand how and why people hear EVP. It's much easier—not to mention much more fun—to just watch a TV show, read a book, or see a talk by a ghost hunting group that shows how easy it is to collect "ghost voices" and run out to do it than it, rather than take the time and effort to understand the processes and pitfalls underlying EVP.

The fundamental problem is that it's not clear what the "anomalous" sounds are, whether they are ordinary random sounds from the environment or even from the ghost investigators themselves. Ghost hunters often create EVPs and "ghost voices" completely by accident through careless investigation techniques. Since the microphones they use are often sensitive, they pick up tiny, ordinary sounds that most people don't notice. Despite a person's best efforts, it is impossible to be completely silent—even when sitting or standing motionless. Involuntary bodily functions like breathing make sounds, as does stomach growling (the result of contracting digestive muscles and gas moving through the intestines, called borborygmus.) Some ghost hunters have even accidentally recorded their farts—a bad scent, but not an evil spirit!

Then there are countless faint sounds in our everyday environments that we hear but don't notice—fish tank bubblers, air vents, clocks, refrigerator motors starting up, dogs barking, wind howling, and so on. All these—and many others—are potential sources of noise contamination. And, lastly, sometimes an EVP sounds like a voice because it *is* a voice... not from beyond the grave, but from someone nearby.

Scientific investigators do not search for EVPs for several reasons. First, of course, there's no logical reason to think that a ghost or spirit would be able to speak, since speech is created by a physical body. Speech requires physical lungs to take in air and physical vocal cords in the larynx to create vibrations that are turned into intelligible speech by physical lips, a tongue, teeth, and a palate. Sound waves by definition must be created by something tangible. It's simple physics: If ghosts don't have a body with lungs, teeth, tongues, and lips, then they simply can't create human speech; there's really no way around it.

Second, the EVPs that have been collected by ghost hunters over the years are exactly characteristic of what are expected from their origins as a sort of mental or auditory illusion: random, ambiguous words and phrases with little or no relevance to the circumstances under which they were recorded. One telltale sign that the EVPs are not actually ghost voices is that the "responses" are almost always nonresponsive (though they can appear to be meaningful, as we will see).

The ghosts who are allegedly communicating don't actually say anything meaningful but instead give random sounds, noises, and faint taps. Something like a ghost saying, "Welcome to my home; my name is Ricardo Sanchez, and I died in 1925 of a gunshot wound" would be especially helpful and compelling for a science-based paranormal investigator. Instead EVPs are almost always random words, and any meaning or connection to the location is supplied by the ghost hunters' imaginations.

Third, it is virtually impossible to rule out all potential sources of sound contamination in just about any haunted location or setting. That is, in order to establish definitively that a given mysterious sound has no possible alternative explanation (and might therefore be a ghost), you must be able to prove that there were no other sources of sound anywhere that could have created the EVP. Haunted houses are often located in neighborhoods with dozens or hundreds of people within earshot—not to mention cars, radios, pets, and so on. Was a faint, mysterious thump created by a ghost trying to communicate or a car door slamming a block away? Unless you carefully monitor and record sounds all around the area (I offer guidance on how to do so later), there's no way to be sure.

...

What follows are a series of real-world case studies drawn from my personal investigation files and other research that illustrate how EVP can be analyzed.

EVP Case Study 1: The Ghost Who Said 'Told You'

Let's take a closer look at the main EVP evidence offered by one prominent paranormal investigation group, the West Coast Ghost and Paranormal Society (GAPS). It's one of the team's most prominent pieces of evidence for ghosts at New Mexico's Old Cuchillo Bar (see chapter 8 in my book *Mysterious New Mexico: Miracles, Magic and Monsters in the Land of Enchantment*), and appeared in several YouTube videos (Note 1). A male and female investigator are heard, apparently while in a barn. The woman comments, "That is a pretty moon." Then there's a faint two-tone sound, followed by the man saying to her, "Did you know the moon used to be a lot closer?"

Upon replaying the two-tone sound, the team believes it's a ghost saying "told you." The validity of this EVP is highly dubious for several reasons. First, it's merely a brief, low sound that could have been created by anything; there's no logical reason to believe that it's a human or ghostly voice. Second, the sound was recorded in an open barn; I personally investigated that barn (see below) and saw many potential sources of random environmental sounds, from small animals to wind. Third, the sound—like most EVP—could be interpreted as nearly anything; though the ghost hunting team interpreted the low two-tone

The author investigating a haunted building in Cuchillo, New Mexico, where a ghostly voice was recorded. Photo by the author.

murmur sound as the phrase "told you," it could just as easily be heard as "toad stool," "toe shoe," "cold glue," "whoa-oo," "old poo," or countless other short words or phrases. Furthermore, even if it *was* a ghost, why would it throw out a random, nonsequitur phrase like "told you" that has nothing to do with anything anyone was saying? The idea that "told you" is an intelligent response by a ghost to the comment, "That is a pretty moon" between two investigators makes no sense. The ghost (if indeed one was present and making the sound) didn't "tell" anyone anything, and certainly nothing about the moon! It's also not clear why these two West Coast GAPS investigators were making random personal conversation during a supposedly serious ghost investigation. Spoken words like these are exactly the sorts of activities that lead to false EVP evidence. Mentioning how pretty a moon is, or the fact that the moon's orbit used to be closer to Earth than it is now, is perfectly harmless small talk—except when you are recording everything and will later be listening for the faintest sounds and interpreting them as ghost voices. This is puzzling behavior for a team that touts its professionalism and adherence to strict scientific protocols. In fact it's even possible that their discussions (and this was only one of many) could have been picked up as muffled EVPs by other members of their team at a different location. Unless strict "no talking" rules are followed, there is a very real risk of cross-contamination (more on this later).

Despite the lack of scientific validity of EVPs—and especially this one—the Ghost Investigations New Mexico team concluded on their website that "Based on the quality of the EVPs and that they are in direct response to our questions[!], we feel very confident in stating that the Cuchillo Bar does indeed have paranormal activity by what would appear to be at least one male spirit." The team returned in October 2010 to do follow-up research in the form of more EVP sessions. The second session, somewhat predictably, resulted in more ambiguous sounds that were once again interpreted as ghostly voices. The team concluded, "Having the opportunity to conduct a follow-up investigation and capturing more and different EVPs, validates our initial findings of an intelligent haunting." The team is convinced that they have scientifically proven they've been in contact with the ghost of a cowboy, and "we need to establish the name of this cowboy. This is an ongoing investigation."

Since their "investigation" consists mostly of going into a building, setting up audio recorders, talking to the room, and later carefully listening for any faint sound that could possibly be interpreted as an intelligible response, it seems likely that they will continue to "validate" their initial findings of a haunting while never collecting any real, usable, scientifically valid evidence. What is needed to prove that ghosts haunt Cuchillo is better quality evidence, not more of the same poor quality evidence.

EVP Case Study 2: Wild Bill Hickok Speaks from the Grave

Some ghost hunters try to re-enact scenes from history in order to provoke ghostly activity or voices. The stars of the Discovery Channel TV show *Ghost Lab*, Brad and Barry Klinge, went to Deadwood, South Dakota, to search for ghosts—including that of Wild Bill Hickok, who was gunned down while playing poker in a saloon (the "Deadwood" episode, airdate January 22, 2011). According to Brian Wierima (2011) of the website DL-Online.com,

"The Klinge Brothers recreated Hickok's murder precisely by bringing in actors, who relived the scene, along with having freeze frames, while the investigators conducted EVP sessions....' We provoked the hell out of Wild Bill, like telling him you never sit with your back to the door and things like that,' Barry said. 'When we got to the part where the gun was to the back

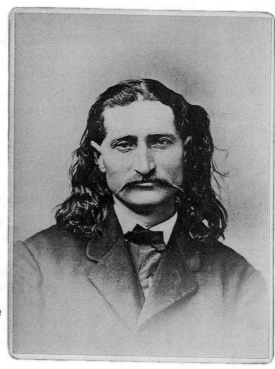

"Wild Bill" Hickok, the gunslinger whose voice was allegedly recorded 135 years after his death by the crew of the *Ghost Lab* television show in Deadwood, South Dakota. From the author's collection.

of his head, we froze it and asked, 'Bill, do you have any last words?' They received an answer. 'The guys out in the truck heard some words and just went crazy,' Brad said. 'We re-listened to the EVP and heard the words, 'Tell my wife I love her.'

To the Klinges—and their TV audience—this must have been a remarkable achievement: They had actually recorded the voice of Wild Bill Hickok, over a century after he died, and he gave them a seemingly meaningful response to their questions.

Or did they? It's disappointing to see high-profile "expert" ghost hunters using such embarrassingly flawed methods—fooling both themselves and their audience in the process. First of all, since the details of Wild Bill's death (like all historical events) are imperfectly known and contain many myths and legends, there's no way to "precisely" re-create his murder, as Brad Klinge claims they did. Different eyewitnesses reported different details about his 1876 murder, and you could spend days or weeks trying to re-enact the event (including the correct dialogue, the people present, the locations of the furniture, the costumes, weapons, props, etc.) and never get very close to how it happened.

Second, there's no evidence that "historical" re-enactments like this lead to increased ghostly activity or better evidence for ghosts. Ghost hunting TV shows like to do it because it makes for interesting visuals, but it has no basis in science or reality. This sort of playacting is what folklorists call *ostension* (Brunvand 2012, Ellis 2001, 200), and it is similar to when teenagers stand in front of a mirror with a candle in a dark room and call "Bloody Mary" three times to evoke a ghost. It's fun (and sometimes scary), but has nothing to do with reality; it's pretending to play a role in a ghost story, half-believing that the participation will make it become real.

And, of course, the "tell my wife I love her" phrase, like most EVP phrases, is faint and ambiguous, and it could be interpreted in many other ways, including "there's a tamale on the floor" (perhaps Wild Bill spied an errant tamale under the poker table as he lay dying on the saloon floor).

Perhaps the most damaging aspect to this "amazing" TV ghost hunting evidence is that the EVP (like the "told you" recorded at the Cuchillo Bar) doesn't make sense. By most historical accounts, Wild Bill Hickok didn't have *any* last words: he was killed instantly by a bullet to the back of the head (see Rosa 2003 for details). In one common legend Hickok's last words were said to have been "The old duffer—he broke me on the hand" (an unlikely comment from someone just mortally wounded by a gunshot to the head). But there's no evidence that his last words were "tell my wife I love her." If the "voice" the *Ghost Lab* crew recorded really was the spirit of Wild Bill, it seems he didn't even know what his own last words on Earth were!

Even if the ghost hunters try to claim that Wild Bill's ghost was addressing *them* with a final message—and not describing what his actual dying words were—that still doesn't make any sense: Why would a spirit tell two TV show ghost hunters to pass along a message to his wife—who (like him) had been dead for over a century? As a ghost dwelling in another realm with other dead souls, presumably Wild Bill would be in a much better position to pass that message along to his wife himself. The *Ghost Lab* crew's whole Wild Bill Hickok ghost investigation fiasco, from re-enactors to random EVP messages, is completely illogical and unscientific. Unfortunately, as is typical, these ghost hunters—who claim to use valid scientific investigation techniques—are seen as role models for many amateur ghost hunters who don't know any better and can't distinguish good science from nonsense.

EVP Case Study 3: The Demon House of Buffalo, New York

In one case I investigated outside of Buffalo, New York, a couple who believed their house was haunted said they sometimes heard faint music on the second story of their home. The couple, Tom and Monica, did their own investigation the day before Halloween: They put a tape recorder at the top of the stairs to record any ghostly sounds. They waited downstairs and did not hear anything at the time, but upon listening to the tape later heard one or more distinct voices they believed to be of ghosts. "What I heard on the [audio] tape scared the shit out of me," Tom said, and this recording was the conclusive evidence that convinced Monica's parents that the house was indeed haunted. That night they ran from the house and had not returned overnight since. (For full details on this investigation see chapter 5 in my book *Scientific Paranormal Investigation.*)

I worked on the case over the next few days. Because of the importance they placed on the audiotape as evidence of spirits, I spent considerable time analyzing it. I suspected that the EVP probably came from somewhere outside the house, not upstairs as Tom and Monica assumed. I wasn't sure if a tape recorder could record street sounds from inside the house on the second story, but it seemed a more likely explanation than ghost voices. If it was a ghost or spirit communicating from beyond the grave, why would it create ordinary background sounds one might hear in a neighborhood?

Tom Flynn, an audio expert I consulted at the Center for Inquiry, analyzed the recordings. He concluded that "there's nothing of obviously paranormal origin" (such as recognized voices of the dead). The 30-minute audiotape contained mostly silence but some noises; much of it was hard to distinguish over the sounds of the tape recorder itself. Flynn used equalization to make some of the noises clearer, but he could not entirely eliminate the sound of the tape recorder's own mechanism because that noise was apparent at every frequency range. Among the sounds were five coughs, four bumps, a dozen or so dog barks, what sounds like some faint music and a conversation, and a train whistle. Most of these were clearly ambient noises from both inside and outside the house.

I then conducted an experiment to test if the EVP they had recorded could have an ordinary explanation. I asked everyone to leave the house except for Monica, who sat in the living room. I instructed Tom to put his small tape recorder in exactly the same position he did the evening of October 30.

I turned it on and we walked down the stairs and out into the driveway below the windows that faced the staircase. We talked about the weather, and he commented that the conditions were exactly as they had been the night he recorded the audiotape: no wind, very calm. We spoke for about

A tape recorder that captured apparent ghost voices (EVP) is placed in its original spot in order to test alternative explanations during a Buffalo, New York, ghost investigation in 2005. Photo by the author.

five minutes, then went back up to get the tape. I wanted to see if voices could be recorded from across the staircase, through the plastic-coated windows, and out toward the sidewalk.

I rewound the tape and played it in front of Tom and Monica. I didn't know what it would show—there were a few suspenseful moments as the leader tape spooled—but my hypothesis turned out to be correct. Our conversation was muffled but clearly audible. Both were surprised at how much the tape recorder picked up. The EVPs they recorded upstairs were from beyond the house instead of beyond the grave. The couple agreed that outside noise was a likely explanation for that ghostly phenomenon. Another EVP created by sincere amateur ghost hunters was explained by environmental audio contamination.

Frank's Box

No discussion of EVPs would be complete without at least a brief discussion of Frank's Box, the so-called "Broken Radio to the Dead." One writer described Frank's Box as: "designed specifically to capture EVP. It was invented by amateur radio enthusiast Frank Sumption, who was inspired by a 'How To' hobby article about recording EVP that appeared in the now-defunct *Popular Electronics* magazine. Upon receiving design instructions from the spirit world and the article, Sumption built a radio receiver that reputedly facilitates real-time communication between the living and the dead, not to mention extraterrestrials, angels, spirits, and assorted entities from other dimensions.... The scan-lock mechanism is disabled on this 'radio.' Therefore, the machine continuously scans radio frequencies at a predetermined rate. This is like twisting the knob on a radio backwards and forwards quickly, producing random noise. This 'sweep method' creates an untunable radio of erratic white noise. The rushing sound of unused frequencies is punctuated by mostly unintelligible fragments of speech or music when the scanner momentarily picks up a station. It is Sumption's belief that 'spirits' and other entities from beyond manifest in an 'echo chamber' built into the unit and harness the random signals to create messages intended for the mortal listener" (Stollznow 2010).

One of the main proponents of Frank's Box is Chris Moon, a ghost hunter and publisher of *Haunted Times* magazine. Moon tours the country with Frank's Box, charging people up to $100 per fifteen-minute session to use his device to contact dead loved ones. During a 2010 ghost investigation at Fort George in Ontario, Canada (see chapter 11) I interviewed Chris Moon about his device and watched as he tried to summon spirits for eager amateur ghost

Ghost investigator Chris Moon demonstrates a device he claims can communicate with the dead. Photo by the author.

hunters during a visit to the site (and later at a formal séance).

The story of Frank's Box and its variants is a fascinating topic that merits a complete discussion beyond the scope of this chapter. For present purposes it's enough to understand that it is simply an active (rather than passive) producer of EVPs. Sumption and Moon acknowledge that the voices generated are those of ambient radio broadcasts instead of actual voices of the dead—but they claim that the ghosts are able to select and use specific sounds, words, and phrases in those broadcasts to communicate their meaning. This, of course, echoes Jurgenson and Raudive's early EVPs from a half-century earlier.

A print analogy would be cutting the pages of a book or newspaper into random words and phrases and putting them into a box, then having a psychic reach into that box and pull out slips of paper until they formed fragments or sentences intended by the spirits. Just as the psychic's hand would be said to have been guided to the correct words and phrases, Frank's Box is said to present audio clips selected by ghosts for human audiences.

There have been several investigations of Frank's Box and other "ghost boxes" (see, for example, Nelson 2011 and Biddle's work with Mitch Silverstein and Stephanie Bohn), and the results have been uniformly negative. As Stollznow (2010) summarizes, "The recordings made by the Frank's Box and similar devices include random words, word fragments, language-like sounds, music, and radio noise. They do not exhibit the features that characterize natural language. There is no grammar; the 'messages' are pieced together, and they do not produce authentic utterances. The most important distinction to make is that these collective sounds do not constitute 'speech.' The data from the Frank's Box may contain bits of speech, but it isn't speech."

EVP Lessons from Real Life

We have seen why many "good quality" EVPs that were originally claimed to be evidence of ghosts turn out to be less than impressive upon closer examination. However, in order to fully understand how EVPs are created, let's examine the same exact principles at work in everyday life, outside of a ghost hunting context. There are many real-life cases in which the meaning and significance of words have been subjected to intense legal and forensic debate. In everyday life meanings in speech are not always clear; far from it. Let's examine some real-world, nonparanormal cases relevant to EVPs.

In February of 2012 a Florida neighborhood watchman named George Zimmerman shot and killed an unarmed black teenager, Trayvon Martin. Zimmerman claimed that Martin had attacked him and that he had shot the young man in self-defense; many, however, believed that the shooting was racially motivated. Those calling for civil rights and homicide charges against Zimmerman referred to a 911 recording of a call in which he muttered "these fucking coons."

Or did he?

Other news media and audio forensic experts heard a very different phrase: "these fucking punks." Did Zimmerman say "punks" or "coons"? The phonetic sounds are quite different ("pəNGks" versus "ko⁻ons"), and most people would have little difficulty telling the words apart. Different experts, however, came to different conclusions. The distinction is very important: one is a general derogatory label that could refer to anyone of any race, and the other is a racial slur referring specifically to black people. How that one word was interpreted could have been key in deciding Zimmerman's future if presented as evidence to a jury or prosecuted under hate crime laws.

After several weeks and more careful audio analysis, the prosecution concluded that Zimmerman had not in fact uttered the racial epithet; he *had* in fact said "punks," just as his defense attorneys had claimed. In explaining why different well-qualified experts had come to contradictory interpretations, Florida state attorney Harry Shorstein "said [prosecutor Angela Corey's] team probably relied on audio enhancing from the FBI or the Florida Department of Law Enforcement. Shorstein called such enhancing 'an indefinite science'"(Schneider 2012).

Audio analysis is indeed an "indefinite science"—even for experts and professionals; unlike DNA testing or fingerprinting, audio analysis has a large measure of subjective interpretation. The more important point is this: If experienced audio experts with the police department and the FBI could not agree on what Zimmerman said in a reasonably clear audio recording (far higher quality than most EVPs), there is little reason to put much faith in the accuracy or validity of interpretations by amateur ghost hunters with no professional training or experience.

We do not, of course, routinely misunderstand one another in everyday conversation (partly because if we don't understand something we can ask the speaker to repeat or clarify—something impossible with EVP), but it happens more frequently than most people notice. Once we acknowledge the frequent difficulty in understanding other people's intent in our everyday discourse in person or by telephone we can appreciate the added difficulty of correctly understanding a ghost's intent (assuming the ghost voice is real).

Elsewhere I describe several other real-world cases where people (including trained personnel such as customs officials and police officers) wrongly claimed to have heard human voices, mistaking ordinary ambient sounds for speech. Those cases, had they been recorded, could easily have been offered as EVP evidence.

The Science of Sound—and EVP

Sounds are the domain of physics and acoustics, but sounds that are also words are the domain of linguistics, the study of language. Since EVPs are, at their core, a linguistic phenomenon, it's somewhat surprising that few if any ghost hunters have examined them from a linguistic point of view.

Mysterious Mondegreens

One way to understand EVP is to examine the common but curious phenomenon of mondegreens. As Gavin Edwards notes in his book *'Scuse Me While I Kiss This Guy' and Other Misheard Lyrics*, "The technical term for misheard lyrics is 'mondegreens,' coined by Sylvia Wright in a 1954 *Atlantic* article. As a child, young Sylvia had listened to a folk song that included the lines 'They had slain the Earl of Moray / And Lady Mondegreen.' As is customary with the victims of misheard lyrics, she didn't realize her mistake for years. The song was not about the tragic fate of Lady Mondegreen, but rather, the continuing plight of the good earl: 'They had slain the Earl of Moray / And laid him on the green'" (Edwards 1995, 7).

Edwards's book contains hundreds of mondegreens. In Elton John's song "Bennie and the Jets," is he singing, "They sell weed and it's wonderful"? Or "They're so weird and wonderful"? Does Carly Simon sing about "clowns in my coffee" or "clouds in my coffee" in her hit "You're So Vain"? Many people misheard Jim Morrison's mumble in The Doors' hit "L.A. Woman," thinking he said "Well I dig a little dog about an hour ago," instead of "Well I just got into town about an hour ago." Then there's the Creedence Clearwater Revival song "Bad Moon Rising," with the inexplicable lyric "a bathroom on the right," which so amused singer John Fogerty that he often sings the misheard lyric in concert.

It's so common that there are even several websites devoted to misheard lyrics; one popular site is BowieWonderWorld.com, which features misheard David Bowie lyrics: In the song Blue Jean, is Bowie singing, "She got leather boots, she's got everything"? Or is it, "She got lead in boots, she got everything"? or "She got language, she got everything"? or "She got lying lips, she got everything?" (Actually the correct verse is, "She got Latin roots, she got everything.") John Lennon singing "cranberry sauce" in the Beatles song "Strawberry Fields Forever" was misheard as "I buried Paul" and taken as evidence that Paul McCartney was dead.

While these wild interpretations seem funny or ridiculous, these mondegreens reveal several important lessons about EVPs. First, these misheard, misunderstood lyrics were recorded by professional singers on high-quality (often state-of-the-art) recording equipment. These were not faint, vague anomalies mined from hours of background static in otherwise apparently dead air recorded by a handheld pocket recorder in a supposedly haunted location; by comparison, song lyrics should be among the easiest words to understand. The fact that so many people can misunderstand these words and phrases shows how easily we can be fooled.

In fact, as Banks notes in *Rorschach Audio*, "One paradox of EVP is that if the voices recorded were of similar quality to normal high-fidelity studio recordings of speech, then nobody would believe them for a minute. If someone came to you claiming that they possessed a recording dictated after death by one of your own close relatives, and they then played a high-quality recording of a stranger speaking in a normal voice, it's reasonable to assume that most people would be not so much convinced but instead quite deeply insulted; and it is a strange fact that it is because of, rather than despite, the very low sound quality of most EVP recordings that at least some listeners are seduced into suspending disbelief. A better production would, ironically, be less convincing" (Banks 16).

Here we see a sort of Goldilocks zone of ambiguity: The EVP cannot be too faint, otherwise it won't be noticed; but it also mustn't be too loud, otherwise it won't be believable. EVPs must sound enough like fragments of human speech, but not be too clear. They must give enough ambiguous, potentially plausible bits of "information" (such as what might be first names, words, or phrases) to be taken seriously, but not too much information (such as "My name is Andrew Prieboy. I'm a musician and have one brother; and I died in 1847 after being hit by a carriage near the corner of Main Street and Markoe Avenue") to be implausible.

Second—and this is crucial to understanding the psychology behind EVPs—*to many people these mondegreen lyrics actually make sense.* Many song lyrics are strange, poetic, and nonsensical, and one interpretation is often just about as good as any other. Take, for example, Duran Duran's hit "The Reflex," which includes the line "The reflex is an only child waiting in the park," but which has also been misheard as "The reflex is a balding child waiting in the park," or "The reflex is a lonely child waiting in a dark." Sure, the idea or image of a reflex being a "balding child" or "lonely child" in a park (or in the dark) is bizarre—but a reflex being an "only child waiting in a park" is equally odd and improbable. When we don't understand something our minds find a way make sense out of the information, and we accept it. The same thing happens with EVPs—our minds go through logical contortions trying to find some way to make the sound or word or phrase make sense. Neither song lyrics nor EVPs are clear, unambiguous, and straightforward, and "understanding" them often involves significant personal interpretation. Further proof that the EVPs are a product of the imagination is evident in the fact that many proponents and "experts" claim that they can hear important messages when the sound is played backward.

If a ghost hunter is convinced that EVPs are reliable (and a ghost is speaking to him), he will often find some way to justify or rationalize it as a personally relevant and meaningful message, even when it may be completely random and meaningless. Just like song lyrics, EVPs are often fragmentary, and instead of concluding that the EVP is not actually a ghost voice, ghost hunters will often rationalize the low-quality, fragmentary nature of the communication by suggesting, for example, that the ghost didn't have enough "spirit energy" to communicate more than a few syllables.

Ghost Linguistics and Misinterpretations

There are other issues that should also be considered when evaluating EVP evidence, such as the issue of ghost mispronunciation. While this may at first glance seem trivial or even humorous, it is relevant to the issue of people correctly understanding and interpreting unknown (and unseen) speakers. Even people who speak the same mother tongue often have difficulty understanding each other—anyone who doubts this should listen to various dialects from Houston, Boston, and Brooklyn.

In real life we sometimes don't understand speakers because of mispronunciation (Elster 1999), and the same word can have different meanings depending on how it's pronounced and where the speaker is from (for example, a live or dead American cowboy would likely use words like *boot* and *torch* differently than a live or dead British milkman). Ghost hunters tend to assume—without any logical justification—that ghosts are communicating with them in their own familiar dialect and level of diction.

To see how an EVP can easily derail a ghost investigation and mislead ghost hunters, let's look at a short, simple example. Let's say a ghost hunter is in a room thought to be haunted; she has an audio recorder out and recording, and she is asking the ghost questions aloud, trying to provoke a response. "Is someone here?" she asks the empty room. "Can you tell us about yourself? What did you do here?" The questions continue until the investigators take a break and review the audio of the session they concluded. After the question, "Can you tell us about yourself?" they turn up the audio and slow down the recording and hear a brief, faint sound or murmur that resembles "abundamurry."

What could this mean? It might or might not be a voice, but if you assume it is (as ghost hunters tend to do), then the question is what it means. And it was in response to the question "Can you tell us about yourself? What did you do here?" So the ghost hunters try to think of possible responses that could be interpreted as an intelligible answer. One possibility is "I want to marry," and might be considered a validation of the question (especially if the location is a church or public building that might host a wedding, for example), and will prompt follow-up questions like, "You said you wanted to marry... who did you want to marry? Why didn't you marry? Did she die?" and so on.

Another possible (and equally likely) interpretation of the sound might be, "I went to Mary." Though this could sound exactly identical to "I want to marry," it has a completely different meaning. Mary is among the most common names for women, and if the ghost hunters do some research and find that a woman named Mary (or Marion, or Maryann, etc.) lived there, visited there, or died there at any time (or even *might* have done so), they might consider this validation of their interpretation. This interpretation would spark follow up questions like, "You said you went to Mary... Who is Mary? Is she your wife? Or your daughter?" and the process begins anew—in a completely different, arbitrary direction, with no real factual information being gained. Yet another ghost hunter might be sure the faint, mumbly ghostly phrase "abundamurry" really means, "I found the money," and use that as a basis for further questions and research: "What money? Did someone steal your money? Were you looking for lost treasure?" and on it goes.

Note also that the response will be interpreted in the context of whatever questions or comments preceded it. Thus if the "abundamurry" sound was a random occurrence, it could have appeared on audio a few seconds or minutes earlier (or later) in response to a completely different and irrelevant question or comment, spawning a set of completely different specious and spurious tangential questions.

The problem is that the conclusions and "answers" that the ghost hunters receive are heavily influenced by their own subjective interpretations. One person may hear one thing while another person may hear something completely different—and each will proceed "investigating" and soliciting further EVPs based on their opinions, with no recourse to verifiable truth or reality and no way to be sure any of their information is accurate. There may be dozens of completely different interpretations of each EVP, and before you know it they have sewn together a patchwork of word associations and guesses into a plausible narrative ghost story about a bachelor ghost who wished he'd wed, or a man happily married to a woman named Mary— or maybe a ghost who found some money. It's like a Choose Your Own Adventure book, with key plot details provided not by a ghost voice but instead by whatever you *think* the ghost might have said. And since you're writing the story, there's no wrong ending.

A review of typical EVPs collected by E.A. Angel in her book *Dead Whispers: Ghostly EVPs* include "come on," "don't," "go away," "now you get," "Amber died," "hello," "farming," "entity," "George," "I'll be at the let's go," "who are you," "god dick get out," "where's mommy," "attuckquock," "defier the beast," "you're mine," "stitch in time saves nine," "my eyes," and so on. Yes, these are all "high-quality" EVPs claimed by a self-proclaimed expert to be ghostly communications.

There's no pattern or structure and no clear evidence that any of these presumed words or phrases are actually coherent or intelligent responses to anything spoken by the ghost hunters. It's merely a record—surely sincere and just as surely wrong—of her personal subjective interpretations of sounds. With no clear connection to the haunted locations where she recorded them (outside of that supplied by her imagination and assumptions), it's no more true or relevant to ghosts than if she'd published a journal about how she interpreted cloud shapes she'd seen or photographed in the sky. (Note 2)

Angel admits (or brags) that many people can't hear the EVPs that seem clear as day to her: "I do show skill with hearing ghost voices; and, over the

"Good job, boys! Keep up the vague, meaningless work!"

Illustration by Celestia Ward of Two Heads Studios

years, by listening to so many recordings, I believe I have developed this skill... I would play some of my recordings for friends. I noticed that most of them would shake their heads, not able to hear what I clearly heard" (15). I've encountered many ghost hunters like her over the years, who have what to them is clear and obvious evidence of ghostly voices. They often get frustrated when I and others don't hear what they hear, or I explain that their interpretation is only one of many. Only rarely have I encountered a ghost hunter or paranormal investigator who acknowledged that their EVPs may be meaningless; much more often they have so much invested in their "developed" ear that they walk away surer than ever that spirits speak to them. It rarely occurs to them that the ghost's words and stories may be the result of their imaginations.

There's another reason ghost hunters are reluctant to question their evidence: If they admit that at least some (perhaps even a sizeable minority) of their best EVPs are in fact not ghostly voices (but instead mistakes, ambiguous sounds, etc.), that admission implicitly undermines the validity of all of them. Though some people classify the EVP recordings into different (and somewhat arbitrary) categories by quality, the simple fact is that even the best of them aren't very good. In other words, if at least some of the best EVPs aren't EVPs at all—and they're all pretty much identical in terms of quality—then how can we be sure that *any* of them are real? Without valid independent corroboration, one is as good as the next. (This evidential pitfall, by the way, has plagued Bigfoot research for decades. When some of the best and most widely accepted-as-authentic Bigfoot tracks were later revealed to have been hoaxed, it forced Bigfoot experts to acknowledge that the authenticity and credibility of some of their best evidence was in fact in jeopardy; see Dennett 1994.)

Most damning of all, all these difficulties in collecting and interpreting EVP are true *even if EVPs genuinely are the voices of ghosts*. To be clear: EVPs almost certainly have nothing to do with ghosts. But even if skeptics, scientists, and psychologists are wrong about this—and the faint murmurs truly are communications from the dead—the irony is that they are still far too ambiguous to be of any use. If EVPs are real, ghosts are providing us with incoherent, fragmentary nonsense.

If a live person communicated with us the way ghosts supposedly do, we'd justifiably conclude he or she was either severely brain damaged, mischievously trying to annoy us with gibberish, or a toddler. Ghost hunters try to explain away this bizarre behavior with myriad theories and excuses about how difficult it must be to pierce the veil into our world, but the fact is that, as "skeptic and entertainment promoter P.T. Barnum put it in 1866, 'none of the ghosts that haunt houses are of the least possible use. They plague people, but do no good. They act like the spirits of departed monkeys'" (Loxton 2016, 69). As an information gathering tool, EVPs are inherently and fatally flawed, generating nothing but Rorschach audio and red herrings.

Guessing Ghost Dialects

I recall during my first visit to Scotland I was baffled to see all the signs and words in English, yet when a Scotsman behind the counter at a restaurant asked me a question he might as well have been speaking Mandarin Chinese. Though we ostensibly spoke the same language his accent was nearly incomprehensible to me. I later came to realize that many EVPs I'd heard over the years—in all their garbled incomprehensibility and seeming gibberish—could have easily been a Scottish ghost speaking my native language, and I'd never have known it.

There's also the complicating issue of different words and speech patterns changing over time. Speech and diction varies greatly by social class, education, geography, race, and other factors—even among those ostensibly sharing a common tongue. A Victorian-era scientist or magistrate will speak very differently than a street urchin or fisherman, for example. Knowing a speaker's approximate age, social class, gender, race, and other factors help greatly in providing context for understanding their words—and conversely *not* knowing factual biographical details about a supposed spirit makes it all but impossible.

The validity of EVPs is dubious because it relies so heavily on the listener being able to correctly and accurately guess a ghost's intent and words. It would be one thing if the spirits spoke loudly and clearly in your own language, but that's never the case. And what if a ghost is bilingual? Many people in the world, especially in decades and centuries past, spoke two or more languages, so the fact that a word or phrase captured in an EVP sounds vaguely like a foreign language doesn't really give any reason to assume it's from one specific spirit instead of another.

EVP researcher Anabela Cardoso's background as a career diplomat (and her consequent familiarity with different languages including Spanish, Portuguese, and English) exponentially increase the likelihood of her gathering (or, if you prefer, "recognizing") supposedly meaningful

Illustration by Celestia Ward of Two Heads Studios

phonemes in otherwise random background noise. A brief string of sounds that may be meaningless in one language may be perfectly clear in another. Without some way of knowing or proving what languages ghosts (or interdimensional beings) speak, there's no way to be sure what, if anything, is being said. For all we know, everyday ordinary background noises and ambient sounds (footsteps, keyboard taps, vehicle rumblings, etc.) may in fact be the unrecognized sounds of an unknown language spoken to us by alien or spiritual entities who simply choose to speak at the exact moment that we would *expect* to hear a sound from whatever source. Such a theory is preposterous, of course, but it cannot be proven wrong and has no less evidence for it than many other common assumptions about ghostly communications.

In her research (described in the next section), Cardoso gives examples of alleged EVPs that are in a different language than the prompts they are supposedly responding to, for example a question in English later followed by an EVP in Portuguese. While this discrepancy passes without comment by Cardoso, it's difficult to know what to make of it, or why a discarnate entity who is supposedly making an effort to communicate would choose to respond in a language unknown to the person who asked the question.

Amateur ghost hunters in New Mexico—my home state, said to be rife with ghosts—would likely assume that any EVPs they collect from haunted locations would be either in Spanish or English, and they would listen carefully for words and phrases in either of those two languages. But those knowledgeable about the state's history would be much more cautious. It is true that English and Spanish are widely spoken in the state—but so are (and were) dozens of other languages, including Native American tongues (Hopi, Navajo, Apache, Comanche, Zuni, etc.), and those brought by European immigrants (thousands of workers and settlers came to the state speaking French, Italian, German, and Portuguese, for example). Speakers of countless languages roamed all over the state, including remote areas. Even assuming a few syllables or words of EVP could be somehow proven to have been spoken by a ghost, you would have to compare it to a large pool of phonemes (the smallest unit of sound used to form meaningful contrast between words) from different languages to even begin to understand its meaning. Ghost hunters usually assume that ghosts speak the same languages they do—not because of any logical or historical reason but because it makes their investigation much easier.

This clearly presents a serious problem for ghost hunters trying to correctly interpret alleged ghost voices. Even if there is a ghost present and it is communicating through EVP, unless it gives specific, detailed identifying biographical information there's no way to know who it is or what it's saying. If a ghost hunter hears what he or she thinks is the sound "da" in an EVP, there's no way to know what—if anything—that means. One person may assume it refers to a father, as in "da-da" while a speaker of another language might have another completely different interpretation.

An English speaker who believes he or she hears the word "da" in an EVP might dismiss it as an irrelevant random sound (or might instead decide it's babytalk for "dad" or "father"); but a person who speaks German would likely take the same "da" as meaningful (it means "there" in German and "yes" in Russian). In Belizean Kriol, "da" can mean "at" or "to"; an Italian or Spanish speaker might interpret it as "to give," while in Norweigan it means "then." A Danish speaker would also hear "da" as "then," but perhaps also "when" or "as." In Japanese, "da" is an informal way of saying "is," and so on.

The point is that what a sound or phoneme means depends entirely on the language of the speaker and the context: because "da" (or any other phoneme) can have so many meanings, it is rendered meaningless to ghost hunters and EVP researchers. Since there is no way to reliably confirm the dead speaker's intent or language (a ghost confirming its preferred language via EVP would be a textbook example of circular logic and question-begging), any interpretation is necessarily derived entirely by the listeners (and is both limited and guided by their native tongue, biases, expectations, and so on). Without some hard scientific evidence (or clear, information-rich EVPs) it's all a guessing game— and thus an unsuitable basis for scientific investigation.

This issue is of course not unique to New Mexico and is far worse in East Coast cities and other areas of high immigration. Those who claim to collect EVPs of slaves, especially in the South, must contend with the fact that dead slaves could have spoken one or more of dozens of African languages. Without knowing for certain the identity and biography of a spirit you're supposedly communicating with, accurately analyzing their words is practically impossible.

Some ghost hunters try to dismiss this problem by assuming (or claiming) that a ghost would only communicate in a language that the listener (i.e., the ghost hunter) would be able to understand. This beggars logic for several reasons, including that it assumes upon dying, spirits can suddenly speak any language in the world and can employ it to suit the individual linguistic preference of anyone trying to communicate with it. It also assumes that the ghost can somehow read human minds to discover which language the listener would prefer—and if they can communicate telepathically, why bother to generate a sound? Anyway, if ghosts really are going to such efforts to be understood, why are EVPs so faint and ambiguous?

Improving Scientific EVP Research

There have been sporadic efforts at bringing some scientific rigor to EVP research. One of the most recent was conducted by the afore-mentioned Anabela Cardoso, a Portuguese career diplomat who often goes by "Dr. Cardoso" (but who does not in fact have an earned doctorate degree). In 2012 Cardoso published an article titled "A Two-Year Investigation of the Allegedly Anomalous Electronic Voices or EVP" in a scientific-sounding journal called *NeuroQuantology*. Cardoso is a former member of the SPR and author of the 2010 book *Electronic Voices: Contact with Another Dimension?*, described in its Amazon.com promotional material as "the story of a normal woman who experienced the impossible: objective contacts with another dimension through loud and clear voices received by electronic means during Instrumental Transcommunication (ITC) experiments. Dr. Cardoso...describes the astounding experiences that transformed her life since she started ITC research in 1997. She presents extracts of conversations with her deceased loved ones and other personalities who insisted that they live in another world."

Cardoso clearly believes that the time, difficulty, and expense she has taken to shield her recorders from outside interference has resulted in strong EVP evidence. In the end, despite the obvious dedication and preparation that Cardoso and her colleagues put into the experiments, they have not convincingly ruled out the possibility of outside interference, nor have they demonstrated that the EVPs are intelligent responses (what she refers to as "semantic reference"). While Cardoso readily admits that "a good number of [EVP] reports might be attributable to pareidolia" and clearly understands many of the fundamental pitfalls inherent in EVP, she does not make a convincing case for what should distinguish a real EVP from auditory pareidolia. Her argument is basically that the "messages" she likes, is impressed with, or finds meaning in are real, and the others are not. Unlike many EVP researchers, Cardoso has a good grasp of EVP recording and interpretation problems—she just doesn't think they apply to her.

Even though collecting EVPs is inherently unscientific, there are methods that ghost hunters could use to improve its scientific validity (should they insist on pursuing this technique). One way to help make sure that the recorders do not accidentally record human voices is by observing a strict "no speaking" rule. Unfortunately this is very rarely done, because the ghost hunters are often trying to elicit an EVP in response to a question or statement. As long as people are talking there is the possibility of aural contamination. It's also important to remember that even if all of the investigators in a room or at a given location agree not to speak (and stick to the rule), it can be difficult or impossible to rule out voices from *outside* the area and beyond the control of the investigator. As anyone who lives near other people knows, voices can and do carry. Unless the location is very remote, and it is conclusively established that there are no people within at least a half a mile or so of the investigation site, there is always a chance that any sound (or apparent voice) may be coming from somewhere else and is being recorded accidentally. Furthermore, even verifying that no one is in the vicinity does not guarantee that human voices cannot be recorded. Humans do not need to be present for human voices to be heard; radios, televisions, music players, and other electronic equipment can convey voices when no one is present. Radio waves carrying voices or music can also, under certain circumstances, be picked up by devices that are not normally considered receivers.

Ghost hunters who wish to validate EVPs should also subject their methods to controlled experiments. One major flaw is that no research has been done on establishing what in science is called a control group in this field—and doing so would be inherently problematic. Since ghosts have not been proven to exist, we cannot compare one location proven to have ghosts with another proven *not* to have ghosts. However one step toward establishing the credibility of EVPs would be to have ghost hunters demonstrate that the ghost voices do not appear in locations that are *not* reputed to be haunted. Think of it this way: If ghost investigators always go to places that are claimed to have ghosts, then how do they know that they *wouldn't* find EVPs in non-haunted locations—since they never look for them there?

If an investigator is trying to scientifically establish the presence or absence of a phenomenon, it is not scientific to only search in places where he or she expects to find that phenomenon—especially one as ambiguous as ghosts, whose signs closely mimic ordinary environmental noises. If EVPs truly are ghost voices then they should not be found in places that are not said to have ghosts. On the other hand, if EVPs are merely the over-interpretation of random environmental sounds—as science and psychology have demonstrated—then it should be possible to record EVPs everywhere that ghost hunters make an effort to find them.

Alternatively, a double-blind experiment could be set up where people are sent randomly to record EVPs at both "haunted" and "nonhaunted" locations, and all the recordings could then be presented blindly to different ghost hunters who are asked to determine whether the EVPs are genuine or false. These sorts of experiments would be a huge step forward in bringing scientific validity to ghost hunting; unfortunately ghost hunters have shown little interest in doing this. It's much easier to merely *assume* that their methods work than to carefully design tests to prove their assumptions scientifically. Without these sorts of experiments and controls, EVP research fails basic science. (Note 3)

Another way for scientific ghost hunters to help rule out the possibility that EVP was accidentally created by one of the investigators (or someone else on the premises) is to equip everyone—without exception—with a lavaliere lapel microphone. These are small wireless mics that people wear when being interviewed outdoors or when giving talks to large groups; they allow the speaker to be mobile and not tied to a podium microphone. If everyone wears one or more microphones set to record the entire time that they are investigating, then if a strange or anomalous (possible) voice is recorded, the investigators can check the time codes on all of the recordings to make sure that no one there was saying any words that might sound like what was interpreted as a possible EVP.

Since few if any ghost hunters use these techniques (or others that are comparably stringent), there's no way to evaluate their EVP evidence. The irony is that it's *possible* that some of these ghost hunters have in fact recorded ghost voices—but because they didn't use good science and research to rule out alternative explanations, there's no way to know. The ghost hunting community's inability or unwillingness to employ methods such as these assure that their evidence will always remain unscientific and thus their mysteries will stay unsolved.

Conclusion

By any scientific standard, EVPs rely far too much on subjective analysis. Given the clear and consistent scientific evidence that EVPs are the products of well-known psychological principles and not spirit voices, why do they remain so popular among today's amateur (and even "professional") ghost hunters? Part of the reason is that people see EVP collection used as standard practice on influential television shows like *Ghost Hunters*, *Ghost Lab*, *Ghost Adventures*, *Paranormal Lockdown*, and *Paranormal State*. Most paranormal groups adopt their procedures from entertainment "reality" shows (Hill 2012), assuming that the methods seen on television are valid and scientific.

A second, and even more significant, factor is that EVPs are so easy to find; anyone can look for (and usually find) ghost voices. Not every ghost hunter or local ghost investigation group can afford high-tech gadgets like infrared cameras and ion detectors (though these devices do not detect ghosts either), but anyone with a $30 audio recorder and an active imagination can find EVPs. EVP has democratized spirit mediumship. Those who wish to speak to the dead don't need to visit a Spiritualist community such as Lily Dale, New York; nor do they need to seek the services of a psychic medium to commune with spirits on their behalf. All they need is some free time and the techical savvy to push "record."

EVPs are also widely touted as among the best pieces of evidence for ghosts; if those who sought EVPs admitted that they are worthless in ghost investigation, they would be forced to throw out countless hours (if not weeks and months) of work recording and analyzing EVP audio. Simply put, they have too much time, money, and faith invested in EVP to question its validity. As one researcher noted, ghost hunters "should not try and force the square peg into the round hole out of sheer frustration. They should instead recognize the long-term value of admitting failure when necessary, and of discarding an incorrect hypothesis, even if much effort had been invested in its formation" (Banks 2012, 27).

Ghost hunters, of course, can use whatever methods and equipment they choose. If the goal is to have fun and scare themselves, their methods are fine. On the other hand if their goal is to collect scientifically valid evidence, they are on the wrong track with the EVP pseudoscience. Science needs more than low-quality, undecipherable sounds that might or might not be human to validate the existence of ghosts or the paranormal.

Does the lack of validity of EVP mean that it is completely impossible that a ghost might be able to speak or communicate through sounds? Of course not; anything is theoretically *possible*, and it could be that one day a ghost hunter will get clear, unambiguous proof and verifiable, falsifiable information from a departed spirit. But until then, all the EVP evidence—every single syllable, odd knock, and faint murmur—shows us that EVPs have nothing to do with ghosts and everything to do with the psychology of misperception. Ghost investigators would be far better served using proven, logical, scientific ideas and methods instead of ones that have a consistent track record of failure, error, and misunderstanding.

One way that EVP might someday prove the existence of ghosts is through voice analysis. For example, let's say that a ghost hunting group investigated the White House and returned with an EVP of President John F. Kennedy speaking about something that happened after his death. Because there are plenty of Kennedy's speeches for comparison, researchers could do a voiceprint analysis of the EVP to verify that it is Kennedy's voice. Of course, to rule out hoaxing (it could be just a sample from one of his recorded speeches), the content of the message would have to refer to something that he could not have recorded while living (alarm over Donald Trump's presidency for example). This would be very, very strong scientific evidence of ghosts. (Of course a ghost hunter desperate to salvage a favored EVP might then use a special pleading fallacy to claim that the spirit's voices have been changed by the process of dying and coming back—but that would beg the question of why some claim they can recognize the voices of the dead.)

Debate and a healthy culture of peer review are elements of the scientific process. The ghost hunting community, by contrast, has little or no peer review of either methods or results. Each ghost hunter group is off doing their own thing, using their own methods, and with no consensus about what constitutes good evidence. Good science also involves making predictions about a phenomenon—and testing those predictions. Sadly, this element is almost completely lacking in ghost hunting.

Notes

Note 1. The "told you" ghost voice can be heard in a YouTube video titled "WCGAPS Investigates the Old Cuchillo Bar Property," available at http://www.youtube.com/watch?v=s2GFHgvlIt0.

Note 2. For an interesting and relevant psychological case study of the personal messages one man believes have been communicated to him through cloud formations see Tom Lumbrazo's book *A Journey to the Clouds: Messages from the Sky*. Many of the captions and messages he offers do seem plausible, but of course that's because another human brain has processed the same ambiguous stimuli in the same way, and many of us can recognize the common forms he sees; Lumbrazo's error is thinking that the messages are actually created by the clouds themselves instead of interpreted (and given meaning) in his mind.

Note 3. Of course a blinded or double-blinded scientific test would not be easy to design or conduct since ghost hunters are often well aware of which locations are said to house spirits and which are not. Even if a supposedly haunted location is not nationally or internationally famous (as is the case with Montego Bay's Rose Hall mansion, Louisiana's Myrtles Plantation, and so on), dozens of directories to spooky sights are available both in print and online. With the proliferation of city- and state-specific guides to oddities and mysteries (such as *Weird California, Mysteries and Miracles of Colorado, Ghosts of Buffalo, The Big Book of Ohio Ghost Stories*, etc.), even lesser-known local and regional ghost reports are easy to find.

Nonetheless such a test of ghost-detection or EVP collection could in theory be conducted using a random sample of private homes in a region, only some of which were thought to be haunted. Psychics mediums and ghost hunters could also be brought in from outside the area, blindfolded to prevent them from knowing what city (or even state) they are visiting and thus preventing them from being tipped off—consciously or unconsciously—about what to expect, or drawing from latent knowledge of local lore. Still, of course, the ghost hunters could always resort to special pleading fallacies, such as claiming that ghosts at a "truly" haunted location merely chose not to reveal themselves during the experiment if they failed to record EVPs there, or that if they recorded EVPs in a nonhaunted location that ghosts from elsewhere were drawn there just for the experiment, or arrived with them at the location.

Presumably a similar scientific protocol could be employed to test various ghostly theories including "stone tape" theory—the idea that events (especially traumatic ones such as murder or suicide) can be recorded onto rock or other objects at a location and "replayed" or re-experienced at a later date by (or as) ghosts or psychics (see Sharon Hill's 2017 article "The 'Stone Tape Theory' of Hauntings: A Geological Perspective" at http://sharonahill. com/the-stone-tape-theory-of-hauntings-a-geological-perspective/). If this is true, then independent investigators with no prior knowledge of the location or its history should elicit identical (or at least very similar) information.

CHAPTER 8

Ghosts in Print:
Spirit Writing and Books

The dead are said to communicate with the living in various ways. The most common are being seen or photographed, being "sensed" in some unspecified way, and speaking (through EVP, for example; see last chapter). However ghosts have also been said to write out their messages from the afterlife. This is a more tangible—and therefore presumably much more provable—form of evidence. Unlike EVPs, whose phonemes are ambiguous and notoriously open to interpretation, there is far more clarity in the written word; a suspected ghostly voice in an EVP may have said the word *blue* (color), *blue* (mood), *blew*, *Belew*, and so on, but if a ghost writes the word *blue*, we presumably have some idea what word is intended and what it means.

Slate Writing

Early ghosts were said to write directly on surfaces, including on chalk slates and paper. Usually this would be done in the context of a séance with a spirit medium. There were various techniques, but typically two blank slates were placed together facing each other, along with a pencil or chalk, and bound with string.

The medium would speak aloud to the spirits, asking that (very short) messages or answers to questions be written on the slates. This could take anywhere from ten minutes to an hour, after which time the slates would be opened and a message from the ghosts revealed. The mediums, however, didn't merely speak to the dead; they—or, less often, a confederate—were busy writing the messages on slates hidden from view, which would later be switched (in a simple magician's move) for the blank ones on the séance table.

In her book *Lily Dale* Christine Wicker describes Pierre Keeler, known as the best slate medium in America, who was caught faking slate writing by investigator Hereward Carrington in 1907. During the attempt to contact ghosts, "As the two men held the bound slates between them, Carrington heard what seemed to be the sound of a pencil writing. This was supposed to be evidence of spirits at work, but watching the medium's wrist, Carrington saw the slight twitching of a muscle produced as Keeler's finger scratched against the underside of the slates. '[H]is wrists are well covered with fatty-tissue, it is very difficult to detect this movement; but, by watching intently, I clearly saw it—corresponding to the [sound of] scratches on the slate.' When the slates were unbound, Carrington also observed that the pencil between the two slates was perfectly sharp and unused." Keeler was exposed and kicked out of Lily Dale, but he was only one of many fakers. Indeed, Wicker states it is undeniable that "there used to be a shocking amount of fraud," something even modern mediums readily admit (Wicker 2003, 67).

I asked Bill Fienning, a longtime member of the International Brotherhood of Magicians and secretary of his local magic club, to describe some of the methods that Spiritualist-era mediums and magicians could have used to create the illusion of automatic writing on slates. "There are several methods for slate writing that I can think of. The sitters at a séance were very naïve, trusting, and gullible. The séance might last quite a while so the sitters would not be continuously vigilant, if at all. I suspect that mediums would simply switch the slates, perhaps while holding them under the table because the spirits are very shy. Another technique is to have several slates in play, then when an extra slate with writing is secretly introduced into the group, no one notices." This would explain how many prewritten messages from the dead might magically appear (often with

A century ago, ghosts were said to communicate through automatic writing, often using chalk and slates. Antique spirit writing slates, from the collection of Mark Edward. Photo by Mark Edward.

universal, banal messages of love such as "I'm always with you" and "Stay strong")—but what about reports of spirit messages that respond to specific questions in real time? Surely that couldn't be faked?

Fienning explains that the spirit mediums had other tricks up their cheesecloth-stuffed sleeves: "Slate writing could also be done by placing the slate 'in the dark' under the table and pressing it to the underside of the table. With some practice and skill the medium could write on the upside-down slate. Also, in a venue that was modified for séances, the medium could sit with his or her back to the wall. This would facilitate a secret panel that could be opened for a confederate to assist in exchanging the slates. The advantage of this method is that the response by the spirits could be created to a question asked by a sitter during the séance" (Fienning 2016).

For a full discussion of early spirit and slate writing—its practitioners, variety, techniques, and so on—see *Secrets of the Psychics* by Massimo Polidoro; *Miracle Mongers and Their Methods* by Harry Houdini; *The Spirit World Unmasked* by Henry Evans; and *The Psychic Mafia* by M. Lamar Keene.

Example of a "ghost written" or spirit-dictated book from 1876, relating details of the life of the ghost of "Hafed of Persia," as told through Scottish medium David Duguid. From the author's collection.

Spirit Authors: Ghost-Written Books

When psychic mediums or ghost hunters write out messages and books they claim (and perhaps believe) are coming from the dead, this is called automatic writing. I have been in the presence of several people who engaged in automatic writing, and it can seem impressive—you get the sense that the person in front of you really is communing with a spirit and not in control of her hand and arm.

The basic problem is of course that you must take a person's word for it that the words and messages they're generating are not coming from them (consciously or subconsciously) but instead from outside their bodies. I'm not suggesting that all or most people who do automatic writing are faking it (though many surely are) but instead that some may truly and sincerely believe that the messages are not their own even though they themselves are the unwitting author. Because the source of the information is at issue and the medium cannot be validated, we must turn to the content of the material to determine whether or not the messages are from the afterlife.

Except for in a few places such as Spiritualist camps like Lily Dale, slate writing has long since vanished. Part of its disappearance is due to the widespread fraud uncovered a century ago, and part of it is that people no longer use writing slates. Automatic writing has lost its nineteenth century trappings and become computerized. There are hundreds of books claimed to have been written by dead people through living writers.

There is nothing new about this; so-called "channeled" books have been very popular through the years. "Perhaps the most prolific and impressive of all automatic writers was Pearl Curran," notes Prof. Richard Wiseman in his book *Paranormality: Why We See What Isn't There:* "Born in 1883 in St. Louis, the first 30 years of her life were uneventful.... Then on 8 July 1913 everything changed. While using an Ouija board to chat with the dead an unusually strong and dominant spirit emerged. The entity explained that her name was Patience Worth and the she had been born in the seventeenth century in Dorset, England but in later life had taken a ship to America where she was eventually murdered by 'Indians.'"

Curran was so successful at channeling Worth that she eventually became quite prolific in writing what she claimed were the words of the dead. She wrote several novels and thousands of poems, becoming something of a celebrity in the process. However, as Wiseman notes, "Unfortunately for Spiritualism, Curran's writings failed to provide convincing evidence of life after death. Try as they might, researchers were unable to find any evidence

Ghost hunters try to interpret spirit communications following an automatic writing session in which a medium claimed to have been possessed by the spirit of a dead soldier at Fort George in Ontario, Canada (see chapter 11).

that Patience Worth actually existed, and linguistic analysis of the texts revealed that the language was not consistent with other works from the period. The case for authenticity was not helped by Patience writing a novel set in the Victorian times, some 200 years after her own death. Eventually even the most ardent believer was forced to conclude that Pearl Curran's remarkable outpourings were more likely to have a natural, not supernatural, explanation" (Wiseman 2011, 166).

Decades later, such "automatic writing" would be interpreted somewhat differently—as contact not with another person's spirit but with one's own from another lifetime, in the context of past lives or reincarnation. In this regard Pearl Curran's channeling of Patience Worth presaged Virginia Tighe's channeling of Bridey Murphy some forty year later.

Channeled books surged in popularity among New Age circles in the 1970s and 1980s. Among the most popular was the book series *Seth Speaks*, dictated by Jane Roberts, who claimed that an energy named Seth possessed her body and dictated esoteric information through her about the soul, the nature of consciousness, spiritual truths, higher planes of reality, and so on.

Channeling remains immensely popular among New Agers; hundreds of books, audiotapes, seminars, and DVDs are devoted to the practice.

In her book *Conversations with History*, claimed psychic medium Susan Lander (2014) wrote that Betsy Ross, widely credited with sewing America's first flag, came out to her as a lesbian about 175 years after her death. According to an interview on Out.com, "When Lander asked Ross why she contacted her, the American icon announced: 'I am gay and I fly the flag of pride and liberty for all of us... I am gay, I am gay, I am gay... I am speaking now as a revolutionary act,' Ross explained [through Lander], saying she no longer wanted to carry this secret. 'I want history to accurately reflect who I was.'"

It's a surprising revelation from Ross—especially since many scholars doubt that she actually sewed the flag she's famous for. According to *The Washington Post*, "There simply is no credible historical evidence that Ross... either made or had a hand in designing the American flag before it made its debut in 1777... it is all but certain that the story about her creating the American flag is a myth" (Leepson 2011). Given Betsy Ross's interest in wanting history to accurately reflect who she was, it's very strange that she would not have offered evidence defending (or disavowing) her claim to fame.

Wendy Weir, sister of the Grateful Dead singer and guitarist Bob Weir, wrote a book titled *In the Spirit: Conversations with the Spirit of Jerry Garcia*, in which she offered 250 pages of what she says the dead singer told her about life, music, and the world, in a series of lessons from the cosmic beyond. Unfortunately little of Jerry Garcia's lyricism seems to have survived death, and most of his messages are indistinguishable from standard New Age platitudes. Here's a typical message: "Joy is love. Joy is peace. Joy is within each and every one of us if only we listen to it calling, follow its song, and open the doors to where we so often keep it hidden behind pressure, guilt, work, obligations, fear, and pain. Allow the light of joy to shine forth from within, allow it to penetrate the Universe, and you will be transformed, for life within you will be raised to a high vibration and the life without you will respond to this shift.... This is a lesson we should incorporate into all of our lives, every day. Open up, allow your joy to shine forth, and feel the radiance, the joy, shining back to you."

One of the problems with channeled writings is that for the most part there's no way to know whether the information is actually coming from the famous dead person's ghost or just being made up by the author. Anyone can claim to communicate with the spirit of anyone, from Jesus to Napoleon to Michael Jackson, and write a book about it.

In his book *The Science of Ghosts: Searching for Spirits of the Dead,* Joe Nickell describes several cases of automatic writing and communication with the dead through Ouija boards and other devices. Regarding famous Swiss medium Helene Smith—who claimed to channel spirits through speech and automatic writing—"an investigator who studied her for many years... concluded [that] 'No one dares tell her that her great invisible protector is only an illusory apparition, another part of herself, a product of her subconscious imagination'" (Nickell 2012, 204). Though not nearly as common as EVP recordings, for example, automatic writing is sometimes done during modern ghost hunts (see chapter 11).

Verifying Ghostly Information

While the vast majority of information imparted through psychic mediums and channelers is impossible to independently verify, every now and then they do offer facts that can be examined. As mentioned earlier, that was done in the case of Patience Worth—and nothing that Curran claimed about Worth's life or biography could be verified. If Worth was anything other than a fictional figment of Curran's imagination, no evidence of that has surfaced in the century since the claims were made.

The problem continues into modern times as well. Before its demise in 2007 as a printed magazine, *Stuff* had a regular column called "Beyond the Grave: Interviews with Dead Celebrities." It's not clear how tongue-in-cheek the readers took it, but the psychic who wrote it, Victoria Bullis, was certainly serious about her work. Like Susan Lander, Wendy Weir, and many others, Bullis "interviewed" many dead celebrities including ex-model Anna Nicole Smith, and when Smith was asked about the then-hyped controversy over the paternity of Smith's daughter, Dannielynn, Smith was clear and unequivocal: "Please tell everyone it's Howard K. Stern."

However soon after the interview was published, DNA tests revealed that in fact Smith's former boyfriend Larry Birkhead was the father. For Bullis (and others who believe that people can talk to the dead) this presents an interesting problem, because the ghost said something that wasn't true. There are several possible explanations: 1) Smith did not know who the father of her child was, and therefore the dead don't have any better information than the living (about paternity, cosmic truths, or anything else); or 2) Smith lied to Bullis and her readers (thus calling into question the truth of anything communicated by a ghost); or 3) "World-renowned psychic" Victoria Bullis cannot really talk with the dead as she claims.

The Psychology of Channeling

So are all these communications with dead people hoaxes or frauds? Not necessarily; surely some are cynically cashing in on dead celebrities, but most of them truly believe that they have been in contact with the dead or some unseen presence. This is neither pathological nor unusual: countless shamans, prophets, priests, and others claim to hear voices or receive supernatural knowledge or messages from the spirit world.

It's an interesting phenomenon with a psychological explanation. When people meditate and relax, random thoughts, images, symbols, and messages may spontaneously arise. If we believe in ghosts or higher powers—and especially if we are actively trying to communicate with them—then in this harmless dissociative state we may interpret our own thoughts as coming from another consciousness outside the body.

Musician David Young, author of *Channeling Harrison*, believes that George Harrison began communicating with him in his dreams, and Young soon began noticing what he considered to be significant coincidences in his life. For example he writes, "I decided to put on a CD, and pulled a handful of random disks out from the glove box. Speaking to God, I said aloud, 'Pick me a good one.' The lucky random CD was a Beatles album, *Sgt. Pepper's Lonely Hearts Club Band*." Thus, in Young's interpretation his CD pick wasn't a random chance (or whatever happened to be in arm's reach) but instead a message that God (or George Harrison) meant for him. Later Young claims that in a dream George Harrison mentioned playing tennis with grass behind him, and a few days later Young picked up an issue of *Rolling Stone* which happened to include a photograph of Harrison playing tennis with Bob Dylan and grass behind him. The photo of the two young musicians was captioned "Forever Young" (a popular Dylan song), which of course was a sign to Mr. Young from Harrison that he was meant to see it. Where others see mere coincidences David Young sees clear signs that George Harrison is communicating with him.

It should be quite possible to prove whether or not specific, verifiable information is something that only a dead consciousness would know. There are any number of things that only a dead person might conceivably know, ranging from whether he or she had a previously unknown child out of wedlock decades ago (provable through DNA testing) to where a particular family heirloom went to details of the person's death. As long as the information given by the ghost is specific, verifiable, and something no one else would know, validating the message should not be difficult.

As with EVP messages, however, the information is almost invariably unverifiable or simply wrong.

It is possible, however, with some confidence to examine ghostly writings and determine the gender of the author based upon computerized lexical analysis. For example "One computer program had a reported accuracy rate of 80 percent in its analysis of language patterns in modern written material. In a study published in 2002 in the journal *Literary and Linguistic Computing*, researchers analyzed 566 published documents in British English using a program they called Winnow. The program was 'trained' on material that was labeled as having been written by men or women. It then analyzed the comparative frequency in unlabeled documents of scores of features of writing judged to be independent of content. The features included parts of speech, like nouns and pronouns, and function words, like 'and' and 'the,' which have little meaning of their own but indicate grammatical relationships within a sentence. It also studied patterns like two- and three-word phrases—for example, 'above the table.' The writings were fiction and nonfiction, and the same techniques can make that distinction accurately 98 percent of the time, the researchers said" (Ray 2015).

Men and women write differently, and so in theory it is possible to tell whether a message was dictated by a spirit of a different gender than that of the psychic or ghost hunter claiming to convey that message. If a sufficiently large variety of supposedly ghost-dictated messages were available for examination, distinct gender differences should be evident in their grammar and might provide indirect evidence toward proving or disproving the authorship of spirit writings. On the other hand if a psychic medium is creating the messages and not a ghost—whether consciously (i.e., fraudulently) or unconsciously (i.e., innocently)—then the writing style of the messages will closely align with his or her gender.

So was Betsy Ross really a lesbian? Does Jerry Garcia really spend his afterlife talking about joy and love? Is David Young really channeling George Harrison? Do people who visit haunted locations really come back with messages from the dead? Unfortunately so far there's no good evidence for any of it. (For more on this, see the chapter on my attempts to verify the biographical details of the Sarah Ann ghost at Canada's Fort George in chapter 12.)

There are a few legends in which ghosts are said to have appeared to the living and directed them to important documents; perhaps the most famous is the Chaffin will case of the early 1900s, in which the spirit of a man's dead father allegedly—and conveniently—led the son to find a previously-unknown "second will" that just so happened to leave money to the son who found it; the will was later revealed to be a forgery.

Overall, as Peter Aykroyd notes in his *History of Ghosts*, "Automatic writing is probably one of the less spectacular feats of a medium, and in truth, it can be very prone to fakery" (Aykroyd 2009, 126). A review of its history shows that ghost writing, like ghost photography, has its roots in fakery and fraud. This does not mean, of course, that every sample of ghost writing is a hoax, nor that all ghost photos or fakes. The lesson is instead to beware of how easy it can be to fake this evidence and how diligent investigators must be in uncovering the truth.

Ghost hunters who wish to follow up or rely on spirit writing should exercise the same scrutiny and skepticism they must bring to EVPs and other alleged forms of communication. Only through close investigation can the validity of ghost communication be proven. Many people want to believe, and those speaking for the dead will always have an audience.

CHAPTER 9

Psychology of the Ghost Experience

While an understanding of the psychology of ghost experiences is a theme throughout this book—it's relevant to everything from understanding how to search for ghosts to what equipment would be best for the search—this chapter is devoted specifically to explaining psychological, physiological, and sociocultural aspects of a ghost experience. After all, given the notable absence of hard, scientific evidence for ghosts, much of it is more subjective and less quantifiable—but no less convincing to those experiencing it.

In my many interviews with ghost believers over the years, one theme surfaces time and again: they believe in ghosts because of some personal experience they could not explain. Certainly, they are influenced by ghost hunting TV shows, spooky images shared on social media, paranormal-themed books and magazines, and so on. But by far the most common source for ghost belief is personal experiences. Thus understanding the science and psychology of a ghost experience—independent of whether ghosts exist or not—is an important and often neglected facet of ghost investigation.

Ghostly Experiences

It's useful to understand what, exactly, people describe when they report ghost experiences. Five people might all claim to have had firsthand encounter with a ghost or spirit but have very different experiences. One might report that she saw a shadowy blur in her hallway late one night, while another describes a time when her cell phone or car keys went missing but mysteriously reappeared, and still another might describe feeling an unexplained sense of fear or dread when entering an unfamiliar room. A remarkably diverse variety of experiences are attributed to ghosts—and most if not all of them can also be attributed to mundane explanations—making it difficult for an investigator to identify with any certainty what is (or is definitely not) a sign of spiritual presence.

When sociologist Dennis Waskul and his wife interviewed ghost experiencers for their book *Ghostly Encounters* they found that "many participants in this study were not sure that they had encountered a ghost and remained uncertain that such phenomena were even possible, simply because they did not *see* something that approximated the conventional *image* of a 'ghost.' Instead, many of our respondents were simply convinced that they had experienced something uncanny—something inexplicable, extraordinary, mysterious, or eerie" (Waskul and Waskul, 2016, 20). Once again we see why defining and explaining ghostly phenomenon is slippery and problematic. Many people who will go on record as having a ghostly experience didn't necessarily see anything that most people would recognize as a classic "ghost," and in fact they may have had completely different experiences whose only common factor is that what seemed to have happened could not be readily explained.

As I describe in my book *Scientific Paranormal Investigation*, context is critically important to understanding the claims: Something "unknown" or "unexplained" in the context of a reputedly haunted house will be interpreted as a ghost, while something "unknown" or "unexplained" in the context of a wilderness hike may be interpreted as a Bigfoot; or as a UFO in the context of something odd in the skies. As Dennis Waskul notes, "I have to admit that I've come to envy the people who reported having poltergeists in their home; they have a ready explanation for anything amiss in their household" (134).

For centuries people believed that flames turned blue in the presence of ghosts. Today few ghost hunters or investigators believe that lore, but it's important to realize that the belief came from *somewhere*, and many people presumably attested to its truth over the years. Perhaps they felt an odd presence when a candle happened to flicker blue, and they made that association, or they passed it along as a cautionary tale to others despite (thankfully) never having had to verify its accuracy. It's likely that many of the signs taken today as evidence for ghosts will be seen as just as wrong and antiquated centuries from now.

Real-life ghost hunters expecting dramatic, unmistakably paranormal events such as those seen in movies (levitating bodies, mysteriously airborne chairs, swarms of insects appearing from nowhere, etc.) will be sadly disappointed; depictions of ghosts and hauntings on television and in films are of course heavily dramatized, sensationalized, and outright fabricated. Countless popular "based on a true story" books and films have turned out to be wholly or mostly false. For example Ray Garton, who wrote *In A Dark Place: The Story of a True Haunting*, which told the supposedly true story behind *The Haunting in Connecticut* film and case, has admitted that the story was fictional and that the family who told him about their "ghostly" experiences couldn't keep their stories straight. Garton was hired at the behest of veteran ghost investigators Ed and Lorraine Warren (lionized in *The Conjuring* and other films), who, Garton says, knew the account wasn't true and advised him to just "make it up and make it scary."

In his book *Paranormality*, Prof. Richard Wiseman describes the work of his colleague James Houran, who has spent years researching the nature of ghost reports. In his analysis of nearly a thousand ghost experiences, "Houran's work revealed that reports of fully fledged apparitions are very rare. In fact, they only account for 1 percent or so of sightings and when such figures do turn up they usually appear at the foot of a bed as people are either waking or drifting off to sleep. Such apparitions have an uncanny knack of looking like a normal person, and their ghost-like nature only becomes apparent when they do something impossible, like suddenly vanish or walk through a wall…. Around a third of Houran's reports involve rather fleeting visual phenomena, such as quick flashes of light, odd wisps of smoke, or dark shadows that move furtively around the room. Another third involve strange sounds, such as footsteps from an empty room, ghostly whispering, or inexplicable bumps and knockings. The remaining third are a mixture of miscellaneous sensations, including odd odors of flowers or cigar smoke, sensing a ghostly presence, feeling a cold shiver down the spine, doors opening or closing of their own accord, clocks running especially fast or slow, dogs being unusually noisy or quiet" (Wiseman 2011, 193).

Virtually all ghost reports are fleeting visual phenomena (flashes of light, smoke wisps, shadows); strange sounds (footsteps, thumps, whispering); or various curiosities such as odd feelings, moving doors, and animals acting oddly. Unfortunately for ghost hunters these are exactly the sorts of ambiguous phenomena that may have ordinary explanations. As discussed there are ways to minimize and even eliminate naturalistic explanations for many of these "anomalies," though not all. For example a mysterious light that is recorded in a carefully light-sealed room might be evidence of a ghost, but there is no way to know for certain whether a cat staring intently at apparently empty space is reacting to an unseen spirit or something else.

Owen Davies notes that "A candle or lantern moving to and fro before the windows of a house or flitting along an alleyway at night, the dark rendering the candle's owner a strange, shadowy figure, could easily be mistaken for a spirit by timid individuals.... One night in October 1851 a couple of hundred people gathered outside an empty house in Northgate Street, Gloucester, after word got around that a pale ghost of a young girl had been seen at an open window at the top of the building. Two intrepid men entered the house to find the ghost but saw nothing. It eventually became apparent that the vision was nothing more than the light of a street lamp reflected by the window onto a whitewashed wall of the room" (Davies 2007, 135). There are countless other examples in which ghosts have been revealed to be reflections, optical illusions, and the like.

It's easy—but completely misguided—to dismiss these historical examples as irrelevant. Though most of the modern world has upgraded from candles and lanterns to electric light, the underlying reasons why we misunderstand and misperceive what's around us are exactly the same. Although most people enjoy the conceit that they are too smart or savvy to be fooled by minor optical illusions, the power of suggestion, and so on, the fact is that we are all susceptible. Though science and technology have greatly improved over the centuries, human brains have not evolved at the same pace and we are all subject to the same psychological limitations and cognitive errors as our forefathers millennia ago. Our brains and perceptual organs—as amazing and usually reliable as they are—remain fallible.

In addition to these odd sights and sounds there is another important type of claimed experiential evidence for ghosts: communication and contact. Among those who most commonly claim contact with ghosts are psychics and mediums.

Psychics and Mediums

Though psychics are used or consulted by many ghost hunting groups, the simple fact is that psychic abilities have never been proven to exist. Some people—especially those who claim to be psychic or "intuitive"— may disagree, but the fact remains that such powers have never been scientifically validated. This is not the place for a lengthy discussion on the reality of psychic powers; the scientific evidence can be found elsewhere (see, for example, Hyman 1996).

For the sake of argument, however, let us suppose that psychic power exists, and that some psychics have an unknown, unprovable ability to provide unique information about a haunted location or spirit. This ability is unfortunately of little or no value to a scientific paranormal investigator.

Elizabeth Saint consults with psychic Lori Johnson during a ghost investigation on the 2016 Destination America television series *Ghosts of Shepherdstown*. Publicity still. Credit: Destination America/MAK Pictures LLC.

I have investigated many locations in which psychics have offered evidence or information claimed to be from "the other side." I have never encountered any information from these psychics that was specific and reliable enough to be useful in a ghost investigation. In fact, more often than not, the information was either useless, a distraction, unverifiable, or completely wrong.

Steve Gonsalves, of the T.A.P.S. group and the *Ghost Hunters* TV show, wrote in the February 2007 issue of the TAPS *Paramagazine* that "the legitimacy and findings of remote viewing [psychics] are obviously questionable, but... if you believe in mind power and ESP, then I say, 'Why not?' It certainly won't hurt." Gonsalves's answer reveals a very shaky grasp of both science and investigation. Real investigation requires knowing that the tools and methods you use to gather information are valid, and that the information from those sources is accurate and useful. To an investigator who wastes hours trying to verify wild leads provided by psychics who can't validate their powers scientifically, it certainly *can* hurt! Furthermore, telling a scared family that a psychic "confirmed" the presence of a demon in their house might not be in the best interest of that family.

The exact same problem occurs with the use of dowsing rods, pendulums, Ouija boards, and other metaphysical and New Age items: they may be fun to play with, but they have never been scientifically proven to work. As discussed in the chapter on equipment, there's no evidence that dowsing rods can detect water, much less ghosts. Any "evidence" that these tools and devices provide are far more likely to be red herrings than valid pieces of evidence.

Telling Stories, Seeing Patterns: Ghostlore, Legendtripping, and Narratives

Daniel Loxton, writing in *Junior Skeptic* magazine, notes that early skeptic Reginald Scot, in his 1584 book *The Discoverie of Witchcraft*, discussed ghost beliefs: "Many people 'imagine that they see or hear visions, spirits, ghosts, strange noises, etc.' Scot acknowledged. But these ghost sightings are 'illusions' with natural causes such as imperfect vision, imagination, alcohol, and fear. People are taught to believe in ghosts: 'in our childhood our mothers' maids have so terrified us' with tales of spirits and goblins 'that we are afraid of our own shadows'" (Loxton 2016, 69).

While this may sound dismissive, there is truth to Scot's words. People *are* taught to believe in—and sometimes fear—ghosts. And this is true whether or not ghosts exist; here's why: all ghostly activity and evidence is inherently ambiguous. It may or may not be paranormal, but the identification of a ghost specifically (and not another unknown or unknowable entity) as the source of the odd event is a culturally and socially determined one.

For example, the vivid and compelling experience of communicating with some external consciousness is hardly unique to ghost hunters and psychic mediums. If that happens in the context of a ghost hunt then obviously the experience will be interpreted as involving spirits of the departed—and specifically those who presumably died at that location under circumstances that ghostlore dictate would create a spirit (murder, tragedy, etc.). However in another situation that exact same experience would be interpreted differently; if it happened to teenager on LSD, it would be interpreted not as a ghostly visit but as a hallucination; if it happened while asleep after watching a scary film, it would be interpreted as a nightmare, and so on. As discussed earlier, the interpretation of ghost experiences is often influenced by the social and cultural contexts in which they appear.

The simple truth is that unexplained sights, sounds, and feelings don't come with clear labels identifying their source as supernatural. That intepretation is provided by TV shows such as *Ghost Hunters*, self-styled paranormal experts, films, bloggers, and so on. Whether you accept their explanation (that ghosts manifest on film as orbs, that a creepy feeling is evidence of a malevolent spirit, etc.) or not, it is clearly a sociocultural explanation—one rooted not in scientific experiments, journal articles, or news reports but instead in entertainment media, ghost hunting books, ghostlore, and the like.

The Lure of Ghostlore

If you ask ghost hunters why they search for spirits you are likely to get several stock answers: they had a ghostly experience and want to know more about ghosts; they want to understand the paranormal; they enjoy being part of a like-minded crowd; and so on. However there is another motivation, one that is rarely explicitly acknowledged but is nonetheless evident in most of their activities: telling stories.

What is the goal of all those countless hours of often-tedious EVP collecting and photographing? Not to compile a spreadsheet of anomalous temperature readings or a catalog of orbs—and judging from the lack of scientific rigor, it's also not to scientifically prove the existence of ghosts. Instead the underlying goal of most ghost hunters and psychics is to uncover and construct a long-lost narrative starring one or more ghosts. Usually the story is a melodramatic legendlike account of love, murder, or tragedy; the spirit who can't rest until his or her death is avenged, the wronged lover, and so on. It's not surprising that books of ghost stories (both fictional and those claimed to be real) are so popular: people love ghost stories and always have. They love spine-chilling tales—not just at Halloween or around the campfire at night but all year long. People love to tell ghost stories and they love to read and hear ghost stories. Whether they recognize or acknowledge it or not, this lure of the narrative is a very strong motivator for most ghost hunters.

The general outlines of the story are provided by local legends, which offer ghost hunters with a cast of characters (some historically real, others completely fictional, and others who lived but whose life's details have been exaggerated or distorted) to choose from. At California's Winchester Mansion, for example, the ghost story will likely revolve around Sarah or William Winchester; at the Whaley House it may include Thomas or Violet Whaley; at Montego Bay's Rose Hall mansion in Jamaica, Annie Palmer will appear; at Santa Fe's Las Posada Hotel the ghost stories may include Abraham and Julia Staab, and so on. There are hundreds of reputedly haunted places, each with their own set of stock characters; often there are secondary ghosts as well, some with nicknames and others with no name at all.

Many ghost hunters are in effect amateur folklorists, though they lack the knowledge or training of folklorists, who are careful not to create their own lore and legends in the process of collecting stories. I do not use the folklore designation disparagingly; I often research folklore and am a member of the American Folklore Society. It's a fascinating, important field of study— but it's not ghost hunting.

In her book *Alas, Poor Ghost! Traditions of Belief in Story and Discourse*, folklorist Gillian Bennett notes that "Once recounted, supernatural experiences start to become subject to cultural processes. The event enters the public domain and social expectations are brought to bear on it. These include ideas about what constitutes both a 'proper' experience of the supernatural and a 'proper' ghost story. As Richard Bauman has pointed out, the relationship between story and event is reciprocal and works in both directions. Storytellers' and audiences' knowledge of what constitutes a proper supernatural event helps create the final shape of the stories that are told on the subject; conversely, knowledge of the stories is part of the shape we give to our supernatural experiences" (1999, 5).

According to Bennett "it was not until the eighteenth century that sudden or unnatural death began to be seen as one of the prime reasons for the dead to be restless (a trend that was accelerated by the publication of numerous popular ghostlore compilations in the second half of the nineteenth century that largely focused on dramatic and exotic hauntings). The connection between ghosts and suicide, murder, untimely death is so set now in our mental habits that it seems strange to reflect that in medieval thought, and in writings of the sixteenth and seventeenth centuries, apparitions were not necessarily even of dead people. They might be wraiths of living people in dire distress, as in the famous case where John Donne 'saw' his wife with a dead baby in her arms while he was abroad in France... or they might be emanations of the spirits of wicked people" (164).

Again we see that ideas about ghosts that ghost hunters and the public take for granted as true (or at least plausible) are very much a product of our age. The idea that the dead remain here in spirit form because they are confused, "lost," unavenged, or for some other reason cannot "cross over"—which is common among today's ghost hunters—can be traced directly back to medieval religious superstitions. As Bennett notes, "In the Middle Ages, a ghost's reasons for walking were customarily linked to its postmortem experiences and underpinned the teaching of the church about the nature of the afterlife. After the Reformation, when the Protestant theology denied the existence of purgatory, ghosts tended to be restless less for what was happening to them in the afterlife and more because of what was happening to their survivors in the mundane world" (164). Only centuries later would the now-common idea of the "bad death" emerge, and "by the end of the nineteenth century, in Britain at least, the relationship between apparitions and untimely or violent deaths was just assumed" (Bennett 1999, 165). This is common among today's ghost hunters, who use well-known ghostlore templates to interpret their experiences. A medium or ghost hunter may believe that a spirit lingers in an area because it is confused and take great personal satisfaction in psychically helping the spirit to "cross over" and find peace.

In his excellent book *The Haunted*, Owen Davies echoes Bennett: "The historical experience of haunting cannot be properly understood without considering the fictional portrayal of ghosts over the centuries. Fiction, whether presented on the page or on the stage, both reflected and shaped popular perceptions about ghosts." Indeed, Davies notes that people who witness ghostly activity are "often participating in the drama rather than being passive spectators. They had to construct their own plots, and literary and theatrical as well as oral traditions shaped how they made sense of what they saw and heard" (216).

Thus "real life" ghost stories are in a very real way completely made up—and this is true whether or not ghosts really exist. That sounds counterintuitive, but here's why:

When ghost hunters and psychic mediums relate and describe the communications they have (or believe or claim to have) with spirits, they are unconsciously imposing their own narrative structures on the information. Ghost enthusiasts are well versed in ghostlore and intuitively understand what makes a good, compelling story. The motivations, melodrama, and so on, are all psychological projections of our own human fears and expectations.

Because human brains are the prism through which the information of supposedly ghostly origin is conveyed, it is impossible to eliminate this confounding factor. As long as there are human ghost hunters and psychic mediums who claim to pass along ghostly messages, this will be an inherent influence (or contaminant) on the information. This same problem plagues other methods of divination including Ouija boards, dowsing, automatic writing, and the like.

In theory there are ways around this problem. For example a ghost or unseen spirit could simply directly manipulate communication tools; if a ghost can—as is often claimed—open and shut cabinet doors, push glasses off tables, and move objects from one place to another, then there's no reason to assume they couldn't simply pick up a pencil or pen and use it to write.

Or, for that matter, ghosts could presumably even type on a computer using a keyboard, with ghost hunters watching the screen intently as an unseen spirit directly tells its own tale. With careful controls it shouldn't be hard to rule out some form of fraud or deception using such a method, and this would be an easy way to prove the existence of ghosts.

Yet this has never happened, and it seems likely it never will. Ghost hunters are unable to explain *why* it doesn't happen, often offering speculative special pleading excuses: perhaps a ghost's energy isn't strong enough to hold a pen or crayon (yet it can manipulate other small objects?), or a human medium—someone to make contact with a pencil or planchette—is (for unexplained reasons and notwithstanding EVP claims) necessary for communication. It is an ironic and curious anachronism that modern ghost hunters use cutting-edge technology (such as laser-assisted infrared devices) in service of centuries-old theories about what ghosts are and how they behave.

Owen Davies emphasizes the importance of context in ghost stories: "A ghost needed to be located in time to make sense of it. This could be achieved by matching a haunting with a real event such as a murder or suicide. This could be a recent incident fresh in the collective or individual memory, or it could be associated with a dim and distant tragic event. Legends could be appropriated to give a ghost a back-story" (40).

Indeed this idea provides the template for most modern ghost hunts. Sometimes the context is provided by the location (the Stanley hotel or the Whaley House, for example) which has a pre-existing legend/history and specific cast of colorful characters for ghost tourists to seek evidence of ("sometimes Mary's ghost is glimpsed in the far corner of the bar late at night"). Other times ghost hunters will search an area not for a specific named ghost or entity (a home's former owner, for example) but instead for generic "types" of ghosts such as soldiers, cowboys, or slaves. In still other cases ghost hunters will go into a supposedly haunted area, seek out some sort of seemingly anomalous event, and then try to communicate with the spirit to learn about its past.

Mass Media Depictions

The public's idea of what ghosts are and how they behave (not to mention how to get rid of them) is heavily influenced by entertainment media and popular culture. Countless paranormal and ghost-themed blockbusters including *The Exorcist* (1971 book and 1974 film); *The Amityville Horror* (1977 book and 1979 film); *Poltergeist* (1982), *White Noise* (2005), the

Paranormal Activity franchise (2007 to present), and so on have themes of psychics contacting dead, spirits communicating through white noise/static, and the like. It's difficult to overstate the influence that fictional pop culture depictions of ghosts have had on the public's idea of spirits.

The paranormal in pop culture is far too vast a topic to cover here, but it's important to recognize this medium in shaping ghostlore. Elsewhere I have written about the true stories behind famous horror films, but with the recent success of supposedly real-life haunting cases from Ed and Lorraine Warrens, I offer an analysis.

In *The Conjuring 2* (2016) Patrick Wilson and Vera Farmiga reprised their roles as Ed and Lorraine Warren, respectively. The first *Conjuring* film was set at a rural Rhode Island farmhouse in 1971, but this new film begins with a wholly unrelated—and far more famous—case, that of murderer Butch DeFeo, who killed his family in their Amityville, New York, home. The killings really happened, and DeFeo's defense lawyer famously tried to claim that DeFeo should be found not guilty because ghosts made him kill. The jury saw right through this flimsiest of Devil-made-me-do-it defenses but the Warrens apparently did not, gullibly taking Butch DeFeo at his word that some unseen evil lurked in the house and had compelled him to kill. The heavily fictionalized story was later made into a novel by Jay Anson and spawned a popular horror film franchise (see Radford 2005 and 2010).

Despite a few early bait-and-switch scenes set in Amityville, the action in *The Conjuring 2* soon moves across the pond to north London, England, where a single mother is raising four children alone in a house plagued by a ghost. It's known as the Enfield Poltergeist case and centers on two teenaged girls who claim to be tormented by spirits. The kids have various nightmares and receive threatening messages from what is apparently a cranky old man named Bill who died in the place years earlier but still causes his favorite rocking chair to spookily move. Things escalate, as they always do in these films, and soon a demon that looks something like a hungover Marilyn Manson in a nun's habit shows up—first in Ed's dream, then in his painting, then in their hallway, always lurching out toward the camera in a suitably scary cinematic fashion. The Warrens, along with TV reporters, a few bobbies, and a token skeptic, soon interview the girls (and Bill, through a séance), trying to piece together what's going on.

The film claims to be "based on a true story," but, as always, such a tagline should be taken with a grain of salt. The true story of the Enfield Poltergeist case is far too complex to go into here, but it is widely acknowledged as being a hoax. Investigators in the real case noted that unusual things only happened when the girls were around, often when the girls knew the cameras were off and investigators were in a nearby room (or had their backs turned). In a series of photographs taken when one of the girls claimed to be levitating, she is seen clearly jumping off her bed into the air. Several of the investigators caught the girls faking poltergeist activity (much more so than is even depicted in the film), and the girls admitted as much but insisted that they hadn't faked *all* of it—raising the obvious question of why someone would fake *any* of it, if genuine, demonstrable ghost activity is going on all around you.

The hoaxing in the real-life case was so obvious, in fact, that the screenplay had to deal with it. Of course admitting the phenomena was faked doesn't make for a compelling or dramatic story—and in any event *The Conjuring 2*'s audience has by then seen many obviously paranormal things going on—so the narrative quickly minimizes the hoaxing in favor of more "scares."

At one point in the film when the ghost hunters are trying to contact the spirit of the dead person who they think is haunting the place, they manage to elicit a stream of clear, verifiable, and coherent information. Not the typical EVP where some faint and ambiguous brief murmur or sound can be variously interpreted as anything from "momma" to "Norma" to "wah-wah," making interpretation difficult if not impossible. No, in this case—and conveniently for the narrative—the ghost happily offers his vitals (including his cause of death) to the Enfield investigators: "My name is Bill Wilkins, I'm 72 years old, and I died of a hemorrhage in this room."

This is virtually unheard of in ghost hunting. If ghosts really could communicate verifiable information so clearly and effectively, the matter of whether consciousness survives death would be settled rather quickly. Of course it's not clear that a person who dies of a hemorrhage would necessarily be aware of that fact; such a determination would be made later by a coroner or medical pathologist upon examination of the brain and corpse. People who have survived them say it involves blacking out, nausea, and "feeling strange," with no authoritative voiceover pronouncement that "You're having a brain hemorrhage." Even if a ghost were contacted, it's quite possible that he or she wouldn't know what killed them—would not the very fact of having a fatal brain hemorrhage likely destroy or at least greatly impair the person's memory or understanding of what happened them at death?

Of the Warrens, one of the principal investigators in the real case revealed in an interview that they had almost no role in the matter. "Guy Lyon Playfair, member of the Society for Psychical Research and one of the chief investigators of the Enfield Poltergeist case, says they showed up uninvited, stayed for only a day, and alleges that they manufactured their own paranormal evidence simply 'to make money out of it,'" according to a June 2016 interview with Playfair on Darkness Radio.

I've not personally met Lorraine Warren (Ed died in 2006), though I investigated a haunted house for a *MysteryQuest* TV show (titled "Return to the Amityville Horror") with one of their protégés. Several of my friends and colleagues have encountered Ed and Lorraine and in some cases even worked with them. All of them describe a pair of self-promoting, opportunistic "ghost hunters" who may or may not have believed in the cases they examined but were happy to exaggerate—or even fabricate—ghostly "evidence" if it made a good story. Their goal was attention and publicity, not truth or helping people. They made a career out of showing up at supposedly haunted locations, presenting themselves as respected paranormal researchers, and injecting themselves into the cases as much as they could with the hopes of getting a book or movie deal.

Writer Ray Garton, who worked with the Warrens on a book about the supposed "true story" behind *The Haunting in Connecticut* case (and 2009 horror film) stated in interviews that the couple would flat-out tell him to make up details about paranormal events in the "true story" books he was hired to write. "If Lorraine Warren told me the sun would come up tomorrow morning, I'd get a second opinion," Garton told me shortly after *The Conjuring 2* was released.

Even though many audiences know (or should know) that a "based on a true story" tagline in a film is no guarantee of truth, there is undoubtedly an influence on the public's perception of ghosts. Many people may assume that the basic facts of a "true" story as depicted in a film are real, even if the dialogue and events are not verbatim or fully accurate. In fact such films are just as likely to be wholly fictional as any other; filmmakers, after all, have no incentive to fact-check their sensational "true story."

The Illusion of Attribution

Another way that human psychology influences anomalous experiences such as ghost hunting is through the illusion of attribution. People often misinterpret and misattribute the events and actions around us, and there's no reason to assume that ghost hunters are immune to these biases.

Cat lovers, for example, often attribute a beloved feline rubbing up against someone as a sign of affection. The truth is that cats have scent glands on their heads and when they rub up against something they are leaving their scent behind in a process called bunting. We like to think that our cats are being affectionate, but in fact cats bunt many objects they presumably have little love for or personal connection to, including coffee table legs, walls, and trees.

The process of attributing human qualities to nonhuman animals and objects is called anthropomorphization. Humans anthropomorphize many things; it's in our nature and psychological makeup. We name things and personalize them. Some people have pet names for their cars and trucks and even use personal pronouns to describe them ("I love my '57 Chevy, she's old but she's got some years left in her"). We describe nonhuman events in human terms, and so on.

This also happens in ghost hunting; we go out of our way to try to frame and make sense of things we experience in our own terms: lights, faint voices, impressions, feelings, and so on. The human brain is very good at finding patterns and trying to make sense of stimuli around us—we do it both consciously and subconsciously every waking moment—thus it's not surprising that ghost hunters will be primed to interpret ambiguous stimuli as relating to them personally.

Michael Shermer, author of several books including *Why People Believe Weird Things*, calls this tendency to infer hidden agents in the world *agenticity*: "Examples of agenticity abound. Subjects watching reflective dots move about in a darkened room, especially if the dots take on the shape of two legs and two arms, infer that they represent a person or intentional agent. Children believe that the sun can think and follows them around, and when asked to draw a picture of the sun they often add a smiley face to give agency to it. Genital-shaped foods such as bananas and oysters are often believed to enhance sexual potency. A third of transplant patients believe that the donor's personality or essence is transplanted with the organ. Psychologist Bruce Hood found that most people say that they would never wear the sweater of a murderer, showing great disgust at the very thought, as if some of the murderer's evil rubbed off in the material of the sweater, but that most people say that they *would* wear the cardigan sweater of the childrens' television host Mr. Rogers, believing that wearing the sweater would make them a better person" (Shermer 2013).

In their book *Anomalistic Psychology: Exploring Paranormal Belief and Experience* Christopher French and Anna Stone note that "Many ghost hunters will attribute intentionality to orbs, describing their 'behavior' as indicating intelligence. If the orbs appear to be close to a person in the picture, they are described as 'friendly.' If they are distant or few in number they are described as being 'shy' (197). Yet when the true nature of orbs is understood (see chapter 6) we realize that they are not in fact displaying any intent, intelligence, or human attributes; it is merely an illusion our mind imposes on the world. An orb appears in a specific spot in a photograph not because that's where someone died but because there happened to be a reflective object in the background.

Of course many ghost hunters recognize that the occasional odd event or possible spirit message is merely a random event with no meaning or significance. But the underlying tendency to interpret external, unrelated events and actions as having a personal significance is pervasive, very real, and easy to succumb to.

Emotional Illusions

An investigator's feelings, emotions, and impressions can be very convincing, and ghost hunting books are filled with countless vivid descriptions of what a person claims he or she felt in a spooky area or in the presence of a ghost. Their subjective personal experiences, whether true or not and however sincerely felt and conveyed, are simply not good evidence of anything. Because personal experience—fallible as it is—is such a powerful source of beliefs, ghost investigators must be vigilant in recognizing and guarding against these psychological processes.

This tendency to discover nonexistent messages is not unique to ghost hunting; it appears in other pseudosciences as well including "backward language" claims and the claim that prophetic messages are hidden in Bible passages (for example in *The Bible Code* books popularized by Michael Drosnin and debunked by David Thomas).

Physicist Leonard Mlodinow, author of several bestselling science books including *The Drunkard's Walk* and *A Briefer History of Time* (cowritten with Stephen Hawking), wrote extensively about this tendency to see intent where none exists in his book *Subliminal: How Your Unconscious Mind Rules Your Behavior*. Mlodinow notes that "It can be difficult to distinguish willed, conscious behavior from that which is habitual or automatic. Indeed, as humans, our tendency to believe in consciously motivated behavior is so powerful that we read consciousness into not only our own behaviors but those of the animal kingdom as well... the cat peed on the suitcase because it was mad at us for going away, the dog must hate the mailman for some good reason. Simpler organisms, too, can appear to behave with humanlike thoughtfulness and intentionality," and Mlodinow gives fruit flies and worms as examples (12).

Though we like to think we are aware of these cognitive biases, in fact "Research suggests that when it comes to understanding our feelings, we humans have an odd mix of low ability and high confidence" (19). People tend to attribute their feelings to whatever they are focusing on, whatever contextual cues seem most salient at the time, and whatever they are wanting or expecting to experience. We assume we immediately and correctly recognize the causes of our feelings and subjective experiences, but in fact it is rarely self-evident: "You might swear you like that fellow for his sense of humor, but you might really like him for his smile, which reminds you of your mother's. You might think you trust your gastroenterologist because she is a great expert, but you might really trust her because she is a good listener. Most of us are satisfied with our theories

Many haunted locations, such as Louisiana's Myrtles Plantation (pictured here) have an inherently spooky and evocative atmosphere with or without ghosts—especially to tourists and visiting ghost hunters. Photo by the author.

about ourselves and accept them with confidence, but we rarely see those theories tested. Scientists, however, are now able to test those theories in the laboratory, and they have proven astonishingly inaccurate" (19-20).

This research helps explain the experiential aspect of a ghost encounter. A ghost hunter walking around in a supposedly haunted location who suddenly feels tired, irritable, or even frightened will often attribute the sensation to the influence of a ghost and interpret it as evidence of a spirit's presence (I've seen it happen firsthand many times). Yet if that person felt the exact same sensation in another context unrelated to ghosts (say, while buying mayonnaise in a local supermarket, or during their daily commute), it would be attributed to something mundane, such as forgetting to eat, needing coffee, a medication issue, or daily stress. The context of a feeling or subjective sensation is a powerful influence on how we interpret it, and it's important to recognize that fact when considering experiential evidence for ghosts. The vast majority of ghost experiences are subtle and subjective (faint sights, sounds, feelings), and exactly the kinds of phenomena that are most likely to be misattributed.

Mlodinow describes a scenario encountered during many ghost hunts: "Suppose you experience the physiological symptoms of emotional arousal [sudden fear, stress, panic, etc.] for no apparent reason. The logical response would be to think, *Wow, my body is experiencing unexplained physiological changes for no apparent reason! What's going on?* But suppose further that when you experience those sensations they occur in a context that encourages you to interpret your reaction as due to some emotion [such as fear or anger] even though there is no actual cause for that emotion. In that sense your experience would be an emotional illusion" (184). Mlodinow goes on to describe several experiments that demonstrate this phenomenon; for an in-depth look at the subject see chapter 9, "Feelings," in his book *Subliminal.*

Because any subjective ghost experience may in fact be indistinguishable from an emotional illusion, it cannot be taken as scientific evidence for ghosts. There are simply too many factors and cognitive biases that can create emotional illusions that mimic ghost experiences to consider them good evidence.

Michael Shermer and Pat Linse, in their booklet *The Science behind Why People See Ghosts*, offer over a dozen scientific and psychological reasons why ordinary people can and do experience seemingly unexplained phenomenon. They write, "All experience is mediated by the brain, which consists of about a hundred billion neurons with a thousand trillion synaptic connections between them. No wonder the brain is capable of such sublime ideas as evolution and big bang cosmology. But it also means that under a variety of conditions the brain is capable of generating extraordinary experiences that are not real."

These conditions include the use of psychoactive drugs, meditation, sleep disturbances, and the action of brain chemicals such as dopamine. They are for the most part not pathological and within the range of ordinary human consciousness and experience. Shermer also discusses "a phenomenon well-known among mountain climbers, polar explorers, isolated sailors, and endurance athletes called the *sensed-presence effect*—the sense that someone or something else is with us. Conditions associated with a sensed presence include: monotony, darkness, barren landscapes, isolation, cold, injury, dehydration, hunger, fatigue, fear, and sleep deprivation. Charles Lindbergh sensed 'ghostly presences' on his trans-Atlantic flight to Paris. The famous Austrian mountaineer Hermann Buhl sensed a presence after summiting the 26,660 foot Nanga Parbat: 'I see two dots. I could shout with joy.... I can hear their voices too, someone calls 'Hermann,' but then I realize that they are rocks.... I set off again subdued. This realization happens frequently. ...I hear voices, hear my name really clearly—[but they are only] hallucinations....I had an extraordinary feeling that I was not alone.'"

Of course most people who sense unseen—presumably ghostly—presences nearby are not making solo trans-Atlantic flights or summiting soaring peaks. But the sensed-presence effect certainly explains some ghostly experiences, and it occurs under precisely the conditions in which ghost hunters often seek their quarry (especially on overnight ghost hunts): monotony, darkness, cold, hunger, fatigue, fear, and sleep deprivation.

Promiscuous Teleology

Ghost hunters often exhibit what Boston University psychologist Deborah Kelemen (1999) calls "promiscuous teleology," or the tendency to overinterpret the world around them to find purpose and goals where none exist. As researcher Stuart Vyse wrote in *Skeptical Inquirer* magazine, "In addition to finding purpose in the design of objects, children also see meaning in events. In a 2015 study, Konika Banerjee and Paul Bloom of Yale University tested children's preferences for natural and purposeful explanations for life events. They selected three groups of participants: young children five to seven years old, older children eight to ten years old, and adults. The participants were given a series of simple life events, such as 'Briana's cat ran away.' For each of these life events, children were given the choice between only a natural explanation (e.g., 'because she left the door open') and a natural and teleological explanation (e.g., 'because she left the door open and to teach her responsibility'). Banerjee and Bloom found that the majority of younger children chose explanations that included an underlying intention, but the preference for intentional explanations decreased with age. Banerjee and Bloom concluded that children have a broad tendency to animate the world with purposeful explanations. They suggested that this tendency diminishes over time because children judge a broader set of events to be more 'significant' than adults, who eventually come to find many of these things trivial; and with age, people become aware of the social norms that label these explanations superstitious" (Vyse 2016, 24).

Indeed, the failure Vyse describes, of accurately discriminating between what is significant and what isn't, lies at the heart of the ghost hunter's mindset. Ghost hunters—like the children in Banerjee and Bloom's studies—have a tendency to set the filter too low, causing many false-positive (Type I) errors. When nearly any sound or light or feeling that cannot be immediately explained is seen as potential evidence for ghosts, it greatly increases the chances of making mistakes. Ghost hunters would likely accuse skeptics of having too stringent a threshold for evidence and making a Type II error (wrongly dismissing valid evidence), but the fact remains that even the best evidence for ghosts falls short on scientific validity. In other words, the problem is not that skeptics are dismissive of seemingly obvious paranormal phenomenon; it's that such evidence is essentially non-existent.

This psychological tendency is one reason that children are often said to be more "open" to spirits and ghosts; it's not—as is often claimed—because their naive innocence helps them retain the world's wonder and magic, but instead because their brains are highly susceptible to magical thinking. They attribute human motivations to nonhuman objects and intuit intention where none exists. Children often grow out of it not because the wonder of the world has been educated or shamed out of them by disapproving adults but instead because they learn enough about cause and effect to realize that if a tree branch falls on a house it's because of a strong wind, not because the tree was angry at the home. It's easy to romanticize childhood naïveté, but the scientific method—the best and most successful prism through which to understand the world around us—is exactly the opposite of this magical thinking. Children's innocent wishes don't build bridges, put robots on Mars, or create lifesaving vaccines.

Ghost Busting with a Higher Purpose

Ghost hunting involves a curious paradox: On one hand ghost hunters apparently risk their lives facing terrors that most people run from—but on the other hand they keep doing so year after year. Yet if ghost hunters genuinely believe that they can and do encounter powerful, evil entities in the course of their investigations, why do they keep doing it?

One answer is that ghost hunting offers a way to appear courageous to lay audiences (TV show viewers, book audiences, social media fans, etc.) whose understanding of what ghosts are—and what they're capable of—comes from dramatically edited and presented "reality" TV shows, horror films, and so on. Books about "real life" ghost encounters often express in breathless prose just how terrifying and dangerous the evil spirits can be, and how courageous the authors are to risk their safety by facing them—despite the fact that there is not a single known death or serious injury proven to have been caused by a ghost. In a form of what folklorists call ostension (akin to legend tripping and role playing), these ghost hunters get to play the hero, whose knowledge of ghosts and courage helps both the living and the dead.

Another, related perspective comes from sociology, in what Stephen Lyng calls "edgework" (a term borrowed from gonzo journalist Hunter S. Thompson). Edgework involves "a type of experiential anarchy in which the individual moves beyond the realm of established social patterns to the very fringes of ordered reality" (Lyng 1990, 855). Though Lyng associates edgework with seemingly dangerous activities such as skydiving, rock climbing, and bungee jumping—risking your life going to "the edge" (of death, of sanity, of human knowledge, etc.) and returning to do it again, often with renewed self-confidence—the concept applies to ghost hunting as well. Indeed, ghost hunters often speak of themselves as pioneers in the field of exploring the edge of the unknown, unafraid to challenge both popular belief and scientific skepticism; they claim to negotiate with ghosts and evil spirits on behalf of terrified homeowners to bring peace and closure to the victims while helping the ghosts to "move on" or resolve lingering issues that presumably keep them Earthbound (Note 1). People who engage in edgework see themselves as risking their physical, mental, or spiritual health in order to develop themselves personally and in other ways, often resulting in "a magnified sense of self." (One need only look at the dramatic "hero shot" photos of the ghost hunters and their groups to see evidence of this.)

A third issue is that many ghost hunters genuinely believe they are doing good and helping families, and indeed altruism is a strong motivation for ghost hunting. Those who do good deeds for others, such as volunteer work, often report feelings of deep satisfaction and happiness. I've encountered many ghost hunters (and psychic "sensitives" in particular) who believe that they are genuinely helping lost souls find peace through communicating with them and helping to resolve issues so they can "transition" to the Other Side. For example a 2015 *USA Today* article noted that a woman who claims to be psychic joined a paranormal investigations group in order to help a ghost involved in the famous Bell Witch case: "A Mississippi clairvoyant, featured on A&E's upcoming five-part series, *Cursed, The Bell Witch,* is claiming to know the real story behind the nearly 200-year-old tale, and she says she got it directly from Betsy Bell, who, according to the legend, was tortured for years by an unseen force on her family's farm. 'Some people will not agree with me, and that's okay, but I gave Betsy Bell a voice to say what really happened,' said Sara Dulaney Pugh, better known as Angel Leigh, a clairvoyant from Leakesville, Miss. 'As a Christian, when I was told that this could be something evil, it scared me. I had to really pray about it. But once I talked to Betsy, I wanted to help as much as I could. For so many years, she was buried and couldn't tell the truth... I had to give this girl a voice,' she said. 'We had to bring this story to light. We couldn't keep sweeping it under the rug'" (Young 2015).

In this person's mind, she is not merely a medium in contact with a ghost; she is a crusader for social justice and a righteous cause, helping right a historical wrong and giving a voice to the voiceless. It's a common theme among many ghost hunters I've met, a sincere sense of self-satisfied accomplishment akin to helping the homeless or volunteering in a domestic violence shelter—except of course that the recipients of their efforts and goodwill are dead, if they ever existed at all: Despite Pugh's claim that she is correcting the record on behalf of Betsy Bell, there is in fact no historical evidence that Betsy Bell ever existed. It would be simple enough to test Pugh's claim by asking two or three other psychics who are unfamiliar with the Bell Witch legend to contact the (fictional) spirit of Bell and see if the ghost tells them the same story she related to Pugh; it's virtually certain the spirit would not. This subtle but powerful motivator helps explain why many ghost hunters are resistant to evidence suggesting that ghosts may not exist; if they entertained the idea that ghosts aren't real, that means that the dozens or hundreds of spirits they helped find eternal peace were in fact imaginary, and the help they provided was only in their imagination.

Often both ghost hunters and ghost experiencers make the mistake of being too invested in their sighting or experience to objectively analyze their evidence. In the ghost-hunting book *The Other Side*, Dave Schrader gives an enlightening (and humorous) account of a woman who sent him what she insisted was a genuine ghost photograph taken in the doorway of an empty room, but which Schrader immediately recognized as a standee (cardboard cutout) of James Dean in a Diet Coke advertisement. He sent her a side-by-side comparison of her photo with a Dean standee, which should have completely debunked it to any reasonable person. This woman, however, had invested so much time, effort, and faith in her ghost photo that she refused to acknowledge his obvious explanation. The authors conclude that often "People want to believe so badly that they throw logic to the wind and are willing to accept any dust particle, tummy rumbling, or smudge on a window as proof of the existence of ghosts. Be smarter than that. You've invested a lot of time in this hobby and on the ghost hunt. Don't negate it all with silly or misleading evidence" (Gibson, Burns, and Shrader 2009, 73).

Psychology of the Paranormal

In their book *Anomalistic Psychology* Christopher French and Anna Stone examine the psychological characteristics of people who tend to believe in paranormal experiences. Among them, "It seems that there is evidence that believers are more likely to see patterns in randomness than non-believers. As a visual bias, this might increase their chances of seeing ghosts.... As a bias in perception of more abstract information, it might increase their chances of believing in horoscopes, handwriting analysis, or even possibly the work of a fortune-teller or spirit medium" (134).

Because ghost hunting investigations produce information that is largely (some would argue nearly entirely) ambiguous, this psychological tendency has the potential to greatly bias an investigator's conclusions. Most images of ghosts are not in focus; they are instead vague mists, orbs, or shadows that might or might not be paranormal. This effect is even more pronounced in the interpretation of alleged recordings of ghost voices or EVPs. If, as the scientific research suggests, people who believe in ghosts are more likely to find meaning in truly random patterns, this suggests that at least some of the "anomalous" images, sounds, and other ghostly phenomena appearing on TV shows and described in books and websites are wrongly attributed to ghosts when they are instead simply random patterns. This does not of course mean that any evidence offered for ghosts must be the result of cognitive biases; indeed some of it may be completely valid and legitimate. But it does offer insight into the psychology of ghost experiences.

As discussed earlier, a person's expectations can be a powerful influence on their experiences. We often see what we want or expect to see, and this has been borne out in countless studies. When people are told in a blind taste test that one wine costs ten times as much as another wine, they consistently rate it as better tasting, even when it's from the same bottle. We *expect* a more expensive wine to taste better than a cheaper one—and it does, but only in our subjective perceptions. For much more on this effect see chapter 10 in psychology professor Dan Ariely's book *Predictably Irrational: The Hidden Forces That Shape Our Decisions.*

Similarly, if we are in a house that we know is reputed to be haunted, we are more likely to interpret anything odd or unusual as being connected to ghosts. Many locations reputed to be haunted are intentionally kept in deteriorating (though not unsafe) condition; at the historic St. James hotel in Cimmaron, New Mexico, for example, the older, "more haunted" part of the building is adorned with antiques, old carpeting, peeling wallpaper, worn floors, and so on that evoke the Wild West's colorful characters and violent past. That is, after all, part of the hotel's appeal and charm, and visitors are of course more likely to imagine ghosts in the venerable hallways that seem right out of a Western film than at a local Motel 6. Ghost sightings are more likely to happen when the "stage" is set and visitors are psychologically primed to seek spirits and potentially odd events.

Another psychological factor that influences ghost hunters is their peers, as French and Stone note: "Researchers have noted that social environment can enhance the likelihood or the perception of an anomalous experience... In a situation where a group of people anticipate the experience of anomalous sensations, this fosters a sense of arousal and expectation. Ghost-hunting team leaders are aware of this and encourage rapport, reactivity, and emotional empathy in a group. In this way, the members of the group can help to raise each other's level of arousal and any anomalous experience becomes shared and magnified within the group" (French and Stone 2014, 156). This often happens in person, but can also be done through reading or hearing about others' ghostly experiences. In fact many haunted inns, hotels, and buildings have a guest book where guests are encouraged to record their own experiences—and read those of others.

Ghosts, EMFs, and the 'God Helmet'

Some researchers have suggested that ghost experiences may in fact be the result of psychological hallucinations, not some external phenomenon seen or felt. Many ghost hunters, including the T.A.P.S. team on *Ghost Hunters*, use EMF detectors to search for electromagnetic fields because they believe that intense magnetic fields can create hallucinations, which in turn might create the illusion of ghosts. The basis for this theory comes primarily from research done by a Canadian cognitive neuroscientist, Michael Persinger. He found that hallucinations (such as out-of-body experiences) could be triggered by stimulating specific areas of the brain with fixed wavelength patterns of high-level electromagnetic fields. He suggested that EMFs might therefore be responsible for everything from UFO sightings to religious apparitions to ghosts. As researcher Chris French notes, "The proposal is that fluctuations in the earth's background magnetic field can interact with the temporal lobe, especially in individuals with a particularly sensitive temporal lobe, to produce a sense of a presence and visual hallucinations...

The interior of the historic part of the St. James hotel in Cimmaron, New Mexico, is intentionally left rustic and rough (peeling wallpaper, antique furnishings, etc.) to provide visitors with a spooky and evocative atmosphere. Photo by the author.

This explanation offers the intriguing possibility that such transcerebral magnetic stimulation may lie behind many reports of ghosts and hauntings" (French and Stone 2014, 99).

It's an interesting theory. Unfortunately for the ghost hunters, it's just a theory—not a proven effect. In fact there's little or no evidence to support the idea that EMFs create ghosts. Ghosts are not being seen in Persinger's experimental laboratory in Ontario; they are being seen in abandoned hospitals and suburban basements. There is simply no evidence that common household appliances can generate EMFs of the frequency and power that induce hallucinations in a clinical setting.

Indeed, Yale neuroscientist Steven Novella says that the theory of EMFs as an origin for ghosts is "speculative at this point." The electromagnetic stimulation used by Persinger "has to be focused, and at a certain frequency in order to have this effect. It seems unlikely that environmental electromagnetic fields would be fine-tuned just enough to cause this effect.... It's an interesting idea, I just don't think it's terribly plausible. At present, I'm not aware of any evidence to suggest it actually happens out there in the world" (Novella 2010).

Richard Wiseman, in his book *Paranormality: Why We See What Isn't There*, notes that several researchers tried to replicate Persinger's results. A team of Swedish psychologists led by Pehr Granqvist "became worried that some of Persinger's participants may have known what was expected of them and their experiences could therefore have been due to suggestion rather than the subtle magnetic fields. To rule out this possibility in his work, Granqvist had all of his participants wear Persinger's borrowed helmet, but ensured that the [magnetic] coils were only turned on for half the participants. Neither the participants nor the experimenters knew when the magnetic fields were on and when they were off. The results were remarkable. Granqvist discovered that the magnetic fields had absolutely no effect.... Worse was to come for Persinger. In 2009, psychologist Chris French and his colleagues from Goldsmiths College in London carried out their own investigation into Persinger's ideas by hiding coils behind the walls of a featureless white room, and then asking people to wander around the room and report any strange sensations. Seventy-nine people visited this most scientific of haunted houses for about 50 minutes each. Following in the footsteps of Granqvist, French and his team ensured that the coils were only switched on for half of the visits, and that neither the participants nor experimenters knew whether the coils were on or off. The magnetic fields had absolutely no effect on whether or not people reported a strange experience" (Wiseman 2011, 219-20).

In their rush to accept this "scientific" explanation for ghost sightings, investigators extrapolate far beyond the evidence. Until it can be demonstrated that generalized, nonclinical EMFs can create the psychological perception of ghostly phenomena, there is no investigative value in detecting such fields. If ghost investigators are certain that common household EMFs can create ghost hallucinations, there are simple ways to test that theory. If Persinger is correct and EMFs are in fact related to ghostly experience, it's because the EMFs are *causing the illusion* of ghosts. If ghosts exist they may or may not be related to EMFs (there's no evidence showing they do), but ghost hunters who cite Persinger's research in support of their methods are unwittingly undermining their own arguments: If you are sure that ghosts are real (and not the product of EMF-induced hallucinations), there is no point in using a device to detect those EMFs.

There are countless mundane visual phenomena that can be perceived as strange or mysterious. Many ghost photos, for example, have been debunked by diligent investigators as mirror reflections, unseen sources of light, clothes hanging from an odd angle, and so on. It would be impossible to provide a full list of all the possible things that could be mistaken for a ghost, and of course it depends on the specific context of a sighting or report; the potential origin of a strange light or shadow will be different for each location.

There are, however, aspects of a potential ghost experience that are hardwired into our brains—psychological, perceptual phenomena that are with us every living moment. Just as ghost hunters need to be aware of ghost doppelgängers in the external world of abandoned buildings and cemeteries, they need to understand how the human brain can make us see and hear things that may not be there. Any given ghost experience may or may not be attributable to one or more of these factors, but they should be considered and ruled out before accepting paranormal explanations for an unexplained experience.

The Psychology of Seeing Things

An experience I had during a ghost investigation of the haunted Old Cuchillo Bar in Cuchillo, New Mexico helped me understand how easily our senses can be fooled. This is what happened, excerpted from chapter 8 in my book *Mysterious New Mexico*.

The front of the old store in the Old Cuchillo Bar, where strange, shadowy forms have been reported; optical illusions may explain some of the ghostly sightings. Photo by the author.

There is no electricity in the main part of the Old Cuchillo Bar; cables and extension cords run from the main house to provide electrical light. In the main room, which used to serve as a general store (and still has piles of dust-covered junk in it), the only natural light comes in through the glass in the door. It was in this area that shadowy figures had been reported on a few occasions. After spending some time examining the area I devised a hypothesis that might explain the shadowy figures.

During the daytime, the area around and just inside the doors is brightly backlit with sunlight glare, making it difficult to see what's there and creating odd shadows. You can see this effect in pictures of people photographed in front of windows or other bright objects in the background. The sharp contrast also creates an optical illusion of a ghostly afterimage as your eyes try to adjust from the bright New Mexico daylight to the near-pitch dark inside. Under such conditions people often see shadowy figures—but it has nothing to do with the netherworld and everything to do with optical illusions.

Why do people report seeing dark shadowy movements that do not really exist? Actually, recent psychological research holds interesting answers that explain some ghost reports. It has been proven that certain patterns of light and dark, and patterns of colors, create the illusion of movement. Many examples can be seen in books about optical illusions.

Researchers Vilayanur Ramachandran and Diane Rogers-Ramachandran of the Center for Brain and Cognition at the University of California-San Diego note that scientists do not know exactly why this illusion happens, but "What we do know is that the odd arrangements of luminance-based edges must somehow 'artificially' activate motion detecting neurons in the visual pathways. That is, the particular patterns of luminance and contrast fool the visual system into seeing motion where none exists" (Ramachandran and Rogers-Ramachandran 2008).

At the Old Cuchillo Bar we have a combination of circumstances that are known to create optical illusions: low light in most of a room combined with bright glaring daylight coming through full-length windows; and direct and indirect light coming from odd angles (not above, as we usually experience it, but from the sides and even below). Furthermore, I realized, the room was full of shadows because it is so cluttered. Normally we don't notice shadows in our everyday lives because light sources are above our heads, so the shadows of ordinary objects (furniture, people, pets, etc.) are cast more or less downward, out of sight, and unnoticed. But throughout the Cuchillo property—and especially in the old storehouse area where most of the shadows were reported—the light is coming from the side, about knee level upwards. This is guaranteed to create unusual shadows (and likely shadowy figures) as you walk through the room. Try this yourself: put a desk lamp on the floor in a darkened room, turn it on, and watch how ordinary shadows jump into your field of view. This does not explain all reports of shadows, of course, but it provides an example of how our vision can deceive us.

The Psychology of Hearing Voices

Not only do people sometimes see things that aren't there, but they also sometimes hear human voices where they do not in fact exist. Ghostly voices are among the most commonly reported experiences, often heard in areas that are believed or assumed to be empty. There are many reported cases in which what sounds to a listener very much like a person speaking or calling out to them is in fact merely an auditory illusion. This is rarely sign of mental illness, but instead a perfectly natural and normal mistake.

Of course most sounds that are interpreted as ghostly voices are not loud, clear, and sustained but instead faint, indistinct, and sporadic—not resembling a person speaking clearly and articulately to your face, more like someone whispering or mumbling to another person from another room in a house. Instead of entire conversations (which a ghost could presumably engage in), the ghostly voices usually seem to utter only snippets of words, sentence fragments, or merely syllables. This is exactly how ambient sounds mistaken for human voice appear to a listener.

When a Voice Is Not a Voice

Much of the evidence for ghosts comes from anecdotes and personal experiences. People who believe they have been in the presence of spirits often offer descriptions such as "I heard footsteps in the hallway, but no one was there," or "There were faint voices coming from upstairs, but no one else was in the house," or "I heard a little girl laughing and giggling," and so on. These are of course very common in "true" ghost stories and first-person accounts of presumably paranormal experiences. When interviewed by skeptics or investigators they typically offer no proof other than "I was there, I know what I heard." Personal experience is incredibly powerful and compelling—after all, if we can't trust our own eyes and ears, what can we trust?

There is, however, a serious and often-unrecognized problem with this sort of personal experience. The fundamental problem is that just because something *looks* convincingly like something else, or *sounds* convincingly like something else, that doesn't mean it *is* that thing. In other chapters I discuss visual misinterpretations, and here I focus on audio misinterpretations (for more, see chapter 7).

To understand the scientific and psychological basis for why we can't always trust our ears, it's important to understand the basic physics of sound and acoustics. If you listen to music CD of, for example, Bob Dylan's voice, or a tambourine, or a humpback whale call, you are not actually hearing Dylan's voice, or a tambourine, or a humpback whale. You are hearing a series of sound vibrations read off a recorded medium and created by audio speakers, which our brains then reassemble and interpret as those sounds.

Sound is not mysterious, but rather very well understood: it is merely a series of physical vibrations which reach our brains through our ears and which our brains try to make sense of. That is not Bob Dylan's voice—it is a *re-creation* of Dylan's voice using magnets and speakers. And that is important for ghost hunters to understand because it highlights the fact that EVPs (like all recordings) do not reflect or represent reality but are instead *re-created illusions of sounds*—in most cases ambiguous sounds.

(An identical process happens when artificial flavors are created in a food laboratory; flavor can be broken down into specific quantities of different chemicals. Thus an artificial flavor can be indistinguishable from that same natural flavor. It tastes the same but is in fact a wholly new re-creation of the original.) Just as the human mouth cannot reliably distinguish a "true" natural flavor from an artificial one (given sufficiently good quality chemical ingredients), the human ear cannot reliably distinguish the "true" or real sound of footsteps or a faint human voice from some identical (or nearly identical) sound. This gap between what we think (or assume) we hear and what we *actually* hear goes unnoticed in our daily lives. Most things we experience have a clear, immediate, and obvious connection: a chair being moved, door being closed, or person speaking makes a predictable, familiar sound. But when the source of that sound is unseen and unknown, the situation changes dramatically.

When a person says he or she heard footsteps or faint voices or mysterious laughing or giggling, what they mean, (and how ghost investigators should interpret) that is that they heard what might be, or what could be interpreted as, footsteps, voices, or laughing. It might be, or it might not be, but such claims—no matter how sincerely conveyed—cannot be accepted as a truthful, factual statements about what happened. That interpretation may be completely accurate, but the only valid scientific conclusion that can be drawn from such statements is that the person claimed to have heard *something* they interpreted as a footstep, voice, etc. Only after you have verified that it is in fact a voice or footstep can you treat is as a likely fact.

Mysterious Messages in Real Life

We have seen why many EVPs that were originally claimed to be good evidence of ghosts turn out to be less than impressive upon closer examination. However in order to fully understand how EVPs are created, let's examine the same exact principles at work in everyday life, outside of a ghost-hunting context. There are many real-life cases in which the meaning and significance of words have been subjected to intense legal and forensic debate. In everyday life meanings in speech are not always clear; far from it. Let's examine several examples of real-world, nonparanormal cases relevant to hearing mysterious voices and EVPs. Though people hearing nonexistent voices is not normally newsworthy, examples do occasionally appear in the news media.

In June 2012, customs officials at a New Jersey port stopped and searched a cargo ship for dozens of hidden stowaways. According to an ABC News report, "The ordeal began around 3 a.m. Wednesday, after a Coast Guard patrol stop at the mouth of New York harbor, when officials conducting a routine check of the cargo ship believed they may have heard faint knocking coming from one of the containers onboard. Within hours, emergency medical teams, police and federal law enforcement converged on the port as customs officials checked each container and port equipment operators raced to dig out the suspected containers. The ship had been out to sea for more than two weeks prior to docking, leading authorities to fear for the health of the alleged stowaways" (Esposito 2012).

Not only had the officials heard knocking from the container, but they also believed that the stowaways were responding to their calls and requests: "officers heard noises 'consistent with the possible presence of stowaways' coming from one of the containers in the ship's hull, said Charles Rowe, a Coast Guard spokesman. 'When we knocked, we heard a knock back,' he said" (Wilson and Newcomer 2012). This didn't just happen once or twice but several times—enough for the officials to believe they were getting intelligent, meaningful responses to their calls and taps.

After more than 150 cargo containers had been opened and thoroughly examined, the search was called off. Not a single stowaway was found, either at the time or in the following weeks; it had all been a mistake, a sincere misunderstanding. The knocking that the customs agents believed was created by humans was not. Perhaps it was something rocking gently on the boat, or maybe it was their imagination. Either way, experienced professionals misunderstood what they heard, misinterpreting apparently random, coincidental knocking sounds and patterns as signs of human contact (and indeed meaningful human interaction). The analogy to ghost hunting is clear, as this is exactly the same process that many ghost hunters go through to "communicate" with ghosts, asking short questions and asking (or expecting) knocks, sounds, or taps for answers. We can see how ghost hunters might easily mistake random or unrelated unidentified knocks, thumps, or other faint sounds as coming from an unseen human intelligence—even responding intelligently to questions and requests.

Four police officers who helped rescue a baby from an overturned car in a Utah river in March 2015 claimed that they heard an unexplained voice calling from the car. The accident occurred after the car, driven by Lynn Jennifer Groesbeck, 25, ran off the road and into the Spanish Fork River. Her 18-month-old, Lily, was found in her car seat upside down just above frigid river water, where she had been for at least 12 hours. According to a CNN report, "A mystery arose from the rescue: The police officers who entered the water say they heard a voice calling for help. The mother was dead, but the officers said that they heard an adult's voice calling to them."

With Groesbeck dead (and her toddler dehydrated, unconscious, and unable to speak anyway) the spooky question arose: Where did the voice in the car come from? It's possible that in the chaos of the recovery effort some unrelated sound nearby (maybe the river waters itself, or nearby cars) was mistaken for a cry for help. It's even possible that some unseen distraught bystander was calling for help and the rescuers heard it but assumed it was coming from the car. However there may have been another psychological factor at work. A comment from one of the rescuers suggests that he was not sure if he actually heard a voice or not: "It felt like I could hear someone telling me, 'I need help,' [officer Bryan] DeWitt told CNN affiliate KSL. 'It was very surreal, something that I felt like I could hear.'" If what DeWitt heard sounded like an ordinary person's voice calling for help, as has been described in news stories, it's unclear why he would describe it as "it *felt* like I could hear" (instead of just "I could hear"), or why hearing an otherwise expected cry for help during a rescue would seem "surreal."

It wasn't until days later, after the rescuers had discussed the incident among themselves, that the topic of the mysterious voice came up. Because the informal discussion wasn't recorded there's no way to know for certain who said what, but it seems likely that one of the men said he heard the voice, and others chimed in with their own stories. It's likely that—regardless of whether all of them actually did hear a voice or not—the rescuers unconsciously cued and prompted one another. This is very common: one person says, "Now that you mention it, I think I *did* hear a voice!" and another might say, "I heard it too, but it didn't sound like a child," and so on. One person's memory might be unconsciously adopted by one or more of the others, who hear it and reinforce one another's recollections afterwards. This is common in everyday life, as well as among ghost hunting groups.

Later that year another audio illusion of a human voice made the news. In late August 2015 a bizarre story from Honduras claimed that a teen girl had been prematurely buried, a day after she had been pronounced dead. According to a story in the U.K. *Telegraph*, "A teenage girl in Honduras had mistakenly been buried alive and apparently woke up in her coffin, only to die before she was freed. Footage shows frantic relatives smashing into the concrete tomb of recently buried Neysi Perez, 16, after they said they heard her screaming from inside." Her husband, Rudy Gonzales, told

Primer Impacto TV news "As I put my hand on her grave, I could hear noises inside. I heard banging, then I heard her voice. She was screaming for help... I couldn't believe it. I was ecstatic, full of hope." He and others immediately began removing the coffin from the above-ground tomb, breaking into the concrete and coffin with hands and hammers.

Perez was then rushed to a hospital in the nearest large city, San Pedro Sula, where she was confirmed dead. A closer look at the case revealed a plausible scientific and psychological explanation: the faint, muffled "scream" heard seemingly coming from Perez's above-ground tomb was not a scream at all but instead some ambient urban sound (perhaps car brakes squealing in the distance, or a siren's wail) that was interpreted by the girl's grieving family as a cry for help. Once the husband began, quite understandably, panicking that his wife may have been buried alive, the others joined in. Hearing a dead loved one's voice is common and harmless, especially in the early stages of grief or panic.

The phenomenon of hearing (or more accurately, thinking we hear) nonexistent human voices is more common than most people realize. If we think we hear someone calling to us and we realize we're mistaken, we just laugh it off as the ordinary, insignificant misperception that it is; however that same thing takes on a very different meaning and interpretation in the context of a place that is thought to be haunted.

Other Mysterious Sounds

Many ambient sounds can sound like a human voice or wail, including wind whistling through trees or over bridges, old radiators warming up, insect calls, and so on. There have even been cases where parrots and other birds have mimicked adult voices singing and talking and crying babies with astonishing clarity and realism. Many birds are amazing mimics and have been heard and recorded producing human speech far beyond the stereotypical sing-song "Polly want a cracker?" David Attenborough, in his television series *Life of Birds* shows a superb lyrebird mimicking not merely the calls of other birds but even distinctly human and mechanical sounds including the familiar click of a photographer's camera shutter, the sound of a camera motor, car alarms, and even a chainsaw (countless videos demonstrating this can be found online).

This is not to suggest that parrots or other mimicking birds are a common cause of ghostly voices or other mysterious sounds, but merely to show that even something that sounds exactly like a human voice may not be. Ghost investigators should be aware of this possibility and establish the presence or absence of mimicking birds when seeking a cause of unexplained voices. In most neighborhoods dwellings are close enough that voices—human or otherwise—can be heard from one house to another, so surrounding homes should be investigated as well to rule out that possibility. Keep in mind that even if an apartment building or rental home has an official "no pets" policy, that does not rule out the possibility that undisclosed pets (including birds) may be present.

And of course it's not just animals that can fool us; people can as well. Comedian and actor Michael Winslow, best known for his appearance in the *Police Academy* comedy franchise, is known as "The King of Sound Effects" and can create an astonishing variety of seemingly nonhuman sounds, including car alarms, birds, and electronic shavers, as well as voice impressions. In 2016 a Russian man named Gennady Tkachenko-Papizh appeared on a talent show and created a long series of astonishingly realistic nature sounds including bird wing flapping, calls, musical instruments, and much more. These are of course talented performers attempting to re-create sounds, but the point is that just because something sounds to our ears as completely and unmistakably a specific, identifiable sound (bird call, footsteps, door closing, or even a voice) that doesn't mean that it is. We can be fooled, and we can fool ourselves. The rampant problem of mistaking (or ruling out) ambient sounds as an explanation for "unexplained" phenomena is rarely addressed in ghost hunting.

For an in-depth look at the phenomenon of mimicry in plants and animals (that is, organisms creating false but convincing visual, auditory, olfactory, and other stimuli to make it appear than a plant or animal is present—or absent—when it is not), see *Cheats and Deceits: How Animals and Plants Exploit and Mislead*, by Martin Stevens (2016, Oxford University Press).

These same principles apply in the case of EVP evidence; any sound that might be mistaken for another when heard live will be just as mysterious when heard later. This is one reason that EVP makes such poor evidence: by the time it is heard hours, days, or weeks later, the opportunity has passed to meaningfully investigate the true source of a sound or apparent voice.

Any unexplained sound or (apparent) voice was recorded under a very specific set of circumstances: a certain time of day or night, in certain weather conditions and at a certain temperature, with certain human activities in certain places, and so on. With every hour that passes the circumstances change—sometimes slightly, sometimes dramatically—and make understanding the context of that recording all the more difficult.

Let's say, for example, that a brief, muffled mysterious staccato growling sound was recorded in an EVP session and considered possible evidence of a ghost. It indeed might be—or perhaps it was made by a bird just outside a window near where the recording was made; the bird might fly away minutes later. Or the sound might have been coming from an unnoticed neighbor doing woodwork in his basement, and weeks or months later that neighbor would likely be unable to recall whether he had been doing any work at the exact time that the sound was recorded. Or the sound could have come from a passing vehicle, or any number of other external sounds from the environment, most of which require immediate investigation (and/or extensive surveillance equipment) to rule out.

Competent ghost investigation necessarily involves ruling out ordinary, mundane explanations for possibly anomalous sights and sounds; unfortunately this is very rarely done in modern ghost hunting for the simple reason that doing so under real-world conditions is incredibly difficult and time-consuming. In fact as a practical matter for all but the largest, best-organized, and best-equipped ghost hunting groups, it is almost impossible. Once you recognize the issues involved in doing real research and documentation of potentially paranormal phenomena, the sloppy methods seen on television and described in books and articles stick out like a red flag.

Note

Note 1. See, for example, a press release for the 2016 television show *Kindred Spirits:* "KINDRED SPIRITS follows former *Ghost Hunters* stars Amy Bruni and Adam Berry as they help real families who are tormented by paranormal activity in their homes. Scared by the mysterious happenings, but hesitant to pick up and leave their homes, these families have turned to two of America's leading paranormal investigators to capture evidence, guide the spirits into the light and bring closure to family. With the added stress that the spirits may be their own late family members, each episode of KINDRED SPIRITS introduces a new family that seeks help from Amy and Adam to figure out who is bothering them, but more importantly, why? It's up to the experts to help each family reach closure by facilitating contact with the other side."

PART III
INVESTIGATION
CASE STUDIES

CHAPTER 10

Film and Video Cases

In this chapter I give an overview of general investigation principles for analyzing ghost photographs and videos, then provide a half-dozen examples selected from my investigations. Because some phenomena—such as the appearance of faces—occur with regularity in ghost images, I have referenced them in the sections where they are relevant; I hope readers will forgive any repetition. I have not included several high-profile ghost photos that I analyzed and discussed in my previous books including *Scientific Paranormal Investigation* and *Mysterious New Mexico*; readers seeking more in-depth investigation and analysis should refer to those.

In most cases I carried out the investigation myself; in others I gave the person who contacted me guidance on how they could research and determine for themselves what the photo or video revealed. Often, through persistence and knowing what questions to ask, it's possible to solve a ghost photograph by piecing together the context in which it was taken.

The Deadwood Ghost Photo

In 2009 I received a ghost photograph taken several years earlier and the accompanying story: "My brother and I stayed at the historic Franklin Hotel in Deadwood, South Dakota. I'm not a big believer in the paranormal, but I'd heard about ghosts there and the room gave me the creeps. We took some pictures of our scary hotel room, including this one. At first I didn't see anything strange, but when I zoomed in to the image on the mirror, I was shocked: There appears to be a face and arms coming out of the mirror underneath my right arm. It looks like two eyes, a nose, mouth, teeth, and a hairline. What do you make of it?"

I closely examined the photo for about a week and did some research on the Franklin Hotel. I wrote out an analysis of what I thought it was and replied to the writer, a Ms. Oliver: "Your experience is a very good example

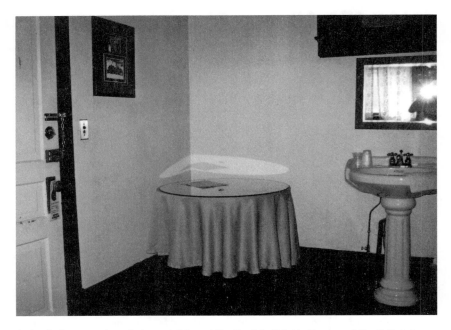

A ghostly face seen in a photograph taken at the Franklin Hotel in Deadwood, South Dakota. Photo by N. Oliver and used by permission.

of how most ghost photos are discovered. My best guess is that the face you perceive is created by a pattern in something behind you and under your arm, formed by your sleeve and shirt. It may be a wallpaper pattern or furniture piece, but more likely a trick of light in the window curtains. The 'face' area appears to be about the same shade, tone, and color as the curtains behind you. To be honest, the 'face' doesn't really look human or ghostly to me, it looks like a stylized carved stone or idol face, like you'd see in *Raiders of the Lost Ark* or on Easter Island."

I noted that the information contained in a single photograph is generally very limited; corroborative evidence might come in the form of a second photograph taken from a different angle that showed something different or unusual, or if the light or dark "face" or entity was seen or videotaped interacting with the environment (such as knocking an object over). Essentially an investigator looks for anything that would help rule out the most common explanation: an optical illusion. As always, you should rule out all the natural explanations before entertaining supernatural ones.

It's not a matter of Oliver photographing a (human or ghost) face, it's a matter of her photographing a random pattern that her brain (and most people's brains) can easily interpret as a face. Add to that, of course, the fact that she and her brother were looking for a ghost when they closely examined the photos. She had a spooky experience there and so she was unconsciously primed to interpret things as potential ghosts. Part of it is imagination, but most of it is simply the way our brains work.

I gave her as thorough an analysis as I could, though I did not (and could not) travel to Deadwood to further investigate. I receive dozens of photographs of alleged ghosts, monsters, and UFOs from around the world every year. It would be impossible for me to fly off to these locations, spending days or weeks (and thousands of dollars) to conduct a definitive, comprehensive investigation into anyone's weird, random photo. If I had the resources of an *X-Files*-type government department I could do it, but as an independent investigator (even one affiliated with a nonprofit educational organization) it's simply not possible. I do the best I can with what I have, and when it's not practical to investigate personally I offer people advice on how to credibly investigate further if they wish to.

I wrote back to her, "In order to fully investigate your photo, we would need to re-create it, ideally as soon after the photo was taken as possible. At this remove, even if you went back to the exact same spot, conditions may have changed. The elements that made up the face may have moved or been replaced, and even under the best of circumstances, a valid re-creation can be very difficult. Unless you took the second photograph at exactly the same height, angle to the room, etc., the flash may not play off the mirror in exactly the same way."

When it comes to investigations, valid recreations can be as elusive as the ghosts themselves. They are useful for helping to determine what might have caused an unknown phenomenon, but investigators need to be very careful to recreate the circumstances as closely as possible and be aware of factors that might have changed (and that might invalidate the results).

In this case, when I presented Oliver with my evidence and explanation, she agreed with me—but it doesn't always work out that way. The person who took the photo (and/or found the ghostly image) has often already made up his or her mind and concluded that there is something mysterious or supernatural about it. An experienced scientific investigator will often have to respectfully and diplomatically offer an alternative explanation, if indeed one can be found.

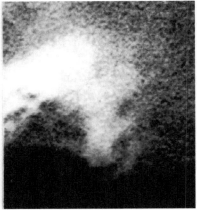

A photograph taken at Cockington Church in Torquay, England, apparently showing one or more ghostly images. Inset: Faces as seen in the Cockington Church ghost photograph by the photographer, showing a bearded man on the left and a horse or dragon on the right. Photos by M. Ingleston and used by permission.

The Cockington Church Ghost Photo

In 2014 I got an e-mail from a Mr. Ingleston with the following query: "While on holiday in England in August 2002 my family and I visited some historic buildings reputed to be haunted near the village of Torquay. At one point I photographed my wife and sister in the main doorway of Cockington Church. Later back home my wife looked at the photos and told me she saw a dragon in one image. When she showed it to me I saw, directly to their left at about their height, two ghostly images: one of a bearded man's face and a second one of a horse's head (which she had seen as a dragon). The photograph was taken at approximately 3 o'clock on a Saturday afternoon. What do you make of it?"

Ingleston sent me the photo and also provided me with a sketch showing where he saw the faces. I could kind of see the faces that Ingleston was referring to, and they appeared to me as white or yellow forms cast against the side of the building (and not, for example, something floating in the air between the photographer and his relatives—who surely would have noticed them at the time but did not).

Before trying to figure out who the ghostly bearded man might be (or what connection, if any, this hypothetical church-going ghost may have with a horse or dragon), it is important to first determine whether those questions need to be answered. As psychologist Ray Hyman points out in the dictum named after him ("Hyman's Categorical Imperative"), before trying to explain a claim, we must make sure that there is something to explain. That is, if the apparent ghostly face is not in fact a ghost's face at all, then we need not spend resources trying to understand the history of the alleged ghost. To avoid a wild goose chase, only after it has been credibly determined that a ghost is indeed the most likely explanation for the image (and not, for example, something mundane) should the investigation turn to trying to explain or construct a history of the ghost.

As with all such photographs, my first step in trying to unravel this mystery was to establish, as closely as possible, the circumstances behind this image. Since the photograph had been taken twelve years earlier on another continent, traveling to Cockington for the purpose of investigating this image was impractical. I replied to Mr. Ingleston asking for a much more detailed description of the photo's circumstances. I gave him a list of specific questions to answer, as best he could, about what else was going on at the time, based loosely on the journalist basics of who, what, where, why, and how.

While I waited for a response I searched the internet for additional photographs of the church and its grounds. I was especially interested to see what was directly behind the photographer: for example was it a parking lot, where the sun might have been reflected off a windshield and onto the church wall, creating odd shapes? Finding such images was not as easy as it seems because, like most tourist attractions, the typical point of interest is what's in front of the camera, not behind it (we've all seen photographs of the Sphinx in Egypt or the White House in Washington, D.C., but it's much more difficult to find photos taken from the Sphinx or the White House looking forward).

Nonetheless with a bit of persistence I was able to find several photographs that showed a wider shot of the church and, specifically, what faces visitors when they walk out those church doors. Ingleston's photo had been taken a dozen years earlier, and, since several of the reference photographs I found online of Cockington Church were undated, I had to use caution when interpreting the results. Of course over the years areas change: fields can be turned into parking lots, parking lots razed for buildings, and so on. But given the terrain and the historic nature of the grounds it seemed a safe assumption that the area immediately surrounding the church has remained relatively unchanged over the past decade or so. Satellite photo references such as Google Earth make this task easier, though it's important to determine the date of the image.

There was no parking lot with a hypothetically reflective windshield, but the results were interesting and fruitful. One image clearly shows a towering copse of trees directly opposite the church, reaching as high or higher than the top of the building itself. Indeed the grounds are covered with grass, shrubs, and trees. This provides an important clue to understanding the curious patterns (including the ghostly image) seen in the photograph. The sunlight is clearly coming from behind the photographer, and at a fairly low angle (which corresponds with Ingleston's statement that the photo was taken in mid-to-late afternoon).

The ghostly "faces" are created by shadows of leaves from trees and shrubs behind and to the left of the photographer. In fact the specific branches that likely cast the shadows that created the faces can be seen in a reference photograph directly below the characteristic three-paned windows. Further evidence of the tree leaves and branches casting the shadows appear in the photograph itself: the reflections of high tree branches can be clearly seen in the windows above the door.

In this case we have at least three different factors working together, any one of which could create the illusion of a ghostly face. The first is the uneven texture of the church's exterior, which is mottled and rough. Like any other rough surface such as stucco or tree bark, natural, random variations in texture and light can create intriguing patterns. Furthermore, the church exterior is stained and weathered from rainwater, moss, and age. This is especially noticeable in a few areas: under the window ledge above the door, the white stains around the doors, and the waist-high band of discoloration around the base of the church. Either one of these factors alone can—and indeed has on many occasions—create "mysterious" images of everything from Jesus to Mary to ghosts.

On top of that—and even more significantly in this case—we have the interplay of light and shadows caused by sunlight filtered through essentially random patches of trees, branches and shrubs. There's yet another random element to this mix, and once again the reflection in the window provides useful information. The sky was neither cloudless nor overcast but had a mix of clouds. Not only was the sunlight being unevenly cast on the church wall through foliage, but the sunlight reaching that foliage was constantly changing as clouds passed overhead. Thus a bright spot of sunlight on the wall might appear in one photo but not another taken only a few moments later—and this might appear mysterious unless the meteorological conditions are taken into account.

The fact that Ingleston, his wife, and others they showed the photograph to found faces in the image is significant. I have encountered many very similar ghost faces in my investigations, including in Deadwood.

This does not, of course, definitively prove that ghosts don't exist, or that the image in Ingleston's photograph cannot possibly be of something unknown or supernatural. However light patches identical in origin and kind (albeit not in exact shape) can be seen in at least a half-dozen other places around the photograph. If we accept that at least some of the amorphous, random patches are the result of sunlight through trees (as is clearly the case here), there's no reason to single one or two of them out as suggestive of supernatural or paranormal origin. The philosophical principle of Occam's Razor requires that, all other things being equal, the simplest explanation (or the one invoking the fewest factors) is likely the best one.

In this case it seems that the faces, dragons, and horses were not in the Cockington Church wall but instead in the minds of those who viewed the images. Like subjective Rorschach blots, each person brings his or her own interpretation to bear on the world around us. In this case the explanation is likely psychological, not supernatural.

The British Footballer Ghost Photo

A ghost photo taken by a young British woman named Natasha Oliver circulated in the news and social media in late July 2015. It depicted about a dozen friends on a lawn and what was said to be a human head and torso in an unfinished building in the background. The form is too dark and fuzzy to be identified, but some have claimed it looks like a ghostly mother and baby. Oliver's photo was taken in 2010 but only got widespread attention five years later after she commented on a Facebook post about a ghost picture she thought was fake—and offered her own. (The photograph Oliver posted is unfortunately too low a resolution to print but can easily be found online.)

The story was featured on several news outlets including *Good Morning America* on July 30 under the headline "'Ghost Woman and Her Baby': Photo Shows Mysterious Figure in Window" (at http://tinyurl.com/ p5rv8r6): According to the story by Avianne Tan, "Oliver said she and her friends 'freaked out' after they saw the photo on her digital camera back in 2010, taken when they were hanging out on the lawn in front of the unfinished home still being built at the time. 'When we saw the ghostly figure, the boys climbed up the scaffolding to see what was up there thinking maybe someone was watching us,' Oliver said. 'But there was nothing up there. There were no floorboards or anything there. The house wasn't finished being built yet at the time.'"

I was asked to investigate the photo for Discovery News and immediately detected several reasons to be skeptical that a phantom had photobombed their party picture. Though there was some speculation that the photo was faked—partly because a famous ghost photo from the same town claimed to be of a little girl killed in a fire was revealed to be a hoax—a misunderstanding seemed more likely in this case.

I noticed that there were only two, nearly identical, photographs provided by Oliver in the news stories, taken two minutes apart (at 21:20 and 21:22). If, as she claimed, the group immediately noticed that an odd figure seemed to be in the window behind them and a few friends were dispatched to investigate, it seemed odd that there weren't more photos of it from a closer point of view. Instead it seems that no one in the group even tried to get a better photo of it. A surprised exclamation of "Look! Is that a ghost?" during a review of a digital photograph taken moments before might be expected to result in a dozen cell phone cameras being produced so others could get their own photographic 'proof' of the paranormal, but that did not happen.

In fact the additional photographic evidence provided by Oliver cast doubt on her explanation of how the photo came to be; because the photos were time-stamped, and because she uploaded dozens of photographs from that June 18, 2010 event to Facebook, there is a photographic record of what the group did after the ghost photos were taken. The image in question was taken at 21:22 and is followed by twenty-six other photos depicting what the group did between that time and 21:52 that evening. There is not a single photograph that shows Oliver or any of her friends searching for a ghost—or even reacting to the discovery that they may have been in the presence of an undead spirit. Instead the two dozen photos show the group laughing, acting goofy, and enjoying an alcohol-fueled footballer (soccer) party.

I discovered that the "ghost" in the photo was first noted four months later, on October 4, 2010, by one of Oliver's friends commenting on her Facebook photo. Therefore her quoted claim that "When we saw the ghostly figure, the boys climbed up the scaffolding to see what was up there thinking maybe someone was watching us" could not be true, since no one in her group saw the figure at the time, which explains why her photos show no investigation. Since there was no investigation at the time—and therefore no one trying to figure out what the strange form might be—the creepy claim that in looking for the ghost they found that "there was nothing up there" also could not be accurate.

There are two second-story windows visible in the ghostly photograph; in another photo later in the series, one of Oliver's friends can indeed be seen on scaffolding in front of one of the windows. But since the ghost wasn't discovered until months later, he was not (and could not have been) searching for the ghostly intruder; he is posing and holding a beer about half an hour after the "ghost" photo was taken.

One may surmise that he looked in the window and saw nothing—but a closer look reveals he is at the wrong window. The ghost was photographed in the *other* window, on the right had side of the photograph. What may have happened is that he told Oliver (months later) that when he had been up there he hadn't seen anything odd and that there was nothing in that window, and he (or she) misunderstood which window he was referring to. There's no evidence that anyone ever looked in the window where the "ghost" was photographed to see what was there.

Perhaps Oliver was misquoted and meant to suggest that, four months after the photo was taken, they returned to the site to search for a cause of the figure. But by then the construction would have likely been completed, the scene changed dramatically, and the scaffolding removed. Either way, the story as it was presented on *Good Morning America* and other news media could not be accurate. A more likely explanation is that Oliver simply misremembered the circumstances of that photo five years after it was taken, and that mistake spawned a ghost mystery.

So what is the light gray, vaguely humanlike figure? It could have been a trick of light, or a piece of plastic or tarp from the construction site behind the group, or wooden planks propped up in the window, or any number of other things. Just because the general shape looks vaguely like a head and chest doesn't mean it is; the human brain is hardwired to look for humanlike patterns. It's impossible to know what was in that window five years after the photo was taken; the building has been finished and all the scaffolding and construction debris long since removed. All we are left with is a ghost story and photo.

In this case the (incorrect) statement that the window had been investigated at the time—and apparently declared free of any ghostly doppelgängers—fueled the mystery. Many ghost photo mysteries are created when people misremember the circumstances under which a photo was taken. Sincere photographers swear, for example, that a strange figure in the background could not have been a person because they didn't see anyone behind the subjects they were shooting—though other witnesses and contemporary photos often tell a different story.

This mistake has been responsible for many "unexplained" photos, including the famous 1964 "Solway Firth Spaceman" image of a five-year-old girl with a strange figure in the background wearing what looks something like a white space suit. The photographer, Jim Templeton, insisted that he had not seen anyone in the background when the photo was taken. It was considered a classic mystery for nearly half a century (often interpreted as an accidentally-photographed UFO or alien, though a ghost would be as plausible an explanation as any other) until it was revealed in 2013 that the image was actually of Templeton's wife (the subject's mother), who had wandered into the background unnoticed, and whose light-colored dress had been overexposed. There's no suggestion that Templeton was lying, merely that he was mistaken.

People and objects in backgrounds can be very easily missed, and a photographer's recollection—perhaps weeks, months, or years later—that there were no humans (or potentially humanlike objects) in the background is simply not good evidence of a ghost.

GHOST VIDEOS
The Kansas Gym Ghost Video Mystery

The video described here is available as of publication on YouTube at https:// www.youtube.com/watch?v=f4Uh6UjCaIc (note that due to the impermanent nature of online media this URL link may change or expire).

On September 12, 2008, a surveillance video from Anytime Fitness, an all-night fitness club in Overland Park, Kansas, captured what many believed to be a ghost. When owner Kim Peterson came in one morning and reviewed the previous night's security footage, she was mystified by what she saw: a glowing, fuzzy light apparently in a workout area, meandering around the weight benches and fitness machines.

The story drew inquiries from press and public around the world. I was asked by my editors at LiveScience.com to investigate the mysterious ghost video. While I prefer onsite field investigations, it's not always practical or economical to visit the scene. As it turned out, the case could be solved from a careful examination of news reports and the footage.

The image appeared at 2:21 A.M., about half an hour after the last person had left the building. It reappeared about nine times over the next two hours, each time briefly moving across the room. It baffled Peterson, her staff and members, and the security company. Lights have never activated the camera before, Peterson said. "I called the security company, and they said 'I don't know why that light would make the camera kick on.'"

It was a genuine mystery. Furthermore, the company told her, 600 other clients have the same security system, but none had reported recording such an incident, so it likely was not some sort of technical software or camera glitch. Various people offered their theories, ranging from a hoax to a bug to headlights from a passing car. Peterson and her security company dismissed all those obvious explanations, and by far the most popular is that a ghost visited the gym for an early-morning workout. Peterson's son was even more specific, suggesting it was in fact his deceased grandfather, looking after his mother's new business. Anytime Fitness asked their members to come up with a name for their resident ghost, and the case remained unsolved.

While theories about the ghost circulated, I carefully reviewed the available footage, gathered additional information about the club layout and location, and noted some interesting clues about the ghost's identity.

Clue Number 1: The object is whitish and out of focus. Security cameras (especially the round "fish-eye" lenses used in the club) are designed to be mounted high above the ground and record activity twenty or more feet away. Things at that distance will be in focus, while objects close to the lens will be out of focus. Therefore the object must have been very close to the camera.

Clue Number 2: The object appears to be glowing, but there's no indication that it is in fact emitting light. It has all the characteristics of something that is instead reflecting white light, perhaps from one of the bright lights mounted around the camera (you can see them clearly in video footage of the story).

Clue Number 3: Though Peterson and news reporters claimed that that ghostly object "spent the night wandering around the weights," a closer look at the video shows that it instead wandered *over or across* them. Its movements do not show any interaction with the objects in the room at all—it does not move *around* them—suggesting it was not in the room or gym floor but instead *above* it.

Clue Number 4: Despite the fact that the gym had at least eight different cameras on and functioning that night, the "ghost" was seen on only one of them. If a spirit had actually been in the room, other cameras should have recorded the same image from other angles. They didn't, and therefore the object or phenomenon, whatever it is, only happened to that one camera.

One explanation, prematurely dismissed by Peterson and others, was almost certainly the correct one: the ghost is a bug. A spider or insect wandered onto the camera; that's why it was out of focus, why it seemed to glow, why it didn't interact with anything in the room, and why it only appeared on one camera. It's true that a moving light wouldn't activate the camera, as they are sensitive to motion, not light. But it was the bug's movement that triggered the sensor and started the recording. This also explains why none of the other 600 clients with the same system reported seeing such a ghost; there's no reason they would unless they also had identical bugs crawling on them. Even if they had, if the person reviewing the video correctly identified the figure as an insect, there's no reason to think that they would have reported such a mundane nonevent to the security camera manufacturers. An exterminator—not an exorcist—could rid the gym of its ghost, but before either could be called, the phenomenon disappeared. A bug on the camera fits all the facts and almost certainly solves the mystery.

The Phoenix Driveway Ghost

On May 4, 2007, I got the following email from a woman named Kay, who lives in a suburb of Phoenix, Arizona:

"I was watching a program on the Discovery Channel and saw you. I have tried very hard to get an explanation as to why this image appears on my driveway every night. I have a security camera that records this strange image, it looks like illuminated smoke or mist. It creeps up from the ground and travels across my driveway. When it reaches the other side it just rolls over the side of the driveway like water falling over a waterfall back into the ground. It's very bright and has no particular shape. It is sometimes big and sometimes smaller. It starts at the driveway nearest the house and every night it moves down further away from the house until it reaches the end of the driveway and then it starts over again. It sometimes changes shapes, sometimes it's smaller and sometimes it's larger. I have hours of video of this strange sighting. I attributed this image to the disturbances I've had in the house such as ringing, bumping, popping and rattling noises. I've had knocks on the front door and nobody's there.... I've had my silverware turned upside down in the drawer and other nuisances in my kitchen. This is just a little of what's been happening to me. Can you review the tape and explain to me what's happening?"

I contacted Kay and asked to get a copy of her video. She sent me a VHS tape of a grainy surveillance video. The time/date stamp read April 30, and the video covered that evening and the early hours of the next day. Sure enough, there was a small, eerie, round, glowing image that appeared from 22:20 (10:20 P.M.) until 2:15 A.M. It crossed the driveway, moving diagonally and very slowly. In fact the glowing ghost (if that's what it was) took about four hours to cross the driveway. I asked for a better quality video on DVD, but she only had a VCR hooked up to her security camera and could not provide it.

A few days later I got another e-mail from Kay: "Just to let you know, this thing on the driveway is very smart. I don't think it wanted to be recorded or it wanted to confuse me. From the 8th of June to the 20th it wasn't there. Then, on the 21st of June just as it was getting dark (about 7pm) I went in to get the system set up and the image was there in the middle of the driveway. Before that, I think it just started early in the day and completed its trip across the driveway before I turned the camera on. That's why I say it's very smart."

Upon reviewing our correspondence it was clear that Kay associated what was going on in her driveway with strange events in her home (such as popping noises, knocks on the front door, etc.), though there was no clear connection. In her mind, these disparate phenomena were somehow related. This is fairly common in paranormal mysteries, where eyewitnesses will often lump things together, confusing the issue and creating red herrings. I had no idea who might be knocking on her door, or why she might hear rattling or popping (traffic, neighbors, and other ambient sounds seemed plausible), but I was not asked to investigate—nor was I given any evidence of—anything other than the driveway entity so that's what I focused on.

It's important in investigations to determine the scope of the claims and not get bogged down with irrelevant information, as it's easy to go on a wild goose chase. I soon realized that I was dealing with a clearly unreliable witness; while her information was interesting, it was important to stick with the facts and the evidence available. She was convinced not only that the glowing orb was sentient—and trying to trick her—but also causing other minor mischief.

After doing some additional research I concluded that the ghost or glowing entity Kay videotaped was in fact the reflection of the moon crossing her driveway. Though most people assume that asphalt, being black, absorbs rather than reflects light, oils in the tar do reflect light. The video itself shows this quite clearly; the white area in the top right hand corner of the image is light reflected from a street lamp. Thus we know that light can be reflected by that surface.

By consulting an almanac I determined that the night of April 30, 2007, was a full moon—which would have provided plenty of light to be reflected. But that hypothesis would fall apart (or be severely weakened) if the weather over Phoenix was overcast that evening. An examination of weather reports revealed that the skies over Phoenix were clear that night, and the city had a high of 98 and a low of 74.

Further evidence for this solution was her information that "From the 8th of June to the 20th it wasn't there." Consulting a lunar calendar I found that June 8, 2007, was the date of the last quarter of the moon, thus the moon would have been about half as illuminated as during a full moon. And, not coincidentally, the ghost reappeared around June 20, which was just before the first quarter of the full moon.

This information was very strong evidence for a solution, but it didn't conclusively prove that the moon was the culprit. I needed to do more, and wanted to test my hypothesis with a falsifiable scientific test. I wrote to Kay and asked her to record the driveway on the night of May 13. Consulting my calendar, I saw that there would be no moon that night; if the mysterious image appeared on that night, then the image could not possibly be the reflected moon, and I'd have to keep looking for a solution. I queried her on May 15, asking to see the videotape. She replied about a week later: "I didn't have the camera pointed at the driveway on May 13. It didn't show itself for about a week."

At that point I considered my investigation complete. I had specifically asked for a key piece of evidence, and for whatever reason Kay didn't do as I instructed to collect that evidence. Perhaps she had in fact recorded the video and was embarrassed that the ghost hadn't appeared, as I predicted. Perhaps she just forgot. But Kay admitted that, recorded or not, the ghost had not appeared that week, so either way my point had been made.

I told Kay what I thought the solution to her mystery was, outlining my evidence, research, and reasoning. Kay wrote back to me, saying, "I'm sorry but I disagree with you unless there is a full moon every night. I have taped this image over and over every night for months on end and I don't believe we have a full moon every night." Of course, the moon would not necessarily have to be full to appear in the video, and the only tapes Kay ever sent me were recorded during full moons.

She continued, "Thanks for your review but I know it is something else. I've even taped this image during the day once and I don't think we can see the moon during the day." Kay never provided the daylight video for me to examine. And though I doubt that even a bright moon would be reflected through full daylight, it just might produce a reflection in the late afternoon since the moon is often visible during daylight. Kay just needed to look at the sky to see if she was wrong, but I had taken it as far as I could. Obviously I didn't have the budget to do an onsite investigation; it would have been both impractical and prohibitively expensive to fly to Phoenix and stake out this woman's driveway for days (or weeks). In any event I had the video evidence I needed in the form of the videotape. With each case you must weigh the costs and benefits of an investigation and work within your means while making a diligent effort to solve the case.

Española Police Station Ghost

Video available as of publication on YouTube at https://www.youtube.com/ watch?v=Qw6iPBb5cqo (note that due to the impermanent nature of online media this URL link may change or expire).

A mysterious object caught on camera outside a New Mexico police department in September 2014 had many people wondering if it might be a ghost. According to a Sept. 26 report on *Good Morning America*, "Police in Española, New Mexico, are trying to figure out what human-shaped, blurry, translucent figured was captured on camera strolling across a locked area of their

The author examines a fence where a ghost appeared outside the police station in Española, New Mexico, spawning national headlines. Photo by the author.

station Saturday night. The video shows the figure walking through a chain link fence and slowly walking out again."

Because the outside lot is a secured area, it would be impossible for anyone to open the gate without an alarm going off, and in any event the figure appears to move through objects in classic ghostly style. Police officer Karl Romero said that at first he assumed the moving figure in the video was an insect, probably a fly or moth. But when he looked again he saw something that made him change his mind: "Then, I saw the legs ... and it was a human," he concluded. Yet it could not be a real human because it appeared to move effortlessly through a high chain link fence. So it was "not a real human," he concluded: "No—a ghost." He reported the strange sighting to his superiors, who apparently were equally puzzled ("officers cannot explain what it is," and "detectives say the video defies logic," according to *Good Morning America*). The fact that the video was captured at a police station gave it instant credibility, and the video soon went viral with thousands of people viewing and commenting on the mystery.

I was asked to research this supposedly spectral visitor by Discovery News. Though the police seemed baffled, after about an hour of research I determined that there was enough information contained in the ghost video, news reports, and independent information about it to plausibly identify the mysterious entity.

I began a video analysis, noting that the ghostly blur doesn't go *through* the objects in the background (such as the fence) as was claimed but instead goes *over* them—a sign that the "ghost" is close to the camera (such as on the camera lens), not out in the secured police yard. (This was also a clue in the Anytime Fitness video ghost mentioned earlier.)

Furthermore, I realized, the object's scale is all wrong: People often report ghosts to be human sized, but what appears in the police video is far too small to be human. At one point when it moves over the silhouette of a metal fence post, it appears about the same size—which would be about three inches in diameter. Because the object is out of focus its edges and exact dimensions can't be measured, but it's clearly a very small ghost. Despite the claim that the object is "human shaped," it is in fact indistinct but small and oval. The fact that the object is out of focus is also revealing; the police surveillance camera is set up to record objects in the yard, not on its lens. Anything on the lens would appear out of focus and translucent, exactly like the ghost in the video.

All evidence suggests that Officer Romero's first guess about the object's identity was the correct one: it is actually an insect on the camera, not a human ghost in the yard. Another important clue to solving this mystery can be found in the way the object moves. As Officer Romero noted, the "ghost" does seem to have legs—six or eight of them, not two. The movement of the glowing mystery fuzz is smooth and even, a sign that its weight is being carried and distributed on four or more legs. In contrast, human movement on two legs creates a distinct vertical bounce with each step as our weight shifts from one leg to another moving forward. Based on the "ghost's" movement alone (and assuming it is a living creature), it's much more likely to be an insect than a human.

There's also something important missing from the video that no one seems to have noticed, suggesting its earthy origins: a shadow. The supposedly human-shaped ghost, which is relatively small but appears large and solid enough to be seen at a distance on a surveillance camera, does not cast a shadow on the ground despite floodlights from above. Shadows of other objects, such as the fence that the ghost is claimed to move through, are clearly visible on the concrete, yet the ghost casts no shadow. An insect on the camera lens, of course, would not cast a shadow in the parking lot because it's not in the parking lot.

In my research I discovered that, ironically—in the very parking lot where the ghost appeared—insects were (accidentally) captured by a local cameraman in footage broadcast on *Good Morning America* (see the bugs in the bottom left hand corner of the screen around 1:20, the video can be viewed at http://abcnews. go.com/US/mexico-police-catch-ghostly-intruder-camera/story?id=25771690).

When filmed up close, in focus, and in daylight the insect doesn't look strange or mysterious at all, but it's not hard to see why a blurry, unidentifiable entity seen late at night would appear spooky. I reported my results in an article on the Discovery News website, providing the first (and only) in-depth skeptical analysis online of this ghost video. Though many ghost videos turn out to be insects accidentally caught on camera, not all of them are.

Ghost Screaming in Haunted Hotel

Though most of my ghost photo and video analyses are informal, on occasion I've been hired to provide a more formal and detailed forensic video analysis, usually on behalf of a television show. Here is one example, adapted from a report I did in 2015.

Video available as of publication on YouTube at https://www.youtube.com/ watch?v=BobA5ujHkvU (note that due to the impermanent nature of online media this URL link may change or expire).

Video title: (A) "Real Cryptid Sighting 2014" / (B) "Ghost Screaming in Haunted Hotel-Full Length"

Photographer / filmer: Unknown / YouTube handle "Supernatural News" has a 2014 post (A), and a "jimmynut22" (identified below) seems to have the original (B), posted September 4, 2012

Camera type: Unknown/ multiple (claimed to be hotel security cameras)

Location: Unknown (unnamed hotel, suggested to be Wingate by some)

Provenance: Client via YouTube; appears to be teaser for a ghost hunting TV show or film

Origin: (A) "Real Cryptid Sighting 2014" (https://www.youtube.com/ watch?v=N4bHdw6Sjtc) (480 p); also (B) "Ghost Screaming in Haunted Hotel-Full Length" (https://www.youtube.com/watch?v=BobA5ujHkvU) (720 p)

Length: 2:31 (entire clip is 3:00 but last 30 seconds are blank)

Video quality: (A) 480 p / (B) 720 p

Date/time stamped: Yes (September 14, 2003)

Date/time verified: NO

First Anomaly: 1:30

Key clips: Noted below

Environmental conditions: The video was shot in an unnamed and apparently empty hotel.

Date uploaded: (A) March 1, 2014 / (B) September 4, 2012

Date recorded: September 14, 2003 (unverified)

Popularity: (A) Viewed 58,620 times as of analysis date / (B) Viewed 6,337,530 times as of analysis date

Other videos from same source: Uploader SupernaturalNews added 26 other closely related videos in a date range from 7 to 12 months earlier. The vast majority of them are claimed to be "real-life" video proof of the paranormal; typical titles include "Real Flying Gnome Sighting" (https://www.youtube.com/watch?v=gQQmvGvOvZk); "Real Fairy Gnome Body Caught 2014" (https://www.youtube.com/watch?v=fJi2BghYJ-g); and "Unexplained Creature Sighting 2014 Lake Monster" (https://www.youtube.com/watch?v=NNAdZpbfHYo). Several of these videos have been definitively debunked (see, for example, http://planetsave.com/2013/05/08/dead-fairy-hoax-derbyshire-mexico-facts-and-pictures/), yet this YouTube poster has left these videos up, indicating that the interest is in sensationalism and mystery-mongering, not investigation or evidence.

However the original poster, "jimmynut22" has 8 other videos (including duplicates) uploaded anywhere from 6 months to 2 years ago (see https://www.youtube.com/user/Jimmynut22/videos), all of which are labeled "scary!" and "ghost." This poster appears to be a man named Turner Clay, an independent / low budget filmmaker who has done special effects for two films (*Disaster L.A.* and *Silent Night*; see http://www.imdb.com/name/nm2571852/).

Captions: "Cryptids can move through walls some are not material. Many call these ghosts, sprites, fairies, rods, and several other names. Either way as of today the events are still unknown." / "The following footage was recorded by hotel security on September 14, 2003. It has not been edited." / "**UPDATE: Due to legal matters, I am not allowed to say any more information regarding the exact location of this hotel. Please stop asking. Thank you!"

Narrative overview: The video features a man named "John" (apparently a maintenance or security man) on camera allegedly recorded in a hotel who is asked to investigate a disturbance in room 209. He exits an elevator (00:18) and proceeds to the room while an unnamed narrator conveys information via radio between John and an unseen woman named "Amy." Faint screams are heard as John verifies that no one is checked into the room

(00:58), and he enters the room (1:15) as seen on several cameras. A faint translucent ghostly figure appears to exit the room before John re-emerges (1:45) and states that the room is in disarray and has been vandalized, the furniture turned upside down. The narrator says that police are to be called and "that's scary... I'm officially freaked out now!" A replay of the video image is then shown, and the viewer is encouraged to look for other similar videos by the poster.

Participant reactions:

• Somehow knowing that the interior of room 209 would be dark, John pulls out and turns on his flashlight before even opening the door, and as he enters he inexplicably fails to simply turn on the light as he enters the room, instead walking right past the light switch.

• Other hotel guests: The hotel seems to be completely and inexplicably empty; though the cameras rotate between about 10 different areas of the hotel (gym, south staircase, exterior entrance, inside one elevator, corner hallway, Room 209, pool, etc.) not a single other hotel guest can be seen anywhere. This is especially suspicious given the alleged circumstances that led to this video being captured: "there's reports of screams coming from that room" (00:23). The narrative clearly suggests that the hotel is occupied by other guests; otherwise who is reporting the screams, and why would the narrator note that "There's no one checked into that room, there should be nobody in there" (00:46-00:48)? This comment only makes sense if other nearby rooms are occupied.

The lack of other participants raises another suspicious issue: if someone else (not Amy, John, or the narrator) is hearing a woman screaming from that room why is he or she (or they) not already at the door, trying to gain entry to see if the apparent victim needs assistance? Surely others on the same floor, or anyone within earshot, would be seen at or near the door (or at least in the hallways) looking out their doors to see what the disturbance is about. The fact that this does not occur strongly suggests fakery and hoaxing.

Footage notes: The claim that "The following footage was recorded by hotel security on September 14, 2003. It has not been edited" contains several dubious statements. First, the positioning of the camera, aimed at the door to room 209—the one that just happens to have the mysterious phenomena occurring in it—is very unusual and quite a lucky coincidence. Hotel surveillance cameras do not typically focus on the entrance to a single room (otherwise they'd need hundreds of them to cover the entire premises at enormous cost) but instead cover many rooms over long hallways and lobbies. This suggests that the claim that the "footage was recorded by hotel security" is in fact false; it was instead recorded by cameras installed by the team (including Amy, John, and the narrator). Furthermore hotel security cameras would likely be in color (or, less likely, black and white), not the faux-infrared green-tinted images typical of ghost hunting shows and appears here.

The second part of the statement, "It has not been edited" is clearly false. The video has obviously been edited, cutting back and forth in dramatic, cinematic fashion between Floor 2, Camera 13 (or 15, it's not clear) and Floor 2, Camera 7 as John enters Room 209 (1:20 to 2:08). This is not raw footage by any definition.

This video would be very easy to fake, involving one actor and two voiceover actors (Amy and the narrator). Obviously if there were more people involved (for example extras to play other guests at the hotel), it would be harder to keep the origin of the video a secret. Note that the alleged damage done to the room (the furniture turned over, the carpet ripped up, etc.) is never seen, only described by John. This, too, is very unusual and suspicious: if someone was going to go to the trouble to record this footage, edit it together, and present it as some sort of evidence of some mysterious encounter, surely they would include video, or at least photographs, of the dramatic, unexplained damage done to the room (or even a police report, since the video claims that police were called).

Related videos analyzed for comparison:
http://hoaxes.org/weblog/comments/the_screaming_ghost_in_room_209

Claimed or popular interpretation: Ghost, "cryptid" (though the term cryptid typically refers to corporeal monsters such as Bigfoot, chupacabra, and the Loch Ness Monster, not faint white misty entities)

Other hypotheses: None

Conclusion: Given the complete anonymity of the participants and the location; the false statements made by the filmmaker; the numerous red flags of hoaxing noted above; and the video's apparent origin with a filmmaker who is credited with doing special visual effects on two films, this video is clearly faked and wholly implausible. Thanks to Kenny Biddle for analysis assistance.

•••

In this chapter I've presented a sample of photos and videos purported to be of ghosts. There are many others I could have used, though in the realm of "ghost images" one encounters a lot of repetition (after being asked to identify the fifth flash reflection-created "orb" or third obvious "ghost app" photo of the month, I get a bit jaded). I've tried to highlight the most important things to look for in establishing the nature of the image anomaly and what's involved in finding a plausible, science-based explanation. There is no single blanket explanation for all ghost photos and videos; though there are common themes and threads, each case is different and must be investigated independently. Intrepid readers can find many more of my analyses, as well as those of other investigators such as Captain Disillusion, Kenny Biddle, and others, online, in *Skeptical Inquirer* magazine, and elsewhere.

CHAPTER 11

Fort George: Canada's Most Haunted Place

My write-up of this case is longer and more in-depth than most, largely because it contains an interesting blend of traditional, old-school ghost communication techniques and modern ghost hunting elements. It is one of the very few ghost investigations I've been on that included such varied elements as séances, EVPs and ghost voices, automatic writing, ghostly possession, television production, a famous ghost story, and even an old-fashioned Agatha Christie / Sherlock Holmes-type locked room mystery.

Located a short walk from the picturesque Canadian town of Niagara-on-the-Lake, Ontario, Fort George is an impressive hidden little gem of history. Comprising about a dozen wooden buildings scattered around a roughly coffin-shaped outer wall supported by six blocky bastions, the fort is a popular attraction for tourists and history buffs alike. Replica

The grounds at Fort George. Photo by the author.

cannons appear at intervals on the ruddy wooden-decked bastions, aimed outward at long-dead enemies. The grounds are covered with grassy berms and ditches from which soldiers could defend against attack, alongside the stone gunpowder and occasional wooden watchtower.

Fort George is under the administration of Parks Canada, which offers the following historical introduction:

"In 1796, the British complied with the terms of the 1783 Treaty of Paris, which had granted Fort Niagara to the United States. To protect their interests in Upper Canada, the British set work immediately to construct a fort across the Niagara River. Control of the river supply route was essential to the survival of the forts west of the Niagara region. By 1802, Fort George had been completed and became headquarters for the British army, local militia and the Indian Department. The imposing new fort stood guard over transportation on the Niagara River and protected Navy Hall, a vital warehouse and wharf facility. It was a substantial installation, boasting six earthen and log bastions linked by a wooden palisade and surrounded by a dry ditch. Inside the walls, the Royal Engineers constructed a guardhouse, log blockhouses, a hospital, kitchens, workshops, barracks, an officers' quarters, and a stone powder magazine. The superbly designed magazine survives still.

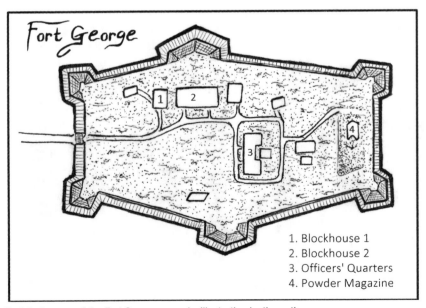

1. Blockhouse 1
2. Blockhouse 2
3. Officers' Quarters
4. Powder Magazine

Sketch diagram of the Fort George grounds. Illustration by the author.

During the War of 1812, Fort George served as the headquarters for the Centre Division of the British Army. These forces included British regulars, local militia, aboriginal warriors, and Runchey's corps of freed slaves.... Fort George was destroyed by American artillery fire and captured during the Battle of Fort George in May 1813. The U.S. forces used the fort as a base to invade the rest of Upper Canada, however, they were repulsed at the Battles of Stoney Creek and Beaver Dams. After a seven-month occupation, the fort was retaken in December and remained in British hands for the remainder of the war. After the war, the fort was partially rebuilt, and by the 1820s it was falling into ruins. It was finally abandoned in favour of a more strategic installation at Fort Mississauga and a more protected one at Butler's Barracks" (Parks Canada 2011).

Fort George is also said to be one of the most haunted locations in North America, home to countless spirits of the war dead: "Thousands died during the war from malnutrition, primitive surgery, disease, and extreme cold weather and many were even burned alive when the Americans set fire to the town. The disturbing nature and abruptness of their deaths is believed to have trapped their spirits on the battlegrounds. There have been so many reported sightings around this fort that it's now considered to be one of Canada's most haunted locations" (Dirty Rig 2005).

Kyle Upton, who has guided ghost tours at the fort since 1994, writes in his book *Niagara's Ghosts at Fort George* that "Most nights you can feel them, out there in the darkness, beyond the circle of illumination thrown by the lantern, watching.... Some nights, though, watching is not enough. The dead are not always passive observers. Sometimes they have a way of reminding us that we are not alone. A misty shape appears and disappears, a waft of perfume, a shadowy figure standing off in the darkness, a door slams shut, a piano plays, a nudge, a tug, a poke" (9). Another source states that "encounters include rapping, swirling orbs of light, footsteps, unearthly moans, crying, and strange breezes, as well as visitors and staff suddenly overwhelmed by feelings of terror, sorrow, anguish, and nausea" (Keenan 2005). Tourists make reservations far in advance for the popular candlelight ghost tours led by storytelling caped figures.

Investigating the Fort: 'Encounters' TV Show

As of 2014 I had visited Fort George four times, spending anywhere from an afternoon to several days there as both a tourist and investigator. My first and most in-depth visit—the one I focus on in this chapter—occurred in 2004, when I was asked to participate in a Canadian television pilot about ghosts. (Note 1)

A producer on the show, Jeanne, asked me if I'd agree to be part of an investigation. She had read of my research and investigations and wanted to have someone with a scientific outlook included. The program, produced by a group from Toronto's Ryerson University called Dirty Rig Productions, was pitched to me as "an in-depth investigation of Canada's most haunted locations. The show brings together spiritual mediums, paranormal scientists, historians, and other local participants in an attempt to investigate occurrences considered to be 'hauntings.' The pilot episode will investigate Fort George, Niagara on the Lake. This site is believed to be one of the most haunted locations in the country based on the number of recorded sightings and its intriguing history that dates back to the 1700s; it was the site of many battles from the war of 1812, and an aboriginal burial ground" (Dirty Rig 2005).

I reviewed the documents and explained to Jeanne that I would be willing to participate, but I wanted a better idea of what my role would be. She said that I would be representing the scientific perspective—she envisioned me

Some of the cast and crew of the *Encounters* television show pilot: Cam, Kim, Michele, myself, and Margaret (holding a directional microphone). Photo by the author.

explaining or trying to disprove what the psychics and ghost hunter cast members were doing. I would basically follow them around in real time, and if they found something odd or mysterious it would be my job to explain it more or less immediately to the cameras (and, by extension, to the show's audience).

To her that made perfect sense. However to a person who had dealt with how psychics and ghost hunters typically operate it was clearly a recipe for failure, a ripe opportunity for me to look bad, and an unfair shift in the burden of proof. I diplomatically explained why during a phone conversation: "Okay, so let's say we're in a room together, and one of the psychics says she feels a ghostly presence in one corner of the room. What am I supposed to do with that?"

"What do you mean?" she asked.

"Well, often the 'evidence' for ghosts that psychics find are personal, subjective experiences like fear or nervousness, or some feeling or psychic sensation. That's not scientifically verifiable—there's nothing for me to investigate or explain. If a psychic or ghost hunter says she senses the presence of some spirit in a room, or has a weird feeling, what am I going to say? 'No, you don't?'"

Jeanne was silent for a few moments; she clearly didn't have much experience with ghost hunters or psychics (nor, for that matter, with skeptics trying to scientifically investigate locations). I didn't blame her: she was thinking like all the other TV producers I've met; her job was to make interesting television. My job was to try and solve mysteries, approach the subject using science and logic, and tease out verifiable, testable claims to understand what was going on, paranormal or not.

"Look," I said, "I'm not trying to be difficult or mess up your show. The psychic ghost hunters are going to do what they're going to do, and that's fine. I'm just saying you need to understand that they may come up with random evidence and claims that neither I nor anybody else can investigate, prove, or disprove. If something physical happens, like a light appears or something flies across a room, I can investigate that, but if it's just personal feelings and mental sensations, there's nothing I can do with that. I'll just shrug and say, 'Well, okay,' and that's not going to make good television."

She said she understood, and the plan gradually coalesced over the course of a dozen emails: We'd gotten special permission from Parks Canada for an overnight investigation at Fort George. The investigations would be conducted at various spots around the fort, including the barracks, the officer's quarters, an outside stone tunnel, and the outposts. Other participants included psychics and ghost hunters from around Ontario including Kim Horaczek, Debby Bennett, Steve Dietrich, Michele Stableford, and Margaret Byl. That was the first I'd met any of them, though since then I've had the pleasure of running into a few of them as guest speakers at paranormal-themed conferences.

In addition to us "professionals," the producers also wanted to include four "ordinary" laypeople who had no particular experience in, or knowledge of, investigation—volunteers who would be given their own infrared cameras and divided into teams to spend the night scaring up spooks. The producers seemed very keen on the idea, which was a brilliant decision from a TV production standpoint (as it essentially quadrupled the chance of getting some sort of spooky footage). The four were Julia, a mother of four from the Niagara region; her daughter Monica, a blonde fashion student in college; an electrician named Dwayne; and a risk management professional named Todd.

The producers seemed to think that the inclusion of these four civilians somehow made the investigation more balanced or scientific because it added a "neutral" element that was presumably neither skeptic nor believer. From my background in scientific experiment research design, however, I immediately saw a problem. I explained to Jeanne that she did not have a random sample of ordinary citizens but instead a self-selecting group of volunteers who were interested enough in ghosts to participate, whether or not they were self-identified skeptics or believers.

Anyway, it shouldn't matter: if there was good evidence of ghosts at Fort George, presumably that would be clear to everyone present; something obviously paranormal should convince anyone—skeptic or believer. Other than meeting the four briefly once or twice throughout the night (for example during dinner at the craft table), I never saw any of the "regular folks" during the investigation at all. I wasn't asked to interview them during or after their investigation, and I saw their activities (and their recorded footage and experiences) for the first time on DVD long after the show was done.

Of course I wasn't running the show; I had no veto power and the producers could do whatever they liked. But I felt it was my responsibility to at least raise the issue; I didn't want anyone coming back to me at a later date saying, "We told you what we were doing, and you never said it was unscientific or invalid." This would become a recurring theme throughout the investigation: My job, as I understood it, was to do my best to bring science to the proceedings and inform people when I saw methods, claims, and procedures that seemed to violate scientific methods and critical thinking principles. Whether they followed that advice or not was out of my hands.

We were all given a list of ghostly phenomena associated with the fort collected by the producers. There were no references or citations (important for judging the credibility of the information—you can't blindly believe everything you're told), and I suspected that much of the information was simply randomly collected on the Internet (Note 2). While this was useful in terms of generally sketching the outline of the claims, it also provided a template for those visiting the fort (including ourselves) and might subconsciously guide their experiences. If you know, for example, that a spooky shadow or sound is said to appear in one certain area, you are more likely to report that shadow through the power of suggestion because you are psychologically "primed" to look for it. Psychologists know that we often see what we expect to see, whether it is there or not.

The Ghostly Claims at Fort George

Using the list provided by the producers as a starting point, I began my own research weeks ahead. Fort George has been popular with ghost hunters for years, and during that time a variety of claims have arisen. In all I found dozens of claims associated with the fort; unfortunately most of the

Interior of the Soldier's Barracks at Fort George; the ghost of a girl named Sarah Ann is reportedly seen here. Photo by the author.

reports were too vague to follow up on or investigate. For example many of the claims were little more than, "A tall man is sometimes seen near the west wall," or "Some people experience uneasiness in the barracks." When I investigate ghosts I try to find cases that offer strong evidence—ideally, first-hand reports that include some sort of objective physical evidence or recordings, not some vague story about what one anonymous person reported seeing or feeling at some point years ago. I knew from experience that second- and third- hand reports were virtually worthless, since (like the children's game of "Telephone"), important details drop out with retellings and false information creeps in (see, for example, Loftus 1980 and 1996). In that spirit, I narrowed the focus to the following main four ghost claims:

1) The Haunted Painting of Lady Charlotte

A painting in one building is said to change before your eyes, morphing from old to young and back again: "It's not just the building that is haunted, but sometimes the objects within it... in the officers quarters is the portrait of Queen Charlotte that was brought to the fort from Great Britain.... The painting is said to be haunted; look closely, for people claim that the portrait changes from a vision of youth to a wrinkled old woman, and back again" (Dirty Rig 2005).

2) Ghost Voices and EVPs

As is often the case, ghost voices or electronic voice phenomena (EVP) were sometimes recorded at the fort: "These have come in various languages, French is the only one identified, there are other languages that the witness doesn't recognize" (Note 3). In the barracks, one person claimed to hear a ghost say, "Sarah, enough!" In the tunnel near the front of the fort, someone reported hearing a "growling cougar" (though how they could identify a cougar's growl from another animal's growl is unclear), and the phrase "Pat, wait for orders, wait for Meurer." Ghost hunters in the field have reported hearing and recording phrases they interpreted as, "Company, company halt!" and "Limbs to cut off." Then there are random ambient sounds including occasional bells, drum beats, the sounds of marching, horses, moaning, whispering, and so on.

3) Random Feelings and Sensations

Reports from the fort also included a fairly typical list of stories of feelings and sensations that had been collected by those conducting ghost tours, including cold spots, feelings of being nudged or pushed, a "creepy feeling," that sort of thing. There were reports of people becoming so scared that they became nauseous. Some said that there was a strong smell of rot or decay near the back wall of the fort, possibly indicating a mass grave. Given the fort's rich history, re-enactors, and many legends, it's easy to imagine what the place might have sounded, smelled, or looked like centuries ago.

4) The Ghost of Sarah Ann

Though a handful of spirits are said to haunt Fort George, one particular ghost stands out as being by far the most prominent. Her name is Sarah Ann (or Sarahann), "a little girl who spends her afterlife in the soldiers' barracks. She often appears sitting on the stairs, and likes to tease the staff members at the fort by tapping on their shoulders and then disappearing" (Dirty Rig 2005). Sarah Ann, according to the show's researchers, is seven years old and died of disease. There seem to be no photographs or videos of her, though one book, *Ghosts of Niagara-on-the-Lake*, states that "This young girl, named Sarah Ann, is certainly the most active and precocious spirit on the site. Over the years, Sarah Ann has been seen numerous times, and her youthful antics never fail to bring a smile to the faces of witnesses. Like a typical child, she's cheerful, mischievous, innocent, and eternally playful. She'll engage in games of peek-a-boo, hiding under beds and behind pillars, and giggling quietly to herself. Sometimes Sarah Ann will playfully tug on someone's clothes and then run away so that the victim of the prank only sees a momentary glimpse of a barefooted girl with shoulder-length curly blonde hair and wearing a flowing white dress before she disappears from view. [One tourist reported] a white cloud, vaguely humanoid in shape and the size of a small child. High-pitched giggling is frequently heard in the barracks, where Sarah Ann seems to spend most of her afterlife hours" (Da Silva and Hind 2009, 133-34).

The Investigation

Finally a date was set for our overnight investigation: Friday, November 26. An email from Jeanne informed us that we should report to the Fort at 11:30 A.M. so that we could be done with M&M (makeup and microphones) by noon. She added, "We are conducting investigations simultaneously to investigate the sightings in various areas of the fort." I quickly realized that this would make my job more difficult, since we'd be split up into at least three groups. I could only be in one place at a time, and I just had to hope that if any good evidence of ghosts materialized, I'd be nearby to examine it.

If one of the other teams saw or recorded something while I was with another group somewhere on the other side of the fort, or deep inside one of the buildings, there would be no way to properly investigate. As I have noted, investigations should be done immediately when the phenomena occurs, not hours or days later. The whole protocol had been developed with no consideration for scientific investigation or methodology but instead to meet the demands of TV producers. Their goal was not to truly investigate, to make an effort to prove or disprove the claims, but instead to make entertaining television. Scientists, on the other hand, are interested in finding out what is true and what is not—regardless of whether or not that search makes for dramatic television.

The ghost hunters on the shoot (like most I've encountered) were engaging in a common (but flawed) "investigation" method called anomaly hunting (see chapter 4). In my ghost investigations I begin by examining the specific claims surrounding the case; amateur ghost hunters, by contrast, spend most of their time trying to generate new information and evidence instead of trying to establish the validity of the earlier claims. I have had this experience on several ghost investigations done in association with a television crew.

The cast was also helpfully informed by the producers in a handout that "ghost photos have historically been better in the dark," a dry statement that amused me for several weeks and was surely meant to encourage us to take plenty of flash photos in the dark in hopes of catching the paranormal. The final instruction from the producers: "Have fun, be yourselves, and think of your actions on camera from a TV perspective: Is this entertaining our audience?" We were explicitly being asked to be animated and excitable. For people who are eager to be on television—as most ghost hunters and laypeople are—there's a clear and an inherent incentive to overact and play to the camera with excited reactions. People who are calm, cool, and collected are rarely selected by directors and casting agents to appear on television.

Investigating Fort George

I arrived an hour ahead of schedule; I wanted to wander around alone to get a sense of Fort George before all the hustle of TV production got in gear. I took photos and video, scribbled notes, gathered information, and generally amused myself until it was time to report to makeup.

We met with the crew and everyone introduced themselves. Margaret Byl was a bespectacled researcher who spent a lot of time with a handheld parabolic microphone, recording sounds around the area. The two psychics, Kim and Michele, both had easy smiles and short hair. Steve was the only male ghost investigator of the lot, and we all got on pretty well. I knew immediately that I'd have a good time with them, whether we found ghosts or not.

It seemed that just about everyone already knew each other. I was introduced to the gang by an assistant producer as the show's token skeptic, though I made sure they understood I was an investigator, not a debunker. I was not there to debunk or disprove anything but instead to help look for legitimate evidence of ghost.

The host of the show was a guy named Cameron Stannard, called Cam by everyone. A handsome and faintly manic (or overcaffeinated) fellow who I suspected came from a theater background, he did a reasonably professional job of hosting the show. It was just after Thanksgiving, and quite cold. Cam did a few takes of introductory footage walking through the gate, and he would take a warm jacket off just before going on camera. He got it after a few takes while the rest of the cast and crew milled around, eating cookies and snacks and sipping hot Tim Hortons coffee, and waited to be told what to do. Soon we were more closely examining the grounds that would be our home for the next eighteen hours.

Scene I: The Soldiers' Barracks

We began our chilly night of specter seeking in Blockhouse 2 of the soldier's barracks, said to be among the most haunted areas of the fort. The two-story wood buildings resembled a huge rectangular barn and were outfitted with replicas of soldier's bunks, wooden storage barrels, and so on. None of it was original, of course; the original barracks had been destroyed, rebuilt, burned down, and rebuilt again over the centuries. But it was designed to give visitors an idea of what it might have looked like in the early 1800s; since no photographs exist from the time, much of the setup is based on historical descriptions and speculation.

Cam and the investigators decided to use what they called "trigger items," objects that we would set up and then ask the ghosts to influence in some way to demonstrate their presence. Cam produced a deck of playing cards and built a house of cards atop one of the wooden tables.

They collapsed once or twice, but eventually the bottom cards bought enough purchase against the rough-hewn wooden surface that it remained standing. The plan, he explained, was that the ghosts would be asked to knock the cards over to show that they were here. I politely pointed out that it was a badly flawed experiment in that the cards could easily collapse for any number of perfectly ordinary reasons ranging from a draft, to the vibrations of a person walking by, to someone accidentally (or intentionally) bumping the table.

Wouldn't it be more impressive and significant, I suggested, if something a little less likely to move or collapse was used to help determine the very significant event of a ghostly presence? For that matter, why not simply ask the ghosts to lift up the table itself, or one of the wooden barrels— something that, if seen and videotaped independently floating, would almost certainly be paranormal. The psychics and crew shook their heads, saying that wouldn't do. They explained, with only a hint of condescension, that the ghosts' power was weak; it took a lot of energy to influence things on "our side," and asking the spirits to do more than move things a tiny bit (or make a sound) was unreasonable. I rather thought they were begging the question—the whole point was to see whether the ghosts were going to create any ghostly phenomena, not prepare excuses and reasons for why they might not. Furthermore, if some eyewitness reports are to be believed then the ghosts of Fort George have done much more than make a deck of cards fall—they have appeared in front of witnesses as full-bodied ghostly apparitions. Surely if a spirit or person (or even their image) materialized in front of us, that would be strong evidence of the paranormal. Aside from that, this argument seemed to assume an awful lot of certain knowledge of ghosts and the spirit world—about how much energy ghosts have, what obstacles

A house of faux antique cards placed on a table in the soldier's bunkhouse and used as a ghost detector. Photo by the author.

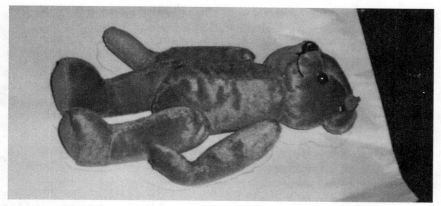

Teddy bear ghost detector. Photo by the author.

they face, what their limitations are. But I was trying to be cooperative and agreeable, so I held my tongue and moved along. Maybe I'd have a chance to ask the ghosts myself during the séance that was soon to come.

Many psychics had visited the fort over the years, often as ghost hunters. According to one writer, "when a group of psychics once arrived there, they could proceed no further. They believe that when people die, their energy enters the ground. Complaining the force was too strong, the group remained fixed to benches while the tour continued" (Keenan 2005).

The cameras and I followed Cam into the next room, where we would try to contact Sarah Ann, coaxing her with something that little girls have loved for well over a century: a teddy bear. Cam put a small plush teddy bear with a tiny rose clipped to its left ear on top of a piece of plain white paper, and placed that on a table. Steve helpfully suggested that they draw an outline around the teddy bear with a pen or pencil, so that way it would be much clearer if the toy moved at all. A few hours later they did the same thing in the officer's barracks with a second, different teddy bear, this one a pudgy red and white figure that was sitting up.

Someone looked in one of the open boxes of war replicas and found a piece of finger-sized wadded cotton, similar to the kind used in rifles and muskets in the 1800s. In all honesty it looked much more like a tampon. Cam took it and tried to come up with some way to turn it into part of the ghost investigation—since, after all, though it wasn't really old or authentic, it was presumably much closer to being something that a solider's spirit might try to manipulate than a deck of modern playing cards or a teddy bear. Not really knowing what else to do with it, he found a small knothole in a floorboard and stuck it there.

We then took seats on the wooden benches and prepared for a séance. I positioned myself so that I could see both the psychics and the camera crew, and so that I was close enough to hear and see what was going on but far enough away so that if I heard or saw something move in another part of the room I could react quickly with the camera and flashlight in hand. Then the lights were turned off. Elsewhere I discuss why turning lights off is a bad idea during an investigation, but apparently that was the procedure that the psychics required, and it had already been agreed to by the producers. Plus, of course, it allowed them to capture spooky-looking infrared footage.

With the lights off and the cameras on, the psychics began concentrating and calling forth spirits. "Is there anyone here?" Debby asked. "Any spirits who wish to communicate with us?" There was silence, except for the cameramen, who moved closer across the wooden floor in the near-darkness to get a better angle. "Can you give us a sign? Something?" More silence, followed about a minute later by a faint but clearly audible car alarm a few blocks away. "That's *not* a sign," I said aloud, only half-joking. The process continued for about fifteen minutes; every now and then there would be a creak or thud, but it was pretty clearly simply sounds from the wooden barracks. A slight wind blew against the walls. Many of the rooms were large and cavernous, which helped create echoes and magnified ordinary sounds—especially in those rooms that had open stairways leading to the second floor. Once again I sat quietly and politely. I was hoping to hear an evil, ghostly or ghastly voice, or maybe some dramatic or loud thump. Maybe the house of cards would explode, sending a three of clubs or ace of spades shooting across the room. Or maybe the teddy bear would suddenly come alive and do cartwheels off the table. Instead we got nothing but occasional ordinary creaks and sounds.

To my mind, virtually everything I was watching was very likely a waste of time because we weren't actually *doing* any investigation. We were sitting in the dark looking around the room and talking to the walls. Still, just because it wasn't how I would have done it doesn't mean that it might not somehow be productive, and I tried to keep an open mind. This was relatively early in my career, and I was eager to interact with ghost hunters of some local stature; seeing how they worked influenced what I did. The producers were less patient: after about forty minutes they realized that they were not getting any interesting video footage and gently urged us to move along.

Skulking the Haunted Barracks

The next scene involved walking slowly around the barracks with the psychics (and, of course, the TV crew) seeking ghostly activity. Though the lights were off and the rooms were dark, the cameras' viewfinders were fairly bright and cast a bluish-gray light behind them (which also created faint shadowy silhouettes of the cameraman's head and torso). The infrared cameras also had small red power lights on them, one or two of which were usually visible at any given time. Though the TV footage I later saw made it look completely dark, our eyes grew accustomed to the low light, which helped us move around the crew without turning our flashlights on.

If the lights had been on and someone who didn't know what we were doing had seen us, they would have found us a queer sight: A cluster of three or four people led slowly through the rooms, circled by cameramen and audio techs, who stopped every minute or two to talk aloud to no one in particular. Because the cameramen needed to look through the viewfinders as they crept along following us, they each had an assistant directly behind them helping guide them around tables, chairs, barrels, and other obstacles. Even so, with nearly a dozen people moving in semidarkness, there was more or less constant background noise—someone bumping something, creating footsteps, the "swish" of nylon jacket sleeves when someone moved their arm, and so on. Even if a ghost had been speaking faintly or giving us some sign or rap, it's doubtful we would have heard it. Every now and then someone would call for silence and we'd all stand motionless while a ghost was addressed, in a futile request to make itself known.

Keeping track of everyone was a critical and difficult task that no one seemed assigned to do; if it had just been myself and one or two other people walking in the room, I could have had some prayer of knowing what was going on. If there's only two of us on the premises, for example, and a voice or noise comes from another room, it's easier to rule out accidental sounds or auditory contamination. If the investigation had been conducted under my supervision I would have run a tight ship, but on this shoot I had no authority to tell anyone what to do (or, more likely, what *not* to do). Though everyone seemed to be taking it very seriously, I couldn't help feeling we were playing roles in some sort of *(This Is) Spinal Tap* satirical version of ghost hunting.

As we wandered, I made note of the items that were giving us false-positive signs for ghosts. For example just after the person ahead of me stepped on a creaking floorboard I whispered into my audio recorder, "the loose board is about five feet in on the right hand side as you come up the stairs on the far corner of the barracks." Locating and noting these spots would help us identify the sources of any potential spooky sounds, and since many of us were following more or less the same path around tables and between barrack bunks, it was likely that they would recur. There were creaky boards everywhere, and treading the floors resembled walking on popcorn.

At one point an investigator commented that she was getting a cold feeling, prompting the man standing next to me to chime in with his own initially spooky observation: "This table is freezing behind me!" he said excitedly. "Is it just me?" He was undoubtedly familiar with the claim that ghosts are sometimes said to create mysterious cold spots in rooms, places where the temperature inexplicably drops in one specific place for no apparent reason. Could this be our first sign of a ghost?

I flicked on my flashlight and aimed it toward his waist, where his hands were. I wasn't sure what to expect: maybe a ghostly, clammy hand or dark shadowy figure? I saw that he was leaning, and his hands were on a large wooden table behind him, propping himself up. It was very strange: though the unheated barracks were cold (and we were all wearing warm jackets), the wood would be cool but not likely "freezing cold." I looked more closely behind him, and he turned to look at where my light was shining. "Um... actually you're sitting on metal," I pointed out, gesturing with the light beam. "There's a metal plate there running along the edge. If you touch the wood itself, it's not cold; you're touching the metal plate so it seems much colder than the table would be." He saw that what I'd said was indeed true; metal is a much better conductor of heat and cold than wood, and the "freezing table cold spot" had a perfectly normal explanation. We moved on.

The psychics paused at various places, talking about the energies and feelings they sensed from one area or room. "I just heard some mumbling," Debby insisted. We strained to hear it, but got nothing. It may have been a real noise, her imagination, or maybe a spirit was speaking only to her. Whatever the case, no one else heard or recorded it, so we moved on.

A Ghostly Assault

As we walked, Michele shuffled forward in near-darkness, with her right hand following the edge of the table for guidance. I was about ten feet behind her and could see her fairly well, silhouetted by a bright bluish LCD camera screen of a cameraman facing her. Suddenly she stopped. "I feel like I'm being pushed forward," she said excitedly. "I'm holding onto the table to brace myself, but I can feel it. Can anyone else feel it?" Everyone else stopped and watched but no one said anything.

"Well, let go and see what happens," I suggested. I wasn't trying to be funny or see her harmed, but if she really was being pushed by some unseen presence, basic physics suggested she should lurch in the direction away from the force. If dramatic—and documented by the cameras present—it could potentially offer real evidence of the supernatural.

"No!" she said almost indignantly. "I'm not going to fall over!"

Another psychic asked, "Are you being pushed forward or backward?"

"I'd be falling forward," she said. "If I let go I'm going to be face-first on the floor, so I'm going to hang on if you don't mind." A few seconds later she reported, "Okay it's easing off now.... I don't think it was trying to hurt me, it was just trying to move me along or something... It was a force that was pushing me forward, and I'm fighting it, pushing onto the table pushing back against it."

I asked if it felt like ghostly hands pushing her and she said no: "It's like if you are pushing two magnets back to back, with opposite poles and they push each other away—that kind of magnetic pushing."

Cam later asked me about it. I had been carefully observing the whole ghostly encounter as best I could, and in this case the low light was actually a benefit compared to no light. "I was watching her silhouette, and I didn't see her being pushed or anything," I said. "I'm not saying she might not have felt a pressure or a push or something, but I am telling you that I could see her body the whole time, and it did not react like it had any force applied to it at all. It just looked like she was leaning against the table, like you or I would." I suggested that it could have simply been her imagination—and that the best way to have found out would have been if she'd not reacted against it but either fallen forward normally (as any of us would if we fainted or leaned too far forward), or let herself be actively pushed so that I (and the infrared cameras) could actually see evidence of these unseen forces acting on her body. Of course that didn't happen; as I suspected might happen, all the evidence we were seeing came in the form of unscientific, personal, subjective feelings which no one could prove or disprove. I didn't blame her for not wanting to be pushed forward (if indeed that's what might have happened), but I was somewhat frustrated that when she had the opportunity to demonstrate that something unexplained was happening, she chose not to take it.

The whole walk-around took a little over an hour, on both floors. Finally we were getting cold and hungry so we headed to a separate building that was our base of operations. It served as the kitchen and dining area, and all the electric outlets spewed long black industrial-weight cables connected to battery chargers for the cameras, lights, and other gear.

Spook Lights in the Locked Room

While fortifying ourselves with Coffee Crisp candy bars, warm coffee, and fruit snacks, I chatted more with the psychics and ghost investigators. I was curious to get their opinions of what we'd seen so far, and gently pointed out that nothing very impressive had happened. Michele suggested that the ghosts were capricious; sometimes they cooperate, sometimes they don't. "If you're looking for it, it's not going to happen," she said.

I pointed out, however, that we had spent much of the night doing exactly that: "If ghosts aren't going to do what we want them to, or give us signs of their presence when we ask them to, then what's the point of all this?" I asked, gesturing to the fort around us. What was the point of Cam creating the house of cards, and the pieces of paper outlining teddy bears, and asking the spirits to give us some communication or sign, if whether those things occur or not is irrelevant and meaningless? By that logic there's no difference between "nothing happened because there are no ghosts here" and "nothing happened because the ghosts decided not to bother." Scientific research uses what's called the *null hypothesis*; it is used to tell whether or not an experiment shows an effect or not, whether whatever is being researched is likely really there or simply a result of random chance. If whatever methods and techniques you're using can't reliably distinguish between "X happening or existing" and "X not happening or not existing," you're merely engaging in playacting, not investigation. It may be interesting and fun—but it's not logical, and it's not science.

She thought about it for a second. "Well, it kind of gave us a sign by pushing me," she replied. "I know you want to feel it, but I'm more open and receptive than you are."

I would have used different words than *open* and *receptive* (perhaps *suggestible*), but I understood what she was saying: If I didn't experience it, in her opinion it was because I was skeptical and not open-minded enough. But of course if you're too open-minded and too willing to accept anything and everything as evidence, then how do you know when the real evidence comes along, if it does?

"Who they pick is who they pick," she explained with a shrug. "Why me? I don't know."

I didn't know either, and I realized that arguing with her about it wasn't going to do any good. We were both open, sincere, genuinely inquisitive people, but we approached the investigation (and indeed the world) in very different ways. I downed the last of a Tim Horton's "Double-Double" (extra cream and sugar) coffee and reached for a doughnut. The TV crew didn't seem to need us for a while, apparently busy dealing with the "civilian investigators" elsewhere on the premises, so I stepped out for some fresh night air.

One of the crew members met me right outside the door. He was very flustered, excitedly saying something about how the lights had mysteriously come on in the barracks. He was one of the TV crew members that had been following us around, and after we left the barracks he'd turned the lights off; nobody else was up there, and he came to join us for food. When he went back to the barracks to get some equipment he'd found the lights back on. Something had spooked him: how had the lights come back on?

"Someone probably went back to get something and left the light on," I said, checking my watch. "We were gone for about forty minutes."

"No," he said. "Impossible. I locked the door behind us, because some of our expensive cameras and audio gear is set up in there." He fished into his jeans and pulled out a small padlock key, holding it out for me to see.

I raised an eyebrow as I peered down at the lock in his hand, reflecting the yellowish outdoor light above. "And no one else has a key?" I asked.

"No, just me. It's been in my pocket the whole time."

"Well, what about the Parks Canada staff? I mean, they work here, they have access to everything. One of them probably went up there while we were eating to check on things."

He shook his head again. "I don't think so. See, this is *our* padlock, we brought it with us. They don't have a key."

A light mysteriously turning on in an empty, locked barracks where ghosts are said to lurk? I wanted to know more! This ghost hunt suddenly became much more interesting, turning from a bunch of imaginative people scaring themselves in the dark to a classic Sherlock Holmes locked-room mystery!

I didn't have a deerstalker hat or a pipe, but I did have some questions. He agreed to show me where the lights were. As I followed him through the barracks, he gave me a little more information. The lights were obviously on, but unfortunately no one else had seen him turn them off earlier; he was the last one to leave the building because the rest of us were headed back to take a break. No one had been videotaping his actions (this scenario, which I've seen repeated countless times, is why the best policy—if you're going to use this method of investigation—is to always tape everything all the time).

I found the lightswitch in a dull grey metal box mounted on the wall. It was not a typical household-style on/off switch but instead a dial which needed to be turned. I turned the lights off myself, just for good measure, and we headed back downstairs. One of the psychics seemed very impressed with the lights coming on and took it as the first real evidence that spirits were indeed present and attempting to contact us. I wasn't so sure: "I don't doubt that he *thinks* he turned the lights all the way off," I said to her. "I don't doubt that at all. In this case I saw for myself that the light was in fact all the way off, so I'm now convinced that unless someone—or something—else touches it, it is in fact off. So if we go outside and no one else touches it and the lights come back on, that's very strong evidence to me, the sort of thing I'd be looking for."

Everyone agreed that by far the best evidence we'd found was the lights mysteriously turning off in the soldier's barracks. Over dinner we swapped theories about what it could be. A ghost was an obvious choice, but I wanted to rule out all the more likely, mundane explanations.

"If the lights are being turned down, the contrast... When we saw them, we'd been in the dark for fifteen or twenty minutes. It might look like they're all the way down unless you're staring right at them."

"It could be the dimmer switch," the crew member added. "I know that sometimes when you push them if you don't push it all the way, they come back."

I was thinking the same thing, and he seemed to sense it.

"It didn't click," he admitted. "But you could tell it was all the way back."

I tested the lightswitch. It went back and forth on one side, and the other side it turned on and off. Could it be a tricky switch? If so, it would not be the first time that a dimmer switch had accidentally turned itself off or on. Though uncommon, sometimes when a switch gets worn out it can do that. I walked over to the nearest metal casing and turned the lights off.

I waited to see if the lights would come back on their own. Ten seconds, then fifteen, went by. Thirty seconds passed. I realized that, if that was the answer, the lights would not have come back on immediately, because obviously the crew guy would have noticed it before he left the room. I waited about five minutes before I realized nothing was going to happen.

I shined my flashlight on the switch and examined it closely. I turned the dial to the left, and it clicked on again. I turned it off and stomped my foot on the floor to see if vibrations might set it off. Still nothing happened. My theory was wrong; I couldn't explain it. I took a few steps back and slumped down on the long wooden bench, discouraged. There must be something else. I spent another ten or fifteen minutes alone there and—just after I discovered an important clue—one of the assistant producers came to fetch me to join the rest of the crew for a séance in the Officer's Quarters.

Scene II: The Officers' Quarters Séance

Michele and the gang had decided to hold an old-fashioned séance to try to contact the ghosts they seemed sure were lurking around, just beyond our ability to really measure or detect them. I was curious to see what would happen; I had researched the history of Spiritualism and was familiar with séances in their traditional historical context, from Victorian-era parlor séances to colorful and controversial mediums such as Eusapia Palladino— as well as the crusading skeptics such as Harry Houdini who often exposed them as frauds.

But modern-day séances are relatively rare outside of specific contexts such as Spiritualist communities like the one in Lily Dale, New York. I had attended a handful of these formal attempts to contact the dead, and I was always eager to experience more of them.

Night vision camera footage of a séance in the Officer's Quarters at Fort George. Still frame from *Encounters* television show.

It was just after one in the morning, and Monica and Julia joined the circle, along with Cam and two other people; it wasn't clear if these two were friends of the ghost hunters, or crew members, but they wanted warm bodies to fill out the circle. For this event, the psychics placed chairs in a circle in the center of the room. I was not asked to join, which suited me just fine, as that left me in a better position to observe the proceedings from a more objective angle and hopefully react quickly to any potential ghostly phenomena that might materialize.

I later found out that the crew had planned the night's activities based on the belief that the hours between 9 P.M. and 6 A.M. (which they dubbed "the psychic hours") were especially important for detecting ghosts (Note 4). There is no scientific validity to the idea that there are any special hours or windows of time when paranormal activity increases (or ghosts are more active), though it is true that ghosts are more often reported at night.

They began with a blessing and holding hands in a circle; the crew was asked to avoid interrupting anything or breaking the circle. The cameramen zoomed in on each of the sitters as they talked to one another and any spirits in the room.

Michele led the effort, moving her head and body as if going into a trance. She stiffened up and a strange expression came over her face. She hunched her shoulders and took several deep breaths. I realized that I was watching a form of spiritual possession, or at least what several people there took as possession. It was nothing as sensational and dramatic as Linda Blair's possession by the demon Pazuzu in *The Exorcist*, but it was basically the same idea: Michele acted as if—and probably believed—that some sort of unknown energy or spirit had entered her body and was at least partly controlling it.

Once Michele felt she was in contact with the spirit, she asked, "Can you make a noise on the piano?" A small piano sat silently on the other side of the room. Nothing happened after about a minute, so she asked again for the ghost to give us a musical sign of its presence. Still nothing happened, and after a minute or so she asked, "Can you set off the sensor in the other room?" We all waited patiently and quietly, but the sensor in the other room remained silent, as did the piano.

Nothing happened except that Michele started to shiver. "I'm freezing!" she said, which was a feeling not unique to her. We were in an unheated, poorly insulated small wooden building in Ontario in late November.

Michele's friend Kim, seated to her right, put her left hand on Michele's

Examining automatic writing allegedly from a ghost soldier immediately following a séance in the Officer's Quarters at Fort George. Photo by the author.

shoulder as she continued the séance. Kim grabbed a nearby notebook and placed it in Michele's lap, and put a pen in her hand. I recognized what they were doing as a phenomenon called automatic writing—a classic technique for communicating messages from spirits for well over a century (Note 5). I watched, eager for messages from long-dead soldiers to appear, hoping they would tell us where they were buried, or give us details of battles centuries ago, or least lead us to some previously undiscovered information.

She wrote in scribbles, looping lines on the page. As soon as one page seemed to be filled up, someone would turn the page for her, and Michele would place her pen back on the notebook and scribble more, not looking down. She was mostly silent, though others would sometimes ask questions of the spirit inhabiting her body, asking it to communicate with us. This went on for several minutes, and then the proceedings suddenly gained some urgency. Michele was breathing more heavily, though not apparently in any pain or danger, and her friends decided they had had enough.

Kim leapt to her feet, stood behind the seated Michele, and began waving her arms over and around her friend, calling for the ghost to release her. "I want Michele back, and I want her back now!" she demanded. She made motions to flick away the energy, sculpting and manipulating the energies as if some soft, sticky invisible spiritual foam encased Michele.

Michele put her hand to her head and grimaced as though deep in concentration. Nothing happened for a while, and finally a man in the room (in the darkness it wasn't clear who) yelled angrily at the spirit inside her, "Fucking give her back!" Within a minute Kim performed what she described as a cleansing ritual to remove any remaining spirit energy from Michele, waving her hands above Michele's head and around her body. She cast a spell making sure that any spiritual energies or ghosts would remain in the building and neither possess our bodies nor follow us when we left.

With that the lights were turned on and the séance ended. Michele talked about how she could feel the spirit inhabiting her body, like her inner self had been temporarily replaced or pushed aside. Michele said that she felt she had been in contact with a male spirit who had been beaten and whipped or tortured, and someone wondered if it might have been the same spirit they sensed elsewhere earlier in the fort. Michele described the ghost that had possessed her, "Oh, he was nasty!" she said, rubbing her eyes. "I didn't like him."

Since the ghost unfortunately didn't give us any real spoken information, our attention turned to the spirit writing that she had channeled. Michele claimed that her hand had been controlled by the spirit that possessed her. Was it truly a communication from the dead? We gathered around to examine it. "Are you right or left handed?" I asked Michele. "Right," she replied. "What if the ghost is left-handed?" I asked with a contrarian smile.

We looked at the pages of scribbles and circles, trying in vain to decipher Michele's automatic writing. If there was a message in there somewhere, it wasn't going to be easy to find. One page began with a cursive word "Hello," though of course it wasn't clear if Michele or the ghost had written that. "I'm trying to follow where I started," she said. Her finger traced the lines her hand had made, supposedly guided by the spirit. "I'm going, going, going, and then it goes up... that could be an F or T if it crosses, O, P, I, T: Stop it."

"'Stop it?'" I asked.

"Maybe when we were arguing," she said, though I didn't remember much of an argument, and anyway why would a ghost say nothing except "stop it?"

We looked at the automatic writing again. One seemed to perhaps spell out "not dead," while another could be interpreted as "someone alone" or "someone help me." Of course I noted that even if these interpretations of the writing were correct, it did not necessarily mean they came from a ghost or spirit inhabiting Michele. She may have been consciously or subconsciously writing those words herself, words that she either imagined or simply chose to write. It's not difficult to write a few words on a piece of paper with your eyes closed; it will look pretty much like the automatic writing we saw: messy and scratchy but possibly decipherable. As long as Michele was the person holding the pen when those words (if indeed they were words) were scrawled, it is impossible to rule out the explanation that she herself was the origin— especially with simple and banal short phrases like "not dead" or "help me."

We hovered over the notebook, turning it in different directions and looking for strings of letters that might form a word. There were lots of O's (because of the circling) and many I's and T's. The "stop it" message only appeared if you filled in the first two letters and decided that the last letter looked like a T instead of an F or an I. Otherwise it read something like "OPIF" or "OPII" or even "GFII" which all of us pretty well agreed was gibberish.

It would be far more convincing if the pen simply began writing on its own, without anyone touching it or being near it. It might look like something out of a Harry Potter or Lord of the Rings film, but it would be very strong evidence of the paranormal if seen, independently witnessed, or videotaped. If ghosts are supposedly strong enough to open and close doors, move objects, and tug or pull on clothing, logically they should be strong enough to put pen to paper and communicate with us. Yet this has never happened.

It was like looking in a big bowl of alphabet soup for possible words and acronyms, except that the process was much more difficult because many of the lines and loops clearly weren't letters. In the end we couldn't come to any consensus about what the ghost was trying to say—if anything. The séance, though dramatic, yielded no information at all, and certainly nothing that could be considered evidence of ghosts. We ended up staying in the room for several hours. The TV crew was apparently more or less done with us for the night, and the cameras and microphones were dispatched to other parts of the fort, presumably to catch up with the "civilian" investigators and get them on tape. Even though the group had been given video cameras to record their spooky exploits, the producers could of course not be certain that any usable footage would come of it, so they used their professional camera teams as a backup.

The Haunted Painting

Since nothing else was really going on after the séance, I eagerly examined the portrait of Queen Charlotte in the officer's quarters to see if it would indeed "change from a vision of youth to a wrinkled old woman, and back again," as some people claimed they had witnessed. I trained a videocamera on it and tried to see if I could catch the change in action. I tried with the lights on and the lights off; I examined it close up, and from a distance, in case it was some sort of illusion created by intended or accidental pointillism by the artist.

No matter what I did, the same woman stared back at me, visibly unimpressed by my efforts and pleading eyes. After about twenty minutes I gave up; I couldn't wait forever, and I had made a good faith effort to see for myself. As I packed up my camera gear I stole a quick glance back up at the painting, in case it had changed when it thought I wasn't looking. But it hadn't. I reasoned that whoever had claimed to see the portrait change probably hadn't stared at it for hours at a time, but had likely seen—or imagined they'd seen—the change while passing by during a ghost tour.

I later researched the subject and after some inquiries about the supposedly haunted painting I discovered a fact almost as strange and bizarre as the story itself: No one had ever videotaped the woman's portrait changing, nor even photographed it in any stages of the transition. All photographs show exactly the same portrait. The idea of a changing painting is a well-known theme in folklore and can be found in countless ghost stories ranging from Oscar Wilde's 1890 gothic novel *The Picture of Dorian Gray* to Disneyland's Haunted House. Fort George is one of several supposedly haunted locations I have investigated with the same legend, and in fact it would be surprising if at least one painting or mirror there (whether authentically antique or a replica) was *not* said to be haunted.

We took a break, which gave me a chance to chat with Steve, whom I found to be refreshingly frank about his assessment of ghost hunting methods. We talked for literally hours, standing in near-darkness in the cold officer's quarters. It was a little after two in the morning. We returned to the soldier's barracks to find everything as we'd left it: the lights were still off, the teddy bear was in the same spot, the house of cards was still standing (which frankly surprised me, since any faint draft from an open door or vibration from a nearby footstep could have brought it down), and even the ghost tampon was still sticking straight up.

I told Steve that I was perfectly open to anything that might happen. I was there, at the ready, patiently waiting to experience (and hopefully capture) some sort of unexplained ghostly phenomenon. The problem was not that I was too skeptical to accept that anything happening could be evidence of ghosts—the problem was instead that *nothing was happening.*

I really enjoyed meeting Steve, Michele, and the other psychics and ghost hunters—they were funny, interesting, sincere, likeable people—who simply didn't approach the subject of ghosts from any perspective I could characterize as scientific. To them, personal experience was evidence, while I was finding plausible alternative explanations for things I was experiencing. I was open, and indeed eager, to experiencing something truly paranormal, but I couldn't in good conscience make up or exaggerate my experiences, either to play along or for the sake of entertaining a television audience.

After about seven or eight hours together, I realized that they already had what they considered to be evidence of ghosts, and they also realized that everything we'd seen or recorded fell far short of hard evidence. We were all on good terms; it was just something we'd have to agree to disagree about. But they, too, still wanted better evidence. Everyone there including me—especially me—wanted to experience something truly extraordinary at one of the most haunted places in North America.

One of the psychics produced a pendulum and held it out. She explained to us that it picked up energies, either positive or negative—depending on which way it moved. Apparently this made sense to nearly everyone else there, but I pointed out that such a test was illogical, since no matter what direction the pendulum swung, it would be seen as evidence of ghostly influence. Apparently the only way that it might *not* detect a ghost would be if it kept unnaturally still, which was quite unlikely given that it's very difficult for the human body (and especially one with an extended hand) to remain perfectly still for more than a few seconds. The whole premise behind what they were doing needed to be examined and established. The pendulum was not being used to see whether ghostly energy was there or not; that was already assumed to be true. Instead the pendulum's actions were being used to divine what specific type of energy was present—without demonstrating that the energy existed in the first place. It was like rolling a die and deciding that if it came up 1, 2, or 3 that meant that the ghost in the room was a female, and if it came up 4, 5, or 6 it was a male—without ever being sure a ghost was even there.

Steve made an interesting observation about ghostly activity: that doors in haunted places much more frequently closed on their own than opened on their own. I actually hadn't thought about that, but after a few moments I offered a skeptical response: "That's an interesting question. It occurs to me that one answer for the door is that, if it's not a ghost, it would make sense because doors can close on their own, but not really open on their own because of the way they latch; you have to turn a knob to open the door. But if it's a draft or a cat, there may be more reasonable explanations for why doors close on their own, and not open on their own."

I pointed out that the creaking board we had all experienced a few hours earlier had been taken as a sign of ghosts—up until its true origin was discovered. If we hadn't found the answer for whatever reason, it would be thought of as a mystery. I challenged the idea that the ghosts weren't showing up because a skeptic was present. (This effect, sometimes dubbed "skeptical shyness effect," is sometimes offered as an explanation for why paranormal abilities or phenomena seem to not occur when disbelievers are around.)

"You yourself, the believer, have asked for the lights to come back on upstairs; they didn't. You yourself the believer have asked for the deck of cards to fall; they haven't. So it's not just like, 'Prove it to the skeptic,'" I pointed out.

"But I'm willing to accept as a sign that the lights went off," Michele said. "He's 100% sure that the lights were off, and I accept that the spirits turned the light off. I accept that." "Right," I replied. "And I don't necessarily because I didn't see him turn it off. The difference is that you're willing to trust his memory about it, and I'm saying that people make mistakes all the time, and we have no proof that the lights were fully off."

I asked Margaret and Michele to help me understand their approach to ghost hunting, and what they thought was going on, how they understood the nature of ghosts and the spirit world.

"What we figured out from the spirits is that they need help to move on... so that's what they'll do. But if they don't want to move on, then that's a harder job for us, because they'll try and stop us, like when I was trying to go up the stairs and it pushed me down, you feel that pressure on your body, like you're being pushed back."

"But why?" I asked. "Why can't the spirits move on?"

"Nine times out of ten, it's because they're scared. They're stuck, they don't know what's on the other side—we don't either, really, and if they've been a bad person, they think they're really going to get it when they get over there. Or they're looking for somebody they left behind, a lot of times that happens."

"But how do *you* know when it's their time to leave or not?" I asked.

"Well, once we find out what's wrong, why they're still here, we can help them see it's their time to leave. We ask them, 'Why are you here? What's making you stuck?' We help them to resolve it so they can move on... We try to help them realize that they don't need to be there anymore. We help them to see that their family is there, waiting for them on the other side."

"But why wouldn't they know that?" I asked. It didn't make sense to me why a human would know more about the spirit world than a spirit would. How did she know what the rules are once you're dead, what ghosts knew or were thinking?

"Why wouldn't they know that? Because they're confused... A lot of times when a spirit is opening cupboards and smashing dishes, they're trying to get your attention. They're not just being mean. They don't know what else to do. Because not everybody can hear a spirit not everyone can see a spirit.... Most people can sense *something*. Like, if you've ever had that weird feeling where the hair stands on the back of your neck, or you feel that you're not alone, sometimes it's a relative, and the thought pops into your head, 'Oh yeah, that's where I left my keys.' It's a spirit that's telling you, 'Hey buddy, you forgot them here.'"

I was listening carefully to what they were saying, and even though I was exhausted, what they were saying didn't really make sense to me. "But how do you distinguish between just happening to remember where your keys are, and a spirit telling you where your keys are?"

"Well usually it's because you've been looking for a long time, and you've tried retracing your steps, and when you finally sit down and relax you can find them."

"Right, but is there a way to know whether that's your subconscious telling you, or your spirit guide?"

"I can distinguish the difference," she said. "I know his voice."

"Oh, so it's a different voice in your head?" I asked.

"Right," she said.

Of course we were back to the unscientific, the untestable, and subjective. I had no idea what voices she heard in her head, whether they were real or imagined. The conversation was interesting, and I was learning a lot about their worldviews, but I wasn't seeing anything anchored in anything scientific or testable. It was mostly a difference in interpretations. It wasn't that we were living in different worlds, it was just that we were approaching our understanding of the world in very different ways. They sensed spirits and ghosts on a regular basis; their lives were built around the idea that they encountered these lost souls and helped them move on. I sensed that they took pride in it, the sort of altruistic pride one feels when doing good works and helping others. I wanted to believe that what they were saying was true and real, for their own sakes if not for mine, but I couldn't help but feel that they might only be communicating with, and assisting toward the afterlife, figments of their imaginations. I headed back to the break room for hot cider and cookies after a brisk walk outside to stretch my legs.

As I surveyed the area, I realized that many of the random and "unexplained" ambient sounds reported at Fort George (bells, whistles, thumps or drum beats, horses, etc.) were in fact coming from outside the fort. In photographs and in brochures Fort George can have a deceptively remote appearance. It looks like it is located miles from civilization, whereas in fact it is part of a town of 15,000 residents. About 3.5 million tourists visit Niagara-on-the-Lake each year, making for a bustling, populated area only a few hundred yards from the fort. While Parks Canada has made efforts to limit light and noise pollution at the historic site, all the sounds of a medium-sized city (voices, shouts, horns, engines, horses transporting tourists, cell phones, dog barks, music, etc.) can be heard from the fort—sometimes loudly and clearly, other times faintly and softly. Furthermore, birds and animals live in the woods nearby, and the Niagara River flows not far away—sometimes with boat traffic. Insects buzz and flutter, ubiquitous squirrels scamper through leaves and trees and across eaves.

This realization put the occasional EVPs or ghost voice's collected there in a slightly different light. The ghost hunters often used very sensitive microphones, including directional handheld parabolic dish microphones that can pick up very faint sounds that could be anything. I have witnessed several occasions when a ghost hunter has assured me that it was absolutely impossible that anyone could have been in the area where a strange sound or voice was recorded—only to discover the sounds had been made by an unnoticed couple out for a stroll in the dark. This of course does not mean that any sound heard at the fort *cannot* be from a ghost or spirit soldier— just that it is extraordinarily difficult (if not impossible) to rule out normal, ambient sounds as possible explanations.

Return to the Luminous Locked Room

I found the crew member who had discovered the ghostly lights on. I'd been looking for him but hadn't seen him for several hours and realized he had been away filming the others. I asked him to follow me up to the barracks for a minute and told him I wanted to show him something. He pulled the key from his jeans pocket and unlocked the padlock. The lights were still off; apparently the playful ghosts had decided against an encore. We entered the chilly wooden structure and I led him to the nearest light switch.

"Exhibit A!" I announced as melodramatically as I could muster at three in the morning. "This light switch here: As you can see, you turn it in one direction and it's all the way on... Do it yourself," I encouraged.

I didn't want him to take my word for it, but see for himself—just as I had wanted to see it for myself. "It goes back and forth on one side, and on the other side it turns it off, right?"

"Yes," he confirmed. Clearly, I noted, the light stays off when it is turned off, as we would expect it to. I turned it on and off once or twice just to be sure. He nodded slowly, clearly wondering where this was going.

"Okay, come look at this one," I said, pointing my flashlight down the darkened barracks and up the stairs to the switch controlling the lights that had mysteriously gone off. I turned the lights on. "This switch is different, try this one. This switch has a little catch on it. Watch this: If I put it right there, the light's off, right?"

He nodded, unable to argue since the light had obviously turned off. "It goes off, and if you don't push it all the way...."

I didn't need to finish the sentence. Instead I let the light speak for me, as it slowly came back on after about five seconds without anyone touching it. It was very dim at first, but within about fifteen or twenty seconds it was on fully. "If you don't turn it all the way off, past the click, then it will slowly come back on as the switch slides back. That's probably how the light came on after you turned it off, left the room, and locked the barracks."

Earlier in the evening I had reviewed the event in my head and re-examined my assumptions and premises, in case there was something I'd missed. That's when I realized that I had made a mistake: Assuming that all the light switches in the building were identical, I tested my theory on the nearest one. It was a logical assumption—and it was wrong. Though the light switches in most buildings we ordinarily enter are the same throughout the structure, this was not the case in the barracks. The first switch I tested acted differently than the second one.

He seemed skeptical of my explanation, and I added, "I'm not saying that it *was*, but this proves that the switch *can* be set in such a way that it's not totally off, and the lights are obviously off, but after a while the lights will come back on by themselves."

"Right," he agreed. "That's possible. But I'm sure I turned it all the way off."

At the time, since I was in the midst of the investigation I hadn't yet reviewed my audio recordings, so I couldn't point out to him that earlier he'd specifically told me that the switch "didn't click" when he turned it off—proving that he had in fact *not* turned it all the way off. I'm sure he believed he had, since of course the lights turned off. But unless he had actually watched the light being turned off and waited for ten seconds to see what happened, it would have been impossible for him to know that he had not in fact turned it off all the way. Of course nobody does that; at night we turn off the light as we leave the room and go into a lighted area. We don't hang around for ten seconds just in case the light comes back on.

And, of course, most people's homes have ordinary residential light switches that are clearly on-and-off, so that's what we are used to. The switches in the Fort George barracks were industrial-grade dial switches that moved in both directions. Furthermore, the light switch was not far from the staircase; it only took a few seconds to walk from the light switch to the staircase and begin descending the stairs. He would have been in another room on another floor and facing the opposite direction by the time the light switched back on upstairs, and he'd never have known it.

What it came down to was this: While it was theoretically possible that the light switch had been flipped on by a ghost, it was much more likely that it had simply not been turned all the way off in the first place. While I couldn't conclusively prove that he *hadn't* turned the light off all the way, I could—and did—prove that the light could be easily (and accidentally) turned off in such a way that it would turn itself back on a short time later, which would of course seem very mysterious and ghostly, especially in Canada's most haunted location.

At this point there were no more scenes to shoot, and there was not much to do except wander around, drink coffee, and wait for the sun to finally shine on our bleary-eyed faces. The more tired we were, the duller our senses, and the more likely we were to misperceive things, from shadows that weren't really there to noises that we imagined. This experience, coupled with my background in psychology, crystallized for me why these sorts of overnight stakeouts are inherently flawed. It is an obvious and indisputable fact that the more exhausted a person becomes, the poorer their judgment is and the less sharp their senses are. This isn't as much of a problem late at night, but by 2 or 3 o'clock in the morning, most people are needing sleep. Nocturnal research by diurnal investigators is a clear recipe for errors and mistakes, especially when engaging in anomaly hunting.

Conclusion

We had seen no sign at all of Sarah Ann, Fort George's most famous ghost—though I later conducted an investigation into sightings and legends of this ghost girl (it appears in the next chapter). While we were there, now and then someone (often one of the psychics) would talk about how she was getting an uneasy feeling from some part of a room, or a particular spot along a path through the grounds, but nothing that could be seen or independently verified. The whole place was cold, so if there had been any ghostly "cold spots" they would have gone unnoticed.

There was plenty of laughing and joking on the set, and as we wrapped up I asked a few crew members what they thought, if they had experienced anything mysterious or unexplained. "No," one of them said to me. "I'll be honest with you, there were times that I was scared, but I'm just looking for something a little more...." His voice trailed off, but I believe he intended to finish with "impressive" or "real." One member of the crew, a friendly fellow named Jesse, admitted to me that the creepy surroundings had made him especially suggestible overnight. Still, he insisted—though he quickly hastened to add that he did not consider himself psychic—at one point after Michele and Debby had described their sensations with ghosts, Jesse claimed he truly felt "the spirit of an old man dying in agony." I then asked this hale and slighty chubby young man of less than two dozen years how he knows what it feels like to be an old man dying in agony, an experience he claimed to recognize. He thought for a few moments. "I imagined it," he said. "I believe that's exactly right," I replied.

Though the on-site investigation was over, I continued doing more research over the next few months. I finally received a DVD of the pilot television show a few months later; my first surprise came upon reading the back of the DVD case: "Our first investigation at Fort George, Niagara On The Lake [*sic*] reveals surprising results: light anomolies [*sic*], strange noises, posessions [*sic*], hundreds of EVP's (White Noise), and ghosts physically harming our participants—all of which have been recorded on over 160 hours of audio and video footage."

There were indeed a few light anomalies, though I had found a very plausible explanation for the most dramatic one, so I wasn't sure what they were referring to. I didn't see any ghosts "physically harming" anyone, though I guessed that the slight push Michele said she felt on her back could be sensationalized into an attack. I had not seen any real EVP evidence, either. The show was a pilot for a TV series, and the whole purpose of a pilot is to drum up interest and excitement, so of course they were going to exaggerate or even fabricate the drama. Why wouldn't they? It was a theme I would come to expect in the following decade of doing investigations on behalf of television shows. The series never got picked up, which was not surprising.

I watched the program, which bore only a passing resemblance to what I and the others had experienced. Hours of investigation were cut down to a few minutes, and in some cases only a few seconds. The show devoted an inordinate amount of time to the mother/daughter team of Monica and Julia, and it soon became clear why. Monica, the daughter, was a young, attractive, and very excitable blonde. The *Blair Witch*-style infrared footage of the pair wandering the fort's grounds scaring themselves and one another was exactly what the producers needed. At one point Monica, wide-eyed and alarmed, wails into the camera "Oh my god... Oh my god... Oh my god... This is so scary!"

A few minutes later, while going up a wooden staircase, she screams, "Oh my god, oh my god... I just heard footsteps behind me!" It is clear from watching the video that the footsteps she hears are her own, echoed back at her in the small enclosed stone space. I had noticed the same effect when I had climbed those stairs earlier in the evening. Of course I was never shown the footage at the time, nor asked to comment on it or explain the ghostly footsteps.

Watching the DVD I learned that investigator Margaret Byl later went to the spot where Monica heard (her own) footsteps and captured what she believed was an EVP that sounded something like a muffled "let's thump it" (or maybe "Len's trumpet," "left open," or even "le muffin"). The DVD also showed another supposed EVP, this one another typical ambiguous sound resembling something like "it's shitty luck for Cameron" (or "a shitty night for Cameron," or "sheer luck for Cameron," or "shitty light for Cameron" or even "should night for Cameron"). It was not Byl's fault—she was clearly sincere and diligent in her quest to capture EVPs at Fort George—but the evidence was simply far too poor to make heads or tails of.

It's not surprising to me that they were able to cull about three or four minutes of "mysterious" or spooky scenes, given that they combed through over 160 hours of footage. Of course, despite a Herculean attempt at editorial turd polishing, nothing happening is nothing happening: The fact is that 99% of the time nothing was going on—and frankly I'm not too certain about that last one percent.

In the DVD extras many of the crew members interviewed one another, and several related their own personal experiences of strange things they claimed happened during their visit. For example one woman said she briefly saw an unknown male figure who immediately disappeared; another said she saw some sort of mysterious smokelike mist that appeared suddenly in a room, lasted for a few minutes, and then vanished; another crew member said he walked through a door, and when he turned around moments later the door had inexplicably shut by itself.

Strangely, not a single one of these half-dozen or so incidents were caught on audio or videotape. For some reason the well-equipped TV crew didn't think to record what they did and where they went. This might be understandable at first—after all, their main job was recording the cast, not themselves behind the scenes as they filmed the show. However after the second, third, or fourth "mysterious event" of the night happened, you'd think that the crew would decide to begin recording *everything* they did, and that with so many professional-grade cameras around, at least one of these supposedly paranormal incidents would have been caught on camera. I of course could not investigate the these spooky events because I was not told about them at the time. Were they real experiences, misunderstandings, or overactive imaginations? Unfortunately once again there is no evidence to go on, and all we are left with are stories.

Encounters show participant Monica emotes into the camera during an overnight ghost investigation. Still frame from *Encounters* television show.

What about the especially bloody history of Fort George? Like many of the ghostly stories, that too seems to have been exaggerated by most of the ghost hunters and spook books. To get a more accurate, historical perspective I contacted Ron Dale, the superintendent of the Niagara National Historic Sites of Canada for Parks Canada. Dale told me that "As for deaths at the fort in battle, there were surprisingly few. The fort was shelled at different times from the American shore but casualties seem to have been light, although ultimately the wooden buildings were destroyed." Dale noted that there were heavy casualties on May 27, 1813 during the Battle of Fort George—"but this was not within the fort but on the plain near the mouth of the river" kilometers away (Dale 2005).

Therefore, if ghosts are said to be found near where their body died, the riverbank should be far more haunted than the fort itself. There would have been occasional deaths from disease, age, or accidents at the fort—as there are anywhere people live or work—but it seems that Fort George is not really the blood-soaked final resting place for so many thousands of souls it is often made out to be in the ghost stories.

With a place as large as Fort George—and with so many ghost-hunting enthusiasts going there looking specifically for anything weird or spooky—the ghost stories aren't going away any time soon. Tours of the fort, whether ghost-themed or not, guarantee that there will be a steady supply of new photos, videos, and spooky stories. I wasn't able to examine every single piece of evidence offered for ghosts—nobody could, and just trying to do so would be a full-time job—but I had done my best to look at the best evidence I could find.

Notes

Note 1. On later visits I interviewed ghost hunter Chris Moon about a device he claims communicates with the dead, Frank's Box (see chapter 7), and conducted a follow-up investigation into the ghostly Sarah Ann. Because of space limitations (and out of respect for the reader's attention span), those in-depth investigations do not appear in this chapter.

Note 2. In my investigations I prefer to do my own research so that I can determine which claims are plausible and which ones are not, and avoid wasting time and effort looking into events that are hoaxes or obvious folklore. Unfortunately few ghost hunters do this; usually they are too eager to visit the location and begin investigating.

Note 3. It's of course a fair question to ask, given the low quality of EVP, why the earwitnesses are certain that the unknown sounds are in an unknown language—as opposed to simply garbled sounds in no particular tongue or even random background noise. As discussed in chapter 7, studies have shown that people will report hearing unknown languages in white noise—in other words, they hear "language" where none exists. This does not of course prove that EVP are necessarily invalid, just that there is good reason to interpret them with caution.

Note 4. Other ghost hunters have followed a similar protocol; Ryan Buell, for example, on his hit TV show *Paranormal State*, investigated during what he called "Dead Time," which many amateur ghost hunters believe is at 3 A.M. when spirits are supposedly most active. Buell admitted that he made up the idea of "Dead Time" for his TV show: it was "created one night when I was trying to explain to some producers our process of investigating" (Buell 2011). However, according to Buell, whose group and TV show popularized it, the common belief that "Dead Time" occurs at 3 A.M. is wrong: "The truth, however, is that Dead Time is whenever it's most quiet. That usually means at night and it usually means late." Buell's remarkable investigative insight— that faint sounds are best heard when it's quiet—has been called a "brilliant concept" by his fans and widely adopted by amateur ghost investigators.

Note 5. The logic behind automatic writing has always puzzled me. If a ghost or spirit is in someone's body, it would seem that the easiest and best thing to do would be to simply communicate through the person's most accessible medium: their voice. Writing is actually a far more complex and difficult process than simply speaking (that's why children learn to speak long before they learn to write, and many adults who can speak perfectly well are illiterate). Writing involves spelling, grammar, punctuation, knowing the alphabet, and other rules, whereas ordinary speech can be freeflowing and ungrammatical and still be perfectly understood. So automatic writing should logically hinder, not help, spirit communication. It's not clear why mediums use it—other than simply following tradition—but it is a flawed investigation technique.

CHAPTER 12

Sarah Ann: Fort George's Most Famous Ghost

Though a handful of spirits are said to haunt Fort George, one particular ghost stands out as by far the most colorful and prominent (and, some claim, the best-proven). Her name is Sarah Ann (or Sarahann), "a little girl who spends her afterlife in the soldiers' barracks or blockhouses. She often appears sitting on the stairs, and likes to tease the staff members at the fort by tapping on their shoulders and then disappearing" (Dirty Rig 2005). Sarah Ann, according to the ghost stories, died from disease at the age of seven, yet remains at the fort. Historians tell us that some soldiers stationed at Fort George (particularly the officers) brought their families to live with them there, and it is said that she was among them.

Soldier's barracks at Fort George, said to be haunted by the ghost of a young girl named Sarah Ann. Photo by the author.

One book, *Ghosts of Niagara-on-the-Lake*, adds, "This young girl, named Sarah Ann, is certainly the most active and precocious spirit on the site. Over the years, Sarah Ann has been seen numerous times, and her youthful antics never fail to bring a smile to the faces of witnesses. Like a typical child, she's cheerful, mischievous, innocent, and eternally playful. She'll engage in games of peek-a-boo, hiding under beds and behind pillars, and giggling quietly to herself. Sometimes Sarah Ann will playfully tug on someone's clothes and then run away so that the victim of the prank only sees a momentary glimpse of a barefooted girl with shoulder-length curly blonde hair and wearing a flowing white dress before she disappears from view. [One tourist reported] a white cloud, vaguely humanoid in shape and the size of a small child. High-pitched giggling is frequently heard in the barracks, where Sarah Ann seems to spend most of her afterlife hours" (Da Silva and Hind 2009, 133-34).

Even though Sarah Ann was a no-show during our investigations for the 2005 pilot episode of *Encounters* (as chronicled in chapter 11), I wanted to dig deeper, to find out if she was just another one of countless baseless legends or bits of ghostly folklore, or if there really was good evidence for her existence, as claimed. I searched in vain for any hard evidence of Sarah Ann; there were no photographs of her, no videotapes, nothing but the rare

A ghost tour guide at Fort George, both collecting and spreading ghost stories about resident ghost Sarah Ann. Photo by the author.

(and curiously varied) eyewitness reports. I decided to see if I could trace back the story of Sarah Ann, find out where it came from, what historical or other evidence there was offered about her. Why was she such a prominent ghost?

Sarah Ann Sightings

Most of the reports about Sarah Ann are either reported to ghost tour guides (who of course have an incentive to make the story as interesting as possible), or later described in blogs or to friends. What can we make of these claims? Unfortunately most of them are ambiguous. For example, how do you scientifically prove an inherently faint or subjective phenomenon such as a tug or a poke? Unless a camera happens to catch a dramatic pulling of clothing down or to one side as if by an unseen hand, it is difficult or impossible to prove that someone experienced a slight tug or tap. Loose clothing such as shirts and jackets (as well as the capes worn by tour guides) may simply momentarily catch on a belt, snag on a rough surface such as a tree branch, shrub, or anything else and give the subjective sensation of a spirit-given tug.

There's another problem with the Sarah Ann story: The eyewitnesses contradict each other, unable to agree on what they're seeing. One person says Sarah Ann is invisible; another says she is barefoot with "shoulder-length curly blonde hair wearing a flowing white dress"; while another says that's all wrong because she has "extremely short hair" and wears a man's shirt. Still another says she looks like a white cloud—yet all of the reports are carelessly lumped together as genuine sightings of Sarah Ann. Even assuming for a moment that ghosts had been proven to exist and were verified as haunting Fort George, there's no reason to assume that it's the same ghost being described by different people in different places. For all we know there are two or more female child ghosts in the area. There's also the curious detail of how a child ghost could reach high enough to tap an adult on the shoulder (though presumably a ghost could do whatever it wished).

Investigating the claims is complicated by the fact that the vast majority of them are second- or third-hand stories, repeated by tour guides on ghost tours, in books, and on websites. Most of the stories are anonymous ("One woman on the tour said she saw....") or semi-anonymous, and happened years earlier so the opportunity to do any real investigation has long since passed. Invariably no credible scientific investigation was conducted at the time of any of these reports. The stories are informal and have little or no investigationally useful information such as names, dates, other witnesses nearby, and the like. This is understandable, since you never know when someone will report some strange experience and a team can't be waiting nearby to investigate anything at a moment's notice. But the inevitable result is that most ghost stories and accounts, while perhaps providing spine-tingling fodder for ghost tours and campfire tales, are simply not detailed enough to be useful evidence proving the existence of ghosts. They are entertainment, not information; stories, not science.

Sarah Ann Appears

One of the first and most in-depth reports of Sarah Ann appears in the book *Ghosts of War*, where author Jeff Belanger (creator of the popular website ghostvillage.com) writes of Sarah Ann as one of the most important ghosts at the fort. Importantly, it also relates what is apparently the original and first sighting of Sarah Ann. It seems that all of the "known facts" about Sarah Ann repeated on ghost tours and in local stories came from this original report. It's rare to be able to so precisely pinpoint the origin of alleged biographical details about ghosts, and, as one of the most famous spirits said to haunt Fort George, her story is worth a close investigation.

Fort George tour guide Jim Hill told Belanger that a woman who had just finished a ghost tour "said that while [fellow ghost guide] Kyle [Upton] was talking, this little figure came down the stairs in what she thought at first was a dress, but she realized that on looking at it a little more closely it looked like a man's shirt. She said the child has extremely short hair and sat and listened to the story, and then followed the group out. When you get to the middle of Fort George there's this lovely, yellow officer's quarters, and when we got to that point the little figure stopped in the path, and this lady said that as the group moved away, she kept looking back and this little figure didn't follow. She said, 'I can tell you that this little person's name is Sarah Ann. Once I saw short hair I thought it was a little boy. But no, her name is Sarah Ann.'" According to Belanger (2007), "When I spoke to Jim, it was clear to me from the context and tone that she was relating a woman's 'psychic impression' of what she saw."

Though presented by Belanger as "a most intriguing ghost encounter," this ghost story is unfortunately so garbled and riddled with non-sequiturs that it's difficult to know what, if anything, it means. If you don't read it too closely it almost makes sense, but if you stop and think about it, none of it makes sense. Many unanswered questions come to mind: Why did she think this apparently human, ordinary child was a ghost? For that matter, how did she "know" the ghost's name? Did the ghost say a name aloud and the woman assumed the ghost was giving her name, or did that name simply pop into the woman's head for some reason? What happened to the girl after that? Did the woman look for her later, or ask anyone else in the group if they had seen her, or even if she was the daughter of anyone on the tour? No one seems to know. Children are not only allowed in Fort George, they are actively encouraged to visit with their families, school groups, and ghost tours, so kids of all ages are often seen in the area.

The fact that ghosts in period costume are occasionally sighted and reported seems especially authentic and spooky—until you remember that staff members and re-enactors hired by Parks Canada regularly dress in period costumes; in fact one Parks Canada brochure highlights Fort George's "knowledgeable, costumed staff who bring the site to life with their tales from the past. Musket and cannon fire and the traditional sounds of fife and drum music fill the air" (Parks Canada 2008). Indeed, "1812-period costumed interpreters" are on hand to guide tourists, and activities are available at the fort in which both children and adults are taught the details and "differences between the uniforms of 1812" (Parks Canada 2008).

In other words, if nobody wandering the grounds was dressed like a figure from centuries ago, then the fact that someone could accurately describe a long-dead soldier's uniform or weapons would seem remarkable—possibly even evidence of ghosts. Where else could they have seen such a sight, except perhaps in illustrated history books? But if visiting tourists are offered extended, close-up looks at what soldiers might have worn 150 years earlier on their tour, then someone seeing a soldier in full costume is hardly mysterious. Even if some tourists are not guided by the costumed staff, there are many depictions of what soldiers of that era looked like in full-color brochures and signage all around Fort George. The staff at Fort George go to great lengths to provide tours with a vivid re-enactment experience and setting, so it's hardly surprising that they succeed.

A Closer Look

Upton and Hill did some research on the history of the area and, for reasons that are not clear, became convinced that several historical details in the woman's report had been independently verified. They spoke to an unnamed "senior history guy" [sic] at Parks Canada and asked him if a young girl in the 1800s might have short hair. "It turns out that to fight lice, the lower classes often kept young kids' hair shorn pretty tight. And why did she stop at the Officer's Quarters? We know that even before the U.S. Army captured the place in 1813, the British were in the process of cutting it in half.... They leveled the Officer's Quarters, cut Fort George almost literally right down the middle, and eventually put a gun battery there" (Belanger 2006, 96). According to Belanger "the spirit of the little girl stopped where the old Fort George would have ended."

They concluded that the girl stopped following the group along the path because a wall had once stood there. Hill told Belanger that "This woman nailed the appearance of a child of a common soldier pretty well for the nineteenth century. She had the location right, why the kid stopped where she did stop, and I mean nobody, not even people who worked at Fort George for many years, knows about it being cut in half. Because you don't want to start your tour saying during the war it looked nothing like this.... This woman nailed the appearance, and she knew bugger all about the history of the area... there were a lot of facts that suddenly came out that I didn't know, all because of this lady who named the kid and had the age about right."

Hill is quoted several times as being amazed that the woman's information was correct, but a closer reading reveals that the woman didn't say anything at all about why the girl stopped where she did. Upton, Hill, and Belanger failed to realize that the woman gave very little of the "amazingly accurate" information they credited to her; it was Upton and Hill—*not their anonymous informant*—who opined why the girl had stopped where she had. *She never said* that the girl's ghost stopped there because that's where the end of the fort was back in 1840—that was all additional speculation from Hill and Upton based on earlier guesses and speculation. Fort George had many different layouts and appearances—structures were built, destroyed, moved, rebuilt, and added over the years. The girl could have stopped at almost any spot on the grounds of Fort George, and Upton and Hill could comb through records and interview historians until they thought up a reason why, at one arbitrary point in history, a ghost might have stopped there.

Though Jeff Belanger endorses Upton and Hill's work as important and insightful ghost investigation, it is actually a deeply flawed and illogical technique called retrofitting. This occurs when a person takes a few theories gleaned from some divination experience (such as a psychic, séance, or EVP) and then combs through history records to see if any of the information might be validated in historical records. On a superficial level this seems like a valid technique, but in practice the information they are trying to check is so vague that just about any historical information can be rationalized as supporting it, even if it takes mental and logical gymnastics to make it fit.

Hill's reasoning has several other logical errors and mistakes, including assuming that a child ghost would not go beyond where a wall used to exist ages ago. Even assuming that a Sarah Ann existed and that what the anonymous woman saw was indeed her ghost, there's no logical reason to think that her ghost would not (or could not) be seen beyond a wall—any more than a person (or ghost) could not be seen outside of a house where they lived. Presumably (again, assuming she was real) in life Sarah Ann did not spend her entire life within the walls of Fort George; like others she could come and go through the fort's gates and be seen down by the river, in nearby fields, and elsewhere (possibly in Halifax, Nova Scotia, or even London, England, if she grew up there). The idea that either in life or in death a girl could not possibly have moved beyond a certain wall or spot (as if blocked by some cosmic force field) is absurd—yet this theory is offered as serious "ghost investigation analysis" by Hill and Belanger.

Furthermore, the soldier's barracks that Sarah Ann seems to favor did not even exist at the time Belanger suggests she was alive; the entire building is a modern recreation based on old descriptions. With the exception of the original stone powder magazine, virtually everything at Fort George that an actual solider or girl might have touched or seen in the early 1800s is long gone, replaced with modern timber, electric lights bought at a nearby Canadian Tire superstore, fake replica items, and so on. Thus by Hill's curious logic Sarah Ann should not be seen in the barracks. Hill's "investigation" into Sarah Ann is a classic (and typical) example of ghost hunters' speculation getting ahead of the facts, poor critical thinking, and failing to question assumptions.

Hill is in effect *claiming to read a ghost's mind*—assuming he knows what the child's ghost would have looked like, what it would have done, and what its motives were for its (apparent) behavior. There is nothing at all unusual or remarkable about the report, and it seems to have mostly been used to manufacture a mystery where none exists, for the sake of a good story.

Even assuming that a girl named Sarah Ann had in fact died there, without knowing what she looked like, we of course cannot know whether the woman "nailed the appearance" of the girl. Belanger and Hill seem astonished at the woman's accuracy in describing a girl, but they fail to notice that the description is meaningless without something to compare it to. We have no way of knowing if her generic description of the child (short hair and a man's shirt that could have been a dress) is what anyone named Sarah Ann looked like. For all we know Sarah Ann was unusually tall (or short) for her age, or may even have had some deformity such as a missing limb. It is logically impossible to say that a description "matches" something without having those two things available for comparison. It's like someone saying that a person "is taller" or "looks like" without saying who or what he is taller than, or looks like. In this case we have Hill confidently claiming that a woman's vague description "matches" someone no one alive has ever seen, nor been depicted in paintings, drawings, photographs for comparison.

How exactly the woman "nailed the appearance" of a soldier's child is never explained, unless Hill assumes that all nineteenth-century children in the region had short hair and wore what looked like a man's shirt. It's likely that a seven-year-old girl who had short hair lived somewhere nearby at some time; it's also likely that a seven-year-old girl who had long hair lived somewhere nearby at some point. People come in all shapes, sizes, and appearances—and those shapes, sizes, and appearances can vary from year to year, week to week, and even hour to hour. Children may wear a wide variety of clothing throughout their childhood; depending on the situation, throughout the course of a week or a month they might wear anything from pajamas to a dress to trousers, swimming wear, church finery, holiday costumes, school uniforms, or even nothing at all. (And let's not forget that children of any age and era are known for experimenting with different looks, styles, and outfits.) There is no rational basis for Hill to claim or think that any particular description by the woman matched anything a specific young girl might have worn, much less "nailed" her appearance. For that matter, it's also not clear why the woman assumed that the young child she saw was a girl. Pre-pubescent children of both genders can be indistinguishable, and a seven-year-old boy with long hair may look exactly like a seven-year-old girl, especially from some distance away.

This, of course, demonstrates the dangers in putting too much stock in one person's uncorroborated eyewitness account. There were apparently no other eyewitnesses and no photographs were taken of these sightings. People are notoriously poor at accurately perceiving and remembering details of what they experience. The woman admitted that at first she didn't understand what she was seeing and mistook a man's shirt for a dress. Perhaps she was wrong, and it actually *was* a dress, as she first thought? And what if the girl she saw didn't have short hair, but it was simply tied back in a braid and looked short from a distance, or from one particular angle? For that matter, what about the fact that other supposedly credible eyewitness accounts of Sarah Ann describe a girl with long hair? Are they wrong? Or does Sarah Ann appear differently to different people, or at different times? If so, which version is correct?

Because we have no answers to these (and many other) questions about ghosts, there is no logical reason or investigative rationale for deciding which of these details to believe. We cannot simply and arbitrarily pick and choose which bits of information to follow up on. An important part of investigation is carefully determining which facts and claims are verifiably true (and therefore should be used as a basis for further investigation), and which are merely guesses and vague possibilities (which often lead investigators on a fruitless wild goose chase).

We don't know for certain that Sarah Ann existed—and even if we did, we don't know for certain what she looked like—and even if we did (through a photograph, for example), we couldn't possibly know what she looked like at any given time. Unless all female children were forced to cut their hair the same way and wear exactly the same clothes at all times (and we have some valid way of independently verifying this), we can't possibly know what a hypothetical "Sarah Ann," or anyone else from nearly 200 years ago, looked or dressed like. It is all guess and speculation—not real investigation, logical deduction, or science. I wouldn't belabor this point or go to such lengths to explain this if not for the fact that this logical fallacy and faulty thinking is very common among ghost hunters and a significant impediment preventing them from honing their investigations toward real evidence. Investigators must question and establish their premises with evidence instead of proceeding on the assumption they are valid.

I don't suggest that the woman, nor Hill, is lying or trying to fool anyone; instead this "mystery" (like many ghost mysteries) is merely a result of confusion, logical lapses, and sloppy analysis. This is a perfect example of how unconfirmed speculation, psychic feelings, and random information can become legitimized and cemented into the "official" information about a ghost or spirit. An identical process occurs when ghost investigators use EVP to collect information about a ghost—it's all unproven speculation with no anchor in reality and no real way to confirm the information. Whatever pops into one person's mind, for whatever reason, is often incorporated into the ghostly legends—and one person's story is as good as another.

A close reading of the information in Belanger's book reveals an even more—and less—astonishing explanation: that the anonymous woman who named and first claimed to see Sarah Ann never actually saw a ghost but instead a real, ordinary human child on the ghost tour and, for whatever reason (whether the power of suggestion or merely to tell a fun story), she mistook it for a spirit. In her entire account there's no reason to think that the child was anything but a flesh-and-blood human; she doesn't say that the child disappeared, or was transparent, or faded away, or anything else that would hint of a spectral origin. By all accounts the little ghost girl looked and acted exactly like a normal human girl (or boy).

Neither the woman, nor Upton, nor anyone else asked other members of the tour group if they had seen the girl at the time. If they had, it is at least plausible that one of them would have said, "Yes, of course, that's my daughter Dorion.... Why would anyone think she's a ghost?" Children are very common on ghost tours, and as any parent knows they don't always walk in lock-step right next to the adults who brought them. Kids often run ahead or lag behind or just wander off doing their own thing, and it would not be at all unusual for a girl to do that.

A 'Real' Ghost Tour?

According to one story, ghost tour guide Kyle Upton himself saw the elusive Sarah Ann—ironically while giving a ghost tour! "For a while Kyle thought that perhaps the young girl was part of the tour, but after doing a quick head count and determining all were present, the truth began to sink in. He realized it had to be the ghost of Sarah Ann, a spirit he had heard about numerous times in the past but wasn't entirely sure he believed in" (Da Silva and Hind 2009, 137). This account rather improbably suggests that Upton's head count proves that a ghost was among his group. With the little girl included, there was one more person than he thought there was. While this is a spooky detail, it's hardly compelling evidence of the supernatural. What if he simply counted wrong in the first place? The number of people on any given ghost tour varies, and may be anywhere from five or six to a dozen or more.

Of course there's another much simpler and more plausible answer: the girl joined the tour on the cheap. Perhaps one of the parents simply decided to save $6 and not buy a ticket for their daughter and let her tag along. Perhaps they simply assumed children could join the group for free. Though the location does sometimes technically close, much of the area is open to the public, including at night, and it's entirely possible that a young girl either departed with the group unnoticed or simply joined them later. The girl did not walk through a wall, suddenly vanish, attract attention from nearby alarmed animals, or anything else. Even if Upton's count was correct and a ghost was present, there is no logical reason to assume that the young girl he saw was the ghost! By Upton's own account, the girl looked and acted in every way like an ordinary child. Perhaps one of the adults or teenagers was a ghost; all a head count tells you is whether you have the same number of people before and after you count, it doesn't tell you which of those is an extra, uninvited guest (alive or dead). While Upton's desire to tell a spooky story is endearing, one extra person found during a head count is simply not good evidence of ghosts.

Furthermore if Upton's headcount had truly convinced him that the most famous ghost in the country had appeared as part of his group, why didn't he say something, or get a photo? I'd hope that if I was on a ghost tour and my guide had what he sincerely believed was a once-in-a-lifetime chance for our group to photograph and experience a genuine ghost among us, he'd say something. I would be furious to find out later that Upton, knowing that his paying customers were hoping to see a ghost close up, had chosen not to mention to us when he saw one standing only a few feet away.

The Real Sarah Ann?

Upton and Hill, following the practice of many ghost hunters, decided to follow up on the anonymous woman's account and see if they could find any historical evidence that matched or supported her information. They scoured records from the War of 1812 looking for any evidence that a girl named Sarah Ann had died there. That effort failed, though they did eventually find a Sarah Ann that seemed to offer evidence for the girl's existence, in a nearby cemetery.

According to *Ghosts of Niagara-on-the-Lake* "A tombstone in St. Mark's Cemetery may provide the answers. There, under a canopy of ageless trees, stands a tombstone to Sarah Ann Tracey, a child who was only seven years old when she died in 1840. She lived at Fort George with her mother, Hannah, and her father, Thomas, the troop sergeant major with the King's Dragoon Guards." No other information is known about her life or death, though as we will soon see, even this brief description takes liberty with the facts. The tombstone reads, "In memory of Sarahann, daughter of Hannah and Thomas B. Tracey, Troop Serjeant Major in the Kings Dragoon

Guards. Who died on the 19th of July, 1840, in the 7th year of her age."

At first glance this does indeed seem to fit at least two things that could match the psychic's description: a female named Sarah Ann (or Sarahann) who died at a young age (assuming, of course, that ghosts appear at the age they died, a common but purely speculative tenet of ghost folklore). According to authors Da Silva and Hind, "The coincidence between the historical Sarah Ann and the spectral girl at Fort George are too eerie to ignore. Many people familiar with the story, Kyle Upton among them, have no doubt that these two children are one and the same."

Jeff Belanger and the Fort George tour guides suggest that the anonymous psychic got much of the information about Sarah Ann correct, including the girl's name, age, cause of death, where she lived, how she looked, and even how she behaved. Unfortunately the validity of this story falls apart upon closer analysis and examination of the historical facts. Instead, as we will see there is little or no connection between Fort George's famous ghost Sarah Ann, the girl said to have lived in the soldier's barracks and died of disease, and Sarah Ann Tracey.

A tombstone in St. Mark's cemetery near Fort George may reveal clues about a real "Sarah Ann" ghost. Photo by the author.

We can begin by noting that there is no indication about why Sarah Ann Tracey died at the age of seven; disease is a plausible reason, but hunting, farming, and other accidents commonly killed children during that era—even murder is a possibility. This is especially true since the woman who came up with "Sarah Ann" never claimed to have an age for her; she merely mentioned a little girl, which might give us an age range from, say, four to fourteen. The designation of Sarah Ann as being seven years old was added to the legend by Upton and Hill *after they found Sarah Ann Tracey's tombstone and decided that she must have been the ghost*—it's not as if the anonymous woman stated that the girl's name was Sarah Ann Tracey, and she died at the age of seven (which would be impressive, assuming of course she was not a historian and had not seen the grave that Hill and Upton eventually found). Thus the fact that Hill and Upton located a grave that seems to confirm the information given to them during a ghost tour is much less impressive (and far more vague) than it first appears.

And what about that all-important name, Sarah Ann, the ghost's most concrete and distinguishing feature? As discussed earlier, there is no hint of where the name Sarah Ann came from; it seems to have simply popped into one anonymous woman's head when she saw a little girl during a ghost tour. In fact, the name the anonymous woman came up with, Sarah, is one of the most popular names for a female child in the world, and has been among the top 150 most common given names since the 1800s. Statistically, the chances of Hill and Upton finding a "Sarah" in one of the dozens of cemeteries in the Niagara region is far higher than for most other female names the psychic could have offered—even dating back 200 years. It actually would have been more remarkable if Upton and Hill had *not* been able to find a tombstone for a "Sarah" from the early to mid 1800s (including one who had died young).

What if the psychic had thought (for whatever reason) that the girl's name was Mary or Margaret, or any of dozens of other fairly common female names? It's likely that Upton and Hill could have found tombstones somewhere in the region that listed those first names as well, seemingly offering supporting evidence for those females as possibly being a ghost.

To investigate this theory, I visited St. Mark's cemetery and after some searching discovered another "Sarah Ann," later to become Mrs. Sarah Ann Putman. This Sarah Ann was born in 1849, only nine years after Sarah Ann Tracey died, though she died in 1895. This Sarah Ann could just as likely have been a candidate for Upton and Hill's ghost—she had the same first two names, she lived not far from Fort George around the same time, and she is even buried in the same cemetery. True, she lived to middle age, but for all we know she might have played in (what was left of) Fort George as a seven-year-old girl, and perhaps her ghost wanted to return to where she had fond memories.

I am not, of course, arguing that the ghost of Sarah Ann Putman haunts Fort George; instead I'm demonstrating that she is no more or less a good candidate than Sarah Ann Tracey, or any number of other Sarahs (or Sarah Anns, or Sarahanns) who lived and died in the area over the centuries. The point is that (with a few logical contortions, rationalizations, and cherry-picking of relevant details) one Sarah Ann is as good as the next. This is a very common error that ghost hunters make when doing research into haunted locations and trying to force-fit the historical facts to match present-day observations, information, or hunches. It is a version of a logical error called the sharpshooter fallacy, in which a few apparent matches are highlighted, and the bulk of criterion that don't match are glossed over or ignored. (It's like an archer shooting at a blank haystack, then drawing a bulls-eye around wherever it struck and claiming it as evidence that she's an excellent shot.)

When Upton and Hill failed to find the evidence they were looking for—confirming the psychic's information about the existence of a young girl who lived at Fort George during the war named Sarah Ann who had short hair and wore men's shirts—they simply broadened the criteria (and lowered the standard of evidence) to include any female named Sarah Ann who lived in the area at some point. Not surprisingly, they eventually found one.

Most damaging to Belanger's and Upton's claims, Sarah Ann Tracey, their candidate for the ghost, died in 1840—*nearly thirty years after fighting stopped at the fort* and after it was in ruins. The claim that Sarah Ann Tracy "lived at Fort George" is simply another myth, an attempt to shoehorn historical facts into the outlines of a fanciful ghost story. *Ghosts of Niagara-on-the-Lake* seems to acknowledge that little Sarah Ann Tracey had nothing to do with the war; instead that while she was alive, "a detachment of cavalry used the decaying grounds of Fort George for grazing [horses and cattle]." Indeed, "By the 1820s, Fort George was no longer being used regularly and the buildings were becoming decrepit."

It seems rather unlikely that a Troop Serjeant Major in the King's Dragoon Guards would be forced to live with his family in decrepit buildings at what was left of a fort. Thus we see that the Traceys likely did not live at the fort when she died, as there was little of the fort standing by then and there was no war going on. Instead the Traceys probably lived elsewhere in the region (likely at nearby Fort Mississauga, which was much newer), and in fact there's no evidence that Sarah Ann Tracey—or any other Sarah Ann—ever lived in, died at, or even visited the fort she is so widely claimed to haunt.

Solving the Mystery?

After researching this case I had many questions, and I contacted Belanger to ask him about these contradictions in one of the most famous ghost reports in Canada. A closer look at the "ghost report" itself helps explain why it's so fragmentary and contradictory. Instead of Belanger doing any investigation himself, he simply relied on what *other people told him about what other people told them.* This sighting is a third-hand story; Belanger is reporting in his book what Jim Hill told him *about what an anonymous woman told him* about something she claimed to have seen. Again we see the difference between a ghost storyteller and a ghost investigator. As any investigator knows, details get garbled and stories change with each retelling—this is why it's important to consult original sources and interview original eyewitnesses whenever possible.

Belanger acknowledged that there were many contradictory and confusing elements to the story he presented, telling me, "You're right, it's a third-hand story. I always prefer first-hand accounts, but Jim was such a good storyteller and I wanted to include what he said.... I don't offer these accounts up as proof of anything. I'm simply passing on what I've learned and heard along the way and I'm trying to do it in an entertaining way. *Ghosts of War* is not meant to be a scientific thesis aiming to prove the existence of ghosts. I don't expect my readers to believe everything they read" (Belanger 2007)(Note 1).

Belanger, like most authors of books of "true" ghost stories and reports, wants to have it both ways; they like to fill books and web pages offering legends, stories, and anecdotes as evidence of ghosts and spirits, while hedging and admitting that at the end of the day they are proof of nothing. Unlike Belanger and other authors of ghost reports, I *do* expect my readers to believe what I write, because I devote substantial time, effort, and scholarship to determining the truth, telling fact from fiction. There's nothing wrong with collecting and retelling ghost stories, but that should not be confused with research or investigation.

The fact that the entire Sarah Ann story can be traced to an anonymous woman (very likely a self-claimed psychic) is revealing, and helps explain why the mystery is so fragmentary. This case is very typical of many ghost investigations and provides another example of the importance of fact-checking, questioning assumptions, and not going too far beyond the evidence with flights of fancy. In his book *Niagara's Ghosts at Fort George,* Upton himself notes that "I feel that some people use the title 'psychic' as a status symbol to impress people, increase their own feeling of importance, and make themselves special, or at least unusual. Because of this, I think that people who claim to be psychic often feel pressured to perform, to see something. As a result, they may exaggerate their experience, add extra details to make a better story, or simply make things up. Certainly the wildest experiences, those that conflict most with historical fact, come from people who claim to be psychic [and because of this] I do take what they say with a grain of salt" (Upton 1999, 11).

Despite this honest assessment (and its refreshing skepticism), it's important to note that virtually all of the information and details about the ghost of Sarah Ann came directly from psychics and is today repeated by Upton and others as a true ghost story—not given "with a grain of salt." For a person who claims to put little stock in psychic impressions, Upton spends a lot of time promoting Fort George's most famous ghost story based on those psychic stories he finds exaggerated or simply made up. I do not think that most psychics or mediums are lying or hoaxing, but merely that their imaginations—like those of the rest of us—may be working overtime during visits at Fort George.

Conclusion

Unfortunately the original Sarah Ann "sighting" that provided the details in this ghost story is largely, if not entirely, built on a foundation of speculation, assumptions, and faulty logic instead of facts. The best evidence for the best-known ghost at Canada's most haunted location is not videotapes, photographs, or hard evidence of any description; it is instead a third-hand account of what an anonymous psychic claims that a ghost told her. Where there is a lack of real evidence to support a haunting, ghost stories, guesses, and anecdotes will inevitably fill the void.

This is normal and natural; humans are storytelling creatures and we make up stories to explain things we don't understand. The ancient Greeks did this millennia ago, constructing stories explaining that the sun shot across the sky each day because it was carried by the handsome god Helios as he drove his chariot over the heavens. Many centuries later the

Aztecs constructed elaborate cosmologies to explain the natural world around them, sacrificing human lives to appease their gods. These human psychological tendencies remain with us and help explain the beliefs and experiences of ghost hunters, who have created their own elaborate (if varying and contradictory) cosmologies about ghosts, spirits, and the afterworld—claiming (through intuition and personal experience) to know what ghosts are, what they do, how they interact, how the afterlife works, and so on. To those who believe, the evidence is obvious, clear, and all around them. And indeed they may be completely correct, but there is no more scientific evidence for their ghost cosmology than there was for Helios or Aztec gods. It's a matter of belief, faith, and folklore—not science.

Of course this inconvenient truth does not help sell ghost books and pack ghost tours. It's much more entertaining to spin a story of a little mischievous ghostly girl who giggles and tugs on clothing in the soldier's barracks than it is to admit that there's little or no evidence that Sarah Ann existed. Ghost stories are always more fun, but the truth should also be honored. There is so much beauty and mystery in history and the real world that fabricating fictional stories is not only unnecessary but also dishonors the very real history of the fort and those who lived in the region. There may indeed be ghosts haunting Fort George, but there's little or no evidence that Sarah Ann is among them.

Note

Note 1. Interestingly, Belanger told me that in the years since his book had come out, I was the first person to call his attention to the contradictions and ambiguities in his account of Sarah Ann. This suggests that many of his readers may not think critically or analytically about the information he presents, or, as he suggested, perhaps I'm "reading Jim Hill's account too literally." Yet scientific investigation requires that information about hauntings and ghost reports be taken literally—not metaphorically, figuratively, or in any other way. Either a ghost was literally seen or recorded, or it was not; there is a huge difference between an eyewitness saying that a room *literally* became colder during a spirit presence and saying that the room *figuratively* became colder. Science operates on literal facts and quantifications: did the room actually get colder—and if so, by how many degrees as measured by a properly calibrated thermometer or other scientific instrument—or did it simply seem to get colder metaphorically, the way a person gives another an icy stare, or a brusque person brings a chill to a conversation. Ambiguity in idea and language often hides illogic and error, and it is a careful investigator's duty to stick to the literal facts and avoid such ambiguity. Suggesting that an investigator—especially a skeptical investigator—is taking some statement or fact claim too literally is tantamount to saying that the investigator is taking the claim too seriously. Yet taking a subject seriously is the scientific process by which we distinguish truth from fiction, accuracy from falsehood.

CONCLUSION AND FURTHER READING

Researcher Sharon Hill, in her master's thesis titled "Being Scientific: Popularity, Purpose, and Promotion of Amateur Research and Investigation Groups in the U.S.," notes that "ARIG (amateur research and investigation group) members, like the growing number of amateurs participating in citizen science efforts, can make contributions. But, to do so would involve substantial changes to their procedures: working under the authority of credentialed scientists, raising the standards and quality of investigations, being open to criticism, and discarding cherished ideas as required. These improvements may encourage qualified scientific investigators to participate. Perhaps new and interesting findings would result. However, the current behavior of many ARIGs suggests that they enjoy the thrill, publicity and personal satisfaction they receive from the existing arrangement and are not willing to institute tight experimental protocol that may improve the quality of their work. Rigorous testing procedures are difficult. Stringent methods would certainly change the public interaction, increase the time, effort and costs associated with investigations and eliminate many current ARIG members from participation. Another option to consider is active collaboration between paranormalist and nonparanormalist ('skeptical') groups; that is, if they can get past the stereotypes and hostility that is evident in their public exchanges. This type of exchange can be a learning experience for groups of differing worldviews" (Hill 2010). Perhaps, then, there is some room for groups working together.

Given the long and thoroughly documented history of fraud, hoaxing, mistakes, and misinterpretation involved in ghost hunting and evidence for ghosts, the common question shouldn't be "Why are you so skeptical?" but instead "Why aren't you more skeptical?" Skepticism—at least on the subject of ghosts and the evidence offered for them—is not a position of cynicism but a logical and rational position informed by knowledge of the history, psychology, techniques, and other factors in ghost hunting.

An 1891 article in the *Pall Mall Gazette* described a lecture titled "Gossip about Ghosts" given by a former chemistry professor at the Royal Polytechnic Institution. The talk began with the following introduction: "Spook hunting has recently become fashionable as Slumming was a few years since, and I fancy the nett [*sic*] result of it all will be to leave matters pretty much where they were before; the believer continuing to believe and the scoffer continuing to scoff" (quoted in Davies 2007, 206). A century and a quarter after that summary, little has changed. As Owen Davies notes, "Whichever way you look at it, sociologically, psychologically, culturally, as long as people believe in ghosts they will continue to exist. Neither science nor religion can exorcise beliefs generated by personal experience, and to be haunted by the dead would seem to be part of the human condition" (Davies 2007, 249). If the spirits of the dead are truly among us, proving that will require more diligence and intellectual rigor than has been brought to bear so far.

OTHER GHOST INVESTIGATIONS

While I have investigated many dozens of ghost reports and hauntings over the years, in this book I focused on just a few in-depth case study investigations that reveal basic principles of how to scientifically evaluate haunting claims. Here is a brief overview highlighting some of my best-known and most comprehensive ghost investigations, and I encourage readers seeking more information to consult those additional resources. Each case is different, presenting new and interesting challenges.

The Demonic Ghost House (Buffalo, New York)

A desperate family contacted me, convinced that their house was haunted by an angry spirit. The disruptions became so bad that the family was driven from their home and refused to sleep there overnight. The family described a wide variety of phenomena, including mysterious lights, demonic faces in photographs, EVPs (ghost voices), and even a ghost attack. See "The Demonic Ghost House," chapter 5 in *Scientific Paranormal Investigation: How to Solve Unexplained Mysteries* (Rhombus Books, 2010).

The Mysterious Santa Fe Courthouse Ghost (Santa Fe, New Mexico)

In 2007, the "Santa Fe Courthouse Ghost"—a mysterious, glowing, moving white orb was captured by a security camera at a courthouse in Santa Fe, New Mexico. While the court personnel who first saw the baffling image didn't know what to make of it, others soon offered their own explanations, and a ghost was among the most popular. The mystery became so well known that it has its own Wikipedia page, and my solution to the mystery made national news. See "The Mysterious Santa Fe Courthouse Ghost," chapter 9 in *Scientific Paranormal Investigation: How to Solve Unexplained Mysteries*, and "The Santa Fe Courthouse Ghost," chapter 5 in *Mysterious New Mexico: Miracles, Magic, and Monsters in the Land of Enchantment* (University of New Mexico Press, 2014).

The White Witch of Rose Hall (Montego Bay, Jamaica)

Rose Hall is a mansion near Montego Bay in Jamaica built in the 1770s, and has a reputation as one of the most haunted places in the Western Hemisphere. Rose Hall is said to be haunted by a woman named Annie Palmer, dubbed the White Witch of Rose Hall, who allegedly killed three husbands, knew black magic, and was infamous for her cruelty and sadism. Psychics and tourists at the site claim to find evidence of Annie Palmer's spirit, but my research revealed an even more fascinating secret. Homicide detective Steve DiSchiavi of the Travel Channel show *The Dead Files* interviewed me about solving the mystery for the 2015 season premiere episode. See "The White Witch of Rose Hall," chapter 12 in *Scientific Paranormal Investigation: How to Solve Unexplained Mysteries* and *The Dead Files*, "Guardians of the Dead," Episode 5.1, airdate April 25, 2015.

The Haunted KiMo Theater (Albuquerque, New Mexico)

The KiMo is one of the best-known haunted theaters in New Mexico and throughout the Southwest, said to house the ghost of a young boy killed there in the 1950s. The ghost (or poltergeist) infamously ruined a play there after a director refused to leave an offering of doughnuts for the ghost. Several local ghost hunting groups claimed to find evidence of paranormal activity, but I found other explanations that were even more amazing. See "Phantom Performances at the Haunted KiMo Theater," Chapter 1 in *Mysterious New Mexico: Miracles, Magic, and Monsters in the Land of Enchantment.*

The Commandery Ghost (Worcester, England)

In 2009 I was asked to research a ghost photo taken in 2001 at the site of the last English Civil War battle in Worchester, England. A visitor had snapped a photo of what appeared to be a soldier at a window, but upon returning to the spot a bit later found it was gone. The visitor, assuming it had perhaps been a costumed mannequin, asked the curator about it and got a chilling response: "she said they had never had a mannequin or exhibit up by the stairs." I examined both the photo and the circumstances behind it and offered an explanation. See "A 'Commandery' Ghost Story," June 19, 2015. Available at http://www.centerforinquiry.net/blogs/entry/a_commandery_ghost_story/.

The Haunted Old Cuchillo Bar (Cuchillo, New Mexico)

Almost literally a ghost town, the small burg of Cuchillo in southern New Mexico has only a handful of living residents, but many nonliving spirits are claimed to linger there. Strange phenomenon have been reported in a ruined bar and store that dates back hundreds of years, and several ghost hunting groups have "verified" paranormal activity there through EVPs and other evidence. See "The Haunted Old Cuchillo Bar," chapter 8 in *Mysterious New Mexico: Miracles, Magic, and Monsters in the Land of Enchantment.*

The Charity Hospital Lights (New Orleans, Louisiana)

It was a Christmas 2015 mystery that had many people scratching their heads—and others smiling appreciatively: a strange lone light spotted inside the window of a dark, abandoned New Orleans hospital. Some thought the light was a Christmas tree propped up to spread cheer, while others suspected a ghost or even something sinister. I reviewed the evidence and discovered the secret of the Charity Hospital Lights. See "Abandoned Hospital Mystery Light Solved," for Seeker.com, January 5, 2016. Available at http://www.seeker.com/abandoned-hospital-mystery-light-solved-1770690021.html.

La Llorona (American Southwest and Mexico)

La Llorona, the wailing spirit who according to legend drowned her children in a river, is among the scariest and deadliest ghosts in the world. Though some dismiss her story as an urban legend, many people have reported real-life encounters with La Llorona. I examine the history and folklore of this murderous ghost and see if there is any truth to the legends. See "La Llorona: Wailing Witches Haunting the Ditches," chapter 11 in *Mysterious New Mexico: Miracles, Magic, and Monsters in the Land of Enchantment.*

The Haunted La Posada Hotel (Santa Fe, New Mexico)

One of the most haunted hotels in the capital city of Santa Fe, the La Posada has a long history of ghost reports. No fewer than five spirits are said to roam the hallways, including Julia Staab, the wife of a former owner of the building who was driven mad by the death of her child. I spent the night in Julia's room and searched the grounds for spectral visitors, debunking some stories but confirming others. See "Santa Fe's Haunted La Posada Hotel," chapter 13 in *Mysterious New Mexico: Miracles, Magic, and Monsters in the Land of Enchantment.*

The Bell Witch Case (Adams, Tennessee)

The Bell Witch case is one of the oldest American ghost stories and also widely said to be one of the most credible and best-documented poltergeist cases in history. It involves a Tennessee farmer named John Bell, Sr., who in 1817 found a mysterious creature with the body of a dog and the head of a rabbit. Soon an unseen evil spirit tormented the Bell family. Not only were the ghostly goings-on seen by dozens of credible eyewitnesses (including a future President of the United States), but was even according to one source the haunting was "validated by the State of Tennessee as the only case in U.S. history where a spirit has caused the death of a human being." I visited the famously haunted property and examined the local and historical evidence for this bizarre story. See "The Bell Witch Mystery" in *Skeptical Inquirer* magazine, 36(1), January/February 2012.

Lincoln's Ghost in the White House (Washington, D.C.)

The White House is famous not only for its living residents but also for the reputed presence of its long-dead ones, including Abraham Lincoln's ghost. In 2015 ghost hunter Joshua Warren claimed to have discovered the image of Lincoln in a 1950 photo taken by longtime White House photographer Abbie Rowe. Warren is convinced that all the evidence—including attempts at a recreation—points to a spirit, but I offer a more earthly explanation. See "Lincoln's Ghost Spotted in White House ... Or Maybe Not," by David Moye for the Huffington Post, November 7, 2015. Available at http://www.huffingtonpost.com/entry/abe-lincoln-ghost-photo-real-or-fake_us_563395c9e4b0c66bae5c2861.

Wolfe Manor (Clovis, California)

As part of the *MysteryQuest* TV series in an episode titled "Return of the Amityville Horror," I investigated a famous haunted house where ghostly figures, a disembodied voice, cold spots, and other phenomena have been reported. The investigative team spent several days at the location and elsewhere (a warehouse in Carson, California) in an effort to document supernatural phenomena. See "Return of the Amityville Horror," *MysteryQuest* show Season 1, Episode 10, Airdate December 13, 2009, from KPI Productions.

Queen Isabella's Ghost (Norfolk, England)

In April 2015 a ghost hunting team visited Castle Rising, a famous fortress in Norfolk, England. It was once the royal residence of Queen Isabella, and the ghost hunters captured what was said to be an image of the queen's spirit, complete with medieval dress—along with what might be a dog or wolf (perhaps a reference to Isabella's nickname as the "she-wolf"). I was asked to examine the photo and determine its credibility. See "Ghostbusters Capture Spooky Image on Ruins of Queen Isabella's Castle" by David Moye of the Huffington Post, May 26, 2016. Available at http://www.huffingtonpost.com/entry/queen-isabella-ghost-uk-castle_us_574475fde4b0613b512b4c65.

REFERENCES

Alcock, James. 2004. *Electronic Voice Phenomena: Voices of the Dead?* Committee for Skeptical Inquiry website. December 21. Available at http://www.csicop.org/specialarticles/show/electronic_voice_phenomena_voices_of_the_dead.

Angel, E.A. 2012. *Dead Whispers: Ghostly EVPs.* Atlgen, Pennsylvania: Schiffer.

Ariely, Dan. 2008. *Predictably Irrational: The Hidden Forces That Shape Our Decisions.* New York: Harper Perennial.

Aykroyd, Peter H. 2009. *A History of Ghosts: The True Story of Séances, Mediums, Ghosts, and Ghostbusters.* New York, New York: Rodale Press.

Banks, Joe. 2012. *Rorschach Audio: Art and Illusion for Sound.* London, England: Strange Attractor Press.

Baker, Emerson. 2015. *A Storm of Witchcraft: The Salem Trials and the American Experience.* New York: Oxford University Press.

Belanger, Jeff. 2005. *Communicating with the Dead: Reach beyond the Grave.* New Page Books.

Belanger, Jeff. 2007. Author interview, February 5.

Bennett, Gillian. 1999. *Alas, Poor Ghost! Traditions of Belief in Story and Discourse.* Logan, Utah: Utah State University Press.

Biddle, Kenny. 2007. *Orbs or Dust? A Practical Guide to False-Positive Evidence.* Paranormal Investigators and Research Association.

Biddle, Kenny. 2016. Author interview, September 15.

Blair, Jenny. 2013. Taking 3-D Polaroids. *Discover,* December 3, p. 14.

Brown, Jennings. 2016. Proton Packs and Teddy Bears: The Pseudoscientific History of Ghost Hunting Gadgets. *Popular Mechanics* magazine, October 26. Available online at http://www.popularmechanics.com/technology/gadgets/a23563/ghost-hunting-gadgets.

Bruce, David. 1956. Effects of context on the intelligibility of heard speech. In *Information Theory,* by Colin Cherry (ed.), Butterworths, London, 245-252.

Brunvand, Jan Harold. 2001. *The Encyclopedia of Urban Legends.* Santa Barbara,

California: ABC-CLIO.

Buell, Ryan. 2011. What is 'Dead Time'?. Paranormal Research Society. April 1. Available at http://paranormalresearchsociety.org/blog/what-is-dead-time/.

Cardoso, Anabela. 2012. "A Two-Year Investigation of the Allegedly Anomalous Electronic Voices or EVP" in *NeuroQuantology*. September, 10(3):492-514.
Christoff-Flowers, Emily. 2014. *The Ghost Journal: Memoirs of a Ghost Tour Guide in Williamsburg, Virginia*. Lulu.com.

Clarke, Andrew. 2004. Price and a flying brick. Available at http://www.foxearth.org.uk/BorleyRectory/TheFlyingBrick.html.

Cutchin, Joshua. 2017. Nosewitness: The Smell of High Strangeness. *Fortean Times*, February, issue 350.

Dale, Ron. 2005. Author interview, April 6.

Da Silva, Maria, and Andrew Hind. 2009. *Ghosts of Niagara-on-the-Lake*. Toronto, Canada: Dundurn Press.

Davies, Owen. 2007. *The Haunted: A Social History of Ghosts*. New York: Palgrave.

The Dead Files (television show). 2015. "Guardians of the Dead." Episode 5.1, airdate April 25.

Dennett, Michael. 1994. Bigfoot Evidence: Are these tracks real? *Skeptical Inquirer.* September 22.

DiMare, Joe. 2014. Author interview, July 10.

Dirty Rig Productions. 2005. *Encounters*. Episode 1: Fort George. Unaired television pilot.

Edwards, Gavin. 1995. *'Scuse Me While I Kiss This Guy' and Other Misheard Lyrics*. New York, New York: Fireside.

Eliason, Eric. 1996. "Ouija" entry in *American Folklore: An Encyclopedia*, edited by Jan Harold Brunvand. New York, New York: Routledge.

Ellis, Bill. 2001. *Aliens, Ghosts, and Cults: Legends We Live*. Jackson, Mississippi: University Press of Mississippi.

Elster, Charles. 1999. *The Big Book of Beastly Mispronunciations*. New York: Houghton Mifflin.

Esposito, Richard. 2012. It's Official: No Stowaways on Cargo Ship. June 28. ABC News.com. Available at http://abcnews.go.com/Blotter/stowaways-cargo-ship/

story?id=16669654.

Emmons, Joanne. 2012. *I Think My House Is Haunted!* Atlgen, Pennsylvania: Schiffer.

Fienning, Bill. 2016. Author interview, November 15.

Finucane, R.C. 1996. *Ghosts: Appearances of the Dead and Cultural Transformation.* Amherst, New York: Prometheus Books.

Flaxman, Larry, and Marie D. Jones. 2011. Not quite dead: When a ghost is not really a ghost. Chapter in *Ghosts, Spirits, & Hauntings: Am I Being Haunted?* Ed. by Michael Pye and Kirsten Dalley. Pompton Plains, New Jersey.

French, Christopher, and Anna Stone. 2014. *Anomalistic Psychology: Exploring Paranormal Belief and Experience.* London: Palgrave MacMillan.

Ghost Hunters (television show). 2008. Episode 401, airdate March 5.
Gibson, Marley, Patrick Burns, and Dave Schrader. 2009. *The Other Side: A Teen's Guide to Ghost Hunting and the Paranormal.* New York: Houghton Mifflin Harcourt.

Harvey, John. 2007. *Photography and Spirit.* London, England: Reaktion Books Ltd.

Hawes, Jason, and Grant Wilson, with Michael Jan Friedman. 2007. *Ghost Hunting: True Stories of Unexplained Phenomena from The Atlantic Paranormal Society.* New York, New York: Pocket Books.

Hill, Sharon. 2010. Being scientifical: Popularity, purpose, and promotion of amateur research and investigation groups in the U.S. Masters thesis, December. University at Buffalo, State University of New York. Available at https://ubir. buffalo.edu/xmlui/handle/10477/46900.

Hill, Sharon. 2012. Amateur paranormal research and investigation groups doing 'sciencey' things. March/April. *Skeptical Inquirer* magazine, (36)2. Available online at http://www.csicop.org/si/show/amateur_paranormal_research_and_investigation_groups_doing_sciencey_things.

Hill, Sharon. 2016. Creator of gadgets for *Ghost Adventures* show says he does not believe in ghosts. October 27. Doubtful News website, available at http://doubtfulnews.com/2016/10/creator-of-gadgets-for-ghost-adventures-show-says-he-does-not-believe-in-ghosts/.

Hyman, Ray. 1996. The Evidence for Psychic Functioning: Claims vs. Reality. *Skeptical Inquirer* 20(2), March/April.

Keenan, Mike. 2005. Niagara's Ghostly Battlefields. *Buffalo Spree* magazine. September/October, 148-149.

Kelemen, Deborah. 1999. Function, goals and intention: Children's teleological reasoning about objects. *Trends in Cognitive Sciences* 3(12): 461–468.

Kindred Spirits (television show). 2016. "Breaking and Entering" episode. Airdate November 18.

Lander, Susan. 2014. *Conversations with History: Inspiration, Reflections, and Advice from History-Makers and Celebrities on the Other Side.* Hay House.

Lecouteux, Claude. 2012. *The Secret History of Poltergeists and Haunted Houses: From Pagan Folklore to Modern Manifestations.* Rochester, Vermont: Inner Traditions.

Leepson, Marc. 2011. Five myths about the American flag. *The Washington Post.* Available at https://www.washingtonpost.com/opinions/five-myths-about-the-american-flag/2011/06/08/AG3ZSkOH_story.html?utm_term=.7a5a94339639.

Loftus, Elizabeth. 1980. *Memory: Surprising New Insights Into How We Remember and Why We Forget.* Addison-Wesley.

Loftus, Elizabeth. 1996. *Eyewitness Testimony.* Harvard University Press.

Loxton, Daniel. 2016. Haunted Houses in *Junior Skeptic* magazine 21(6).

Lyng, Stephen. 1990. Edgework: A social psychological analysis of voluntary risk taking. *The American Journal of Sociology.* January. (95)4: 851-886.

Maher, Michaeleen. 2015. Ghosts and Poltergeists. Chapter 25 in *Parapsychology: A Handbook for the 21st Century.* Ed. by Etzel Cardena, John Palmer, and David Marcussen-Clavertz. New York: McFarland.

Mancuso, Christopher, and Brian Cuno. 2010. The Urban Explorer's Backpack. *Haunted Times* magazine. Issue 4(3), Winter.

Manjoo, Farhad. 2014. An officer's eyes and ears, recording all. *The New York Times*, August 21, p. B1.

Middleton, Jacob. 2013. Spurious Spirits. *Fortean Times*, February, issue 297.

Mlodinow, Leonard. 2012. *Subliminal: How Your Unconscious Mind Rules Your Behavior.* New York: Pantheon Books.

Moye, David. 2015. Lincoln's Ghost Spotted In White House ... Or Maybe Not. *The Huffington Post*, November 7. Available at http://www.huffingtonpost.com/entry/abe-lincoln-ghost-photo-real-or-fake_us_563395c9e4b0c66bae5c2861.

Moye, David. 2016. Ghostbusters Capture Spooky Image In Ruins Of Queen Isabella's Castle. *The Huffington Post*, May 26. Available at http://www.huffingtonpost.com/entry/queen-isabella-ghost-uk-castle_us_574475fde4b0613b512b4c65.

Murdie, Alan. 2011. Ghostwatch column. *Fortean Times*, Issue 279, September, p. 20.

Murdie, Alan. 2014. Ghostwatch column. *Fortean Times*, Issue 316, August, p. 18-19.

MysteryQuest (television show). 2009. "Return of the Amityville Horror." Season 1, Episode 10, airdate December 13.

Nelson, Bobby. 2011. A pathetic grasp at trying to validate the ghost box. *The Bent Spoon* magazine, No. 9, p. 4-7, Available at http://thebentspoonmag.files.wordpress.com/2012/03/issue09.pdf.

Newman, Rich. 2011. *Ghost Hunting for Beginners: Everything You Need to Know to Get Started*. Woodbury, Minnesota: Llewellyn Publications.

Nickell, Joe. 2012. *The Science of Ghosts: Searching for Spirits of the Dead*. Amherst, New York: Prometheus Books.

Novella, Steven. 2010. Getting into the Spirit of Things. MonsterTalk podcast, March 2.

Paranormal Lockdown (television show). 2016. "Monroe Demon House" episode, airdate December 16.

Polidoro, Massimo. 2001. Final Séance: *The Strange Friendship Between Houdini and Conan Doyle*. Buffalo, New York: Prometheus Books.

Polidoro, Massimo. 2003. *Secrets of the Psychics*. Buffalo, New York: Prometheus Books.

Parks Canada, 2011. Cultural Heritage: Fort George / The Battle of Fort George. Available at http://www.pc.gc.ca/eng/lhn-nhs/on/fortgeorge/natcul/natcul2.aspx.

Price, Harry. 1946. *The End of Borley Rectory: The Most Haunted House in England*. London, England: George G. Harrap & Company.

Radford, Benjamin. 2002. Messages From Beyond at a Spiritualist Meeting. *Skeptical Briefs* newsletter, June.

Radford, Benjamin. 2005. Is Reel or Real? The Truth Behind Two Hollywood Ghost Stories. *Skeptical Briefs*, March 15(1). Available at http://www.csicop.org/sb/show/reel_or_real_the_truth_behind_two_hollywood_ghost_stories.

Radford, Benjamin. 2010. Is the *Amityville Horror* House Really Haunted? Live-Science.com. May 25, available at http://www.livescience.com/6528-amityville-horror-house-haunted.html.

Ramachandran, Vilayanur, and Diane Rogers-Ramachandran. 2008. "A Moving Experience." *Scientific American Reports*, Special Edition on Perception.

Randi, James. 1995. *An Encyclopedia of Claims, Frauds, and Hoaxes of the Occult and Supernatural*. New York, New York: St. Martin's Press.

Ray, C. Clairborne. 2015. Reading into gender differences. *The New York Times*, September 1, p. D2.

Riddle, Nate. 2011. *Lone Star Spooks: Searching for Ghosts in Texas*. Atglen, Pennsylvania: Schiffer.

Roach, Mary. 2005. *Spook: Science Tackles the Afterlife*. New York: W.W. Norton and Company.

Rosa, Joseph. 2003. *Wild Bill Hickok, Gunfighter: An Account of Hickok's Gunfights*. Norman, Oklahoma: University of Oklahoma Press.

Rutter, Gordon. 2013. What's the frequency, Victor? *Fortean Times* 301. May.

Schmerler, Jessica. 2016. You Don't Know as Much as You Think. *Scientific American Mind*. January/February 2016, 13.

Schneider, Mike. 2012. Prosecutors: No racial slur in call. *Albuquerque Journal*, April 14, A8.

Searley, Carrie. 2011. Author interview, November 13 and 14.

Shaw, Eva. 1995. *Divining the Future: Prognostication from Astrology to Zoomancy*. New York: Random House.

Shermer, Michael, and Pat Linse. 2013. *The Science Behind Why People See Ghosts. The Skeptics Society*. Available at http://www.skeptic.com/downloads/why-people-see-ghosts.pdf.

Spratley, Charles. 2012. *Piercing the Veil: Examining San Diego's Haunted History*. Atglen, Pennsylvania: Schiffer.

Stinson, Liz. 2013. Odor camera turns your favorite smells into memories. July 15. Wired.com, available at http://www.wired.com/2013/07/this-machine-is-a-camera-for-your-smell-memories/.

Stevens, Hayley. 2012. The Ethics of Ghost Research. Blog at Hayleyisaghost. June 5. Available at http://hayleyisaghost.co.uk/the-ethics-of-ghost-research/.

Stollznow, Karen. 2010. Frank's Box: The Broken Radio. Committee for Skeptical Inquiry. Available at http://www.csicop.org/specialarticles/show/franks_box_the_broken_radio/.

Townsend, Catharine. 2016. "Update: TV Ghost Hunter Ryan Buell's Mom Says 'He's Ill, But Not From Cancer,'" Crimefeed News, September 22. Available at http://crimefeed.com/2016/09/25338/.

Upton, Kyle. 1999. *Niagara's Ghosts at Fort George.* Newmarket, Ontario: Self-published.

Vos Savant, Marilyn. 1994. *Ask Marilyn.* New York: St. Martins, p. 68.

"Verklagekasper" (pseud.) 2012. "Ghost Hunting Flashlight Trick" Available on YouTube at https://www.youtube.com/watch?v=wqNwGe XTQJk. Uploaded March 24.

Vyse, Stuart. 2016. Fate: Inventing Reasons for the Things That Happen. *Skeptical Inquirer* September/October 40(5): 24.

Warren, Joshua. 2003. *How to Hunt Ghosts: A Practical Guide.* New York: Simon and Schuster.

Waskul, Dennis, and Michele Waskul. 2016. *Ghostly Encounters: The Hauntings of Everyday Life.* Philadelphia, Pennsylvania: Temple University Press.

Wicker, Christine. 2003. *Lily Dale: The True Story of the Town that Talks To the Dead.* New York: HarperCollins.

Wierima, Brian. 2011. Bringing science and technology into the world of the paranormal. November 10. Available at http://www.dl-online.com/event/article/id/64169/.

Wilson, Diane. 2016. "Celebrity Ghost Hunter Ryan Buell Arrested." September 21. ABC News 11. Available at http://abc11.com/entertainment/celebrity-ghost-hunter-jailed/1520780/.

Wilson, Michael, and Eric Newcomer. 2012. No Stowaways Found in Port Newark Search. *The New York Times*, June 28, A25.

Willin, Melvyn. 2007. *Ghosts Caught on Film: Photographs of the Paranormal.* Cincinnati, Ohio: David & Charles.

Wiseman, Richard. 2011. *Paranormality: Why We See What Isn't There.* London: Pan Macmillan.

Vaughn, Lewis. 2005. *The Power of Critical Thinking: Effective Reasoning About Ordinary and Extraordinary Claims.* New York, New York: Oxford University Press.

Young, Nicole. 2015. Psychic: I know the real Bell Witch story. October 27. *USA Today*, available at http://www.usatoday.com/story/life/nation-now/2015/10/27/psychic-bell-witch-story/74713998/.

INDEX